A-Level Year 2

Biology

Exam Board: OCR A

Revising for Biology exams is stressful, that's for sure — even just getting your notes sorted out can leave you needing a lie down. But help is at hand...

This brilliant CGP book explains **everything you'll need to learn** (and nothing you won't), all in a straightforward style that's easy to get your head around. We've also included **exam questions** to test how ready you are for the real thing.

There's even a free Online Edition you can read on your computer or tablet!

How to get your free Online Edition

Go to **cgpbooks.co.uk/extras** and enter this code...

4489 1107 0794 5256

This code only works for one person. If somebody else has used this book before you, they might have already claimed the Online Edition.

A-Level revision? It has to be CGP!

Contents

Module 6: Section 5 — Cloning and Biotechnology

Module 6: Section 6 — Ecosystems

Module 6: Section 7 — Populations and Sustainability

Do Well In Your Exams

Published by CGP

From original material by Richard Parsons.

Editors:
Charlotte Burrows, Christopher McGarry, Claire Plowman, Rachael Rogers, Hayley Thompson.

Contributors:
Gloria Barnett, James Foster, Derek Harvey.

ISBN: 978 1 78294 337 2

With thanks to Karen Wells for the proofreading.
With thanks to Laura Jakubowski for the copyright research.

Cover image © duncan1890/iStockphoto.com
With thanks to Science Photo Library for permission to reproduce the images on pages 11, 20, 22 and 36.

Clipart from Corel®
Printed by Elanders Ltd, Newcastle upon Tyne.

Communication and Homeostasis Basics

Ah, homeostasis. What a lovely topic — all about your body making sure that everything is just right.

Responding to their Environment Helps Organisms Survive

1) **Animals increase** their **chances** of **survival** by **responding** to **changes** in their **external environment**, e.g. by **avoiding harmful environments** such as places that are too hot or too cold.
2) They also **respond** to **changes** in their **internal environment** to make sure that the **conditions** are always **optimal** for their **metabolism** (all the chemical reactions that go on inside them).
3) **Plants** also **increase** their **chances** of **survival** by **responding** to **changes** in their **environment** (see p. 38).
4) Any **change** in the internal or external **environment** is called a **stimulus**.

Receptors Detect Stimuli and Effectors Produce a Response

1) **Receptors detect stimuli.**
2) Receptors are **specific** — they only **detect one particular stimulus**, e.g. light or pressure.
3) There are **many different types** of receptor that each detect a **different type of stimulus**.
4) Some receptors are **cells**, e.g. photoreceptors are receptor cells that connect to the nervous system. Some receptors are **proteins** on **cell surface membranes**, e.g. glucose receptors are proteins found in the cell membranes of some pancreatic cells.
5) **Effectors** are cells that bring about a **response** to a **stimulus**, to produce an **effect**. Effectors include **muscle cells** and cells found in **glands**, e.g. the **pancreas**.

Communication can Occur Between Adjacent and Distant Cells

1) To produce a **response**, **receptors** need to **communicate** with **effectors** and effectors may need to communicate with **other cells**.
2) This happens via **cell signalling**.
3) Cell signalling can occur between **adjacent** (nearby) cells or between **distant** cells. For example, cells in the **nervous system** communicate by secreting **chemicals** called **neurotransmitters**, which send signals to **adjacent** cells, such as other nerve cells or muscle cells. The **hormonal** system works by cells releasing **chemicals** called **hormones**, which travel in the blood and act as signals to **distant** cells.
4) **Cell-surface receptors** allow cells to **recognise** the chemicals involved in cell signalling.

This communication makes sure that the activities of different organs are coordinated to keep the organism working effectively.

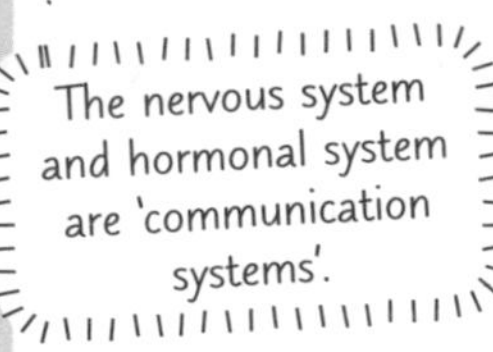

Homeostasis is the Maintenance of a Constant Internal Environment

1) **Changes** in your **external environment** can affect your **internal environment** — the blood and tissue fluid that surrounds your cells.
2) **Homeostasis** involves **control systems** that keep your **internal environment** roughly **constant** (within **certain limits**).
3) **Keeping** your internal environment **constant** is vital for cells to **function normally** and to **stop** them being **damaged**.
4) It's particularly important to **maintain** the right **core body temperature**. This is because temperature affects **enzyme activity**, and enzymes **control** the **rate** of **metabolic reactions**:
   - If **body temperature** is **too high** (e.g. 40 °C) **enzymes** may become **denatured**. The enzyme's molecules **vibrate too much**, which **breaks** the **hydrogen bonds** that hold them in their **3D shape**. The **shape** of the enzyme's **active site** is **changed** and it **no longer works** as a **catalyst**. This means **metabolic reactions** are **less efficient**.
   - If body temperature is **too low enzyme activity** is **reduced**, **slowing** the rate of **metabolic reactions**.
   - The **highest rate** of **enzyme activity** happens at their **optimum temperature** (about **37 °C** in humans).
5) It's also important to **maintain** the right **concentration** of **glucose** in the **blood**, so there's always enough available for respiration.

There's more about control of body temperature on p. 12-13 and control of blood glucose on p. 14-15.

Communication and Homeostasis Basics

Homeostatic Systems Detect a Change and Respond by Negative Feedback

1) Homeostatic systems involve **receptors**, a **communication system** and **effectors** (see the previous page).
2) Receptors detect when a level is **too high** or **too low**, and the information's communicated via the **nervous** system or the **hormonal** system to **effectors**.
3) The effectors respond to **counteract** the change — bringing the level **back** to **normal**.
4) The mechanism that **restores** the level to **normal** is called a **negative feedback** mechanism.
5) Negative feedback **keeps** things around the **normal** level, e.g. body temperature is usually kept **within 0.5 °C** above or below **37 °C**.
6) Negative feedback only works within **certain limits** though — if the change is **too big** then the **effectors** may **not** be able to **counteract** it, e.g. a huge drop in body temperature caused by prolonged exposure to cold weather may be too large to counteract.

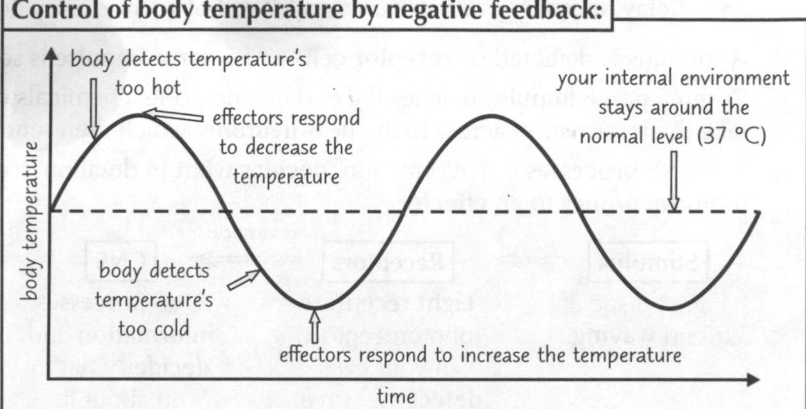

Positive Feedback Mechanisms Amplify a Change from the Normal Level

1) Some changes trigger a **positive feedback** mechanism, which **amplifies** the change.
2) The effectors respond to **further increase** the level **away** from the **normal** level.
3) Positive feedback is useful to **rapidly activate** something, e.g. a **blood clot** after an injury:

- **Platelets** become **activated** and release a **chemical** — this triggers **more platelets** to be activated, and so on.
- Platelets **very quickly** form a **blood clot** at the injury site.
- The process **ends** with **negative feedback**, when the body detects the **blood clot** has been **formed**.

4) Positive feedback **isn't** involved in **homeostasis** because it **doesn't** keep your internal environment **constant**.

Practice Questions

Q1 Why do organisms respond to changes in their environment?

Q2 What is a stimulus?

Q3 Give two types of effector.

Q4 What is cell signalling?

Q5 What is a negative feedback mechanism?

Q6 What type of mechanism amplifies a change from the normal level?

Exam Question

Q1 a) Define homeostasis. [1 mark]

b) Describe the role of receptors, communication systems and effectors in homeostasis. [3 marks]

Responding to questions in an exam helps you to pass...

Multicellular organisms respond to internal changes so that they can keep conditions just right for all their bodily reactions. Maintaining this constant internal environment is called homeostasis — basically you just need to remember that if one thing goes up too high the body responds to bring it down, and vice versa.

Receptors and Neurones

The nervous system helps organisms to respond to the environment, so you need to know a bit more about it...

*The **Nervous System** Sends Information as **Nerve Impulses***

1) The **nervous system** is made up of a **complex network** of cells called **neurones**. There are **three main types:**
   - **Sensory neurones** transmit nerve impulses from **receptors** to the **central nervous system** (**CNS**) — the **brain** and **spinal cord**.
   - **Motor neurones** transmit nerve impulses from the **CNS** to **effectors**.
   - **Relay neurones** transmit nerve impulses **between** sensory neurones and motor neurones.

Nerve impulses are electrical impulses. They're also called action potentials.

2) A stimulus is detected by **receptor cells** and a **nerve impulse** is sent along a **sensory neurone**.
3) When a **nerve impulse** reaches the end of a neurone, chemicals called **neurotransmitters** take the information across to the **next neurone**, which then sends a **nerve impulse** (see p. 8).
4) The **CNS processes** the information, **decides what to do** about it and sends impulses along **motor neurones** to an **effector**.

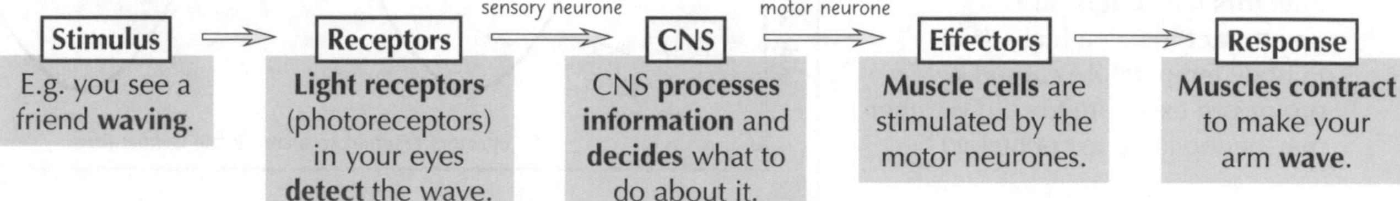

Sensory Receptors** Convert **Stimulus Energy** into **Nerve Impulses

1) **Different stimuli** have **different forms** of **energy**, e.g. light energy or chemical energy.
2) But your **nervous system** only sends information in the form of **nerve impulses** (electrical impulses).
3) **Sensory receptors convert** the energy of a **stimulus** into **electrical energy**.
4) So, sensory receptors act as **transducers** — something that **converts** one form of energy into another.
5) Here's a bit more about how receptor cells that communicate information via the **nervous system** work:

- When a nervous system receptor is in its **resting state** (not being stimulated), there's a **difference in charge** between the **inside** and the **outside** of the cell — this is generated by ion pumps and ion channels. This means there's a **voltage** across the membrane. Voltage is also known as **potential difference**.
- The **potential difference** when a cell is at **rest** is called its **resting potential**. When a stimulus is detected, the cell membrane is **excited** and becomes **more permeable**, allowing **more ions** to move **in** and **out** of the cell — **altering** the **potential difference**. The **change** in **potential difference** due to a stimulus is called the **generator potential**.
- A **bigger stimulus** excites the membrane more, causing a **bigger movement** of ions and a **bigger change** in potential difference — so a **bigger generator potential** is produced.
- If the **generator potential** is **big enough** it'll trigger an **action potential** (nerve impulse) along a neurone. An action potential is only triggered if the generator potential reaches a certain level called the **threshold** level.
- If the stimulus is **too weak** the generator potential **won't reach** the **threshold**, so there's **no action potential**.

Example — Pacinian corpuscles

Pacinian corpuscles are **mechanoreceptors** — they detect **mechanical stimuli**, e.g. **pressure** and **vibrations**. They're found in your **skin**. They contain the end of a **sensory neurone**, called a **sensory nerve ending**. The sensory nerve ending is **wrapped** in lots of layers of connective tissue called **lamellae**.

When a Pacinian corpuscle is **stimulated**, e.g. by a tap on the arm, the lamellae are **deformed** and **press** on the **sensory nerve ending**. This causes **deformation** of **stretch-mediated sodium channels** in the sensory neurone's cell membrane. The sodium ion channels **open** and **sodium ions diffuse into** the cell, creating a **generator potential**. If the **generator potential** reaches the **threshold**, it triggers an **action potential**.

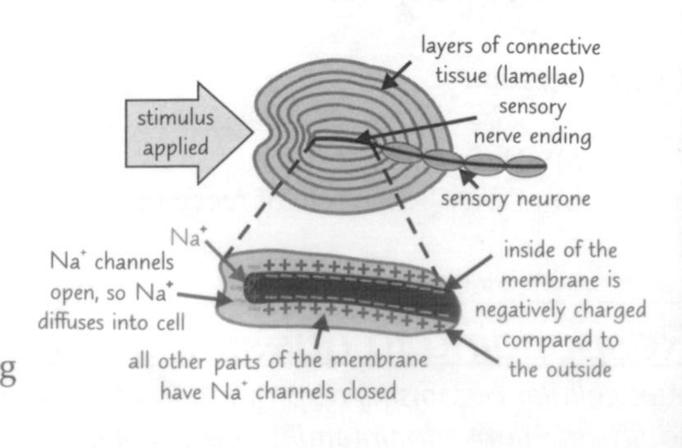

Receptors and Neurones

You Need to Learn the Structure of Sensory, Motor and Relay Neurones...

All neurones have a **cell body** with a **nucleus** (plus **cytoplasm** and all the other **organelles** you usually get in a cell). The cell body has **extensions** that **connect** to **other neurones** — **dendrites** and **dendrons** carry nerve impulses **towards** the **cell body**, and **axons** carry nerve impulses **away** from the **cell body**.

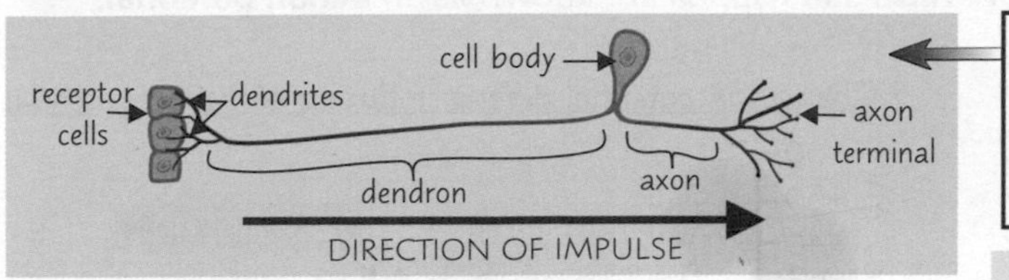

Sensory neurones have **short dendrites** and **one long dendron** to carry nerve impulses from **receptor cells** to the **cell body**, and **one short axon** that carries impulses from the **cell body** to the **CNS**.

Motor neurones have **many short dendrites** that carry nerve impulses from the **central nervous system** (**CNS**) to the **cell body**, and **one long axon** that carries nerve impulses from the **cell body** to **effector cells**.

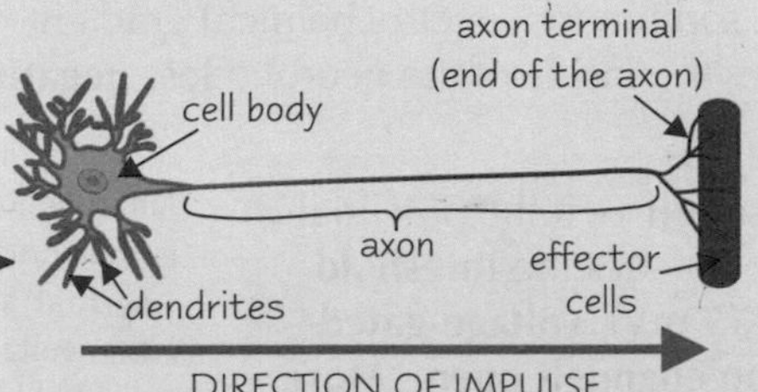

This is a non-myelinated motor neurone — see p. 7 for the structure of a myelinated one.

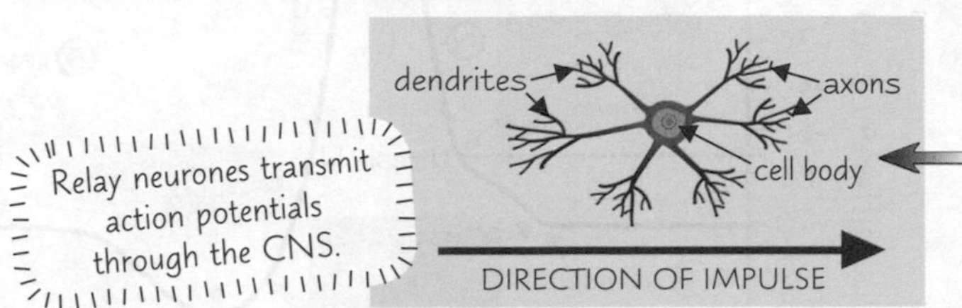

Relay neurones transmit action potentials through the CNS.

Relay neurones have **many short dendrites** that carry nerve impulses from **sensory neurones** to the **cell body**, and **many short axons** that carry nerve impulses from the **cell body** to **motor neurones**.

Neurone Cell Membranes are Polarised at Rest

1) In a neurone's **resting state** (when it's not being stimulated), the **outside** of the membrane is **positively charged** compared to the **inside**. This is because there are **more positive ions outside** the cell than inside.
2) So the membrane is **polarised** — there's a **difference in charge**. The voltage across the membrane when it's at rest is called the **resting potential** — it's about **–70 mV**.
3) The resting potential is created and maintained by **sodium-potassium pumps** and **potassium ion channels** in a neurone's membrane:
4) The sodium-potassium pumps move **sodium ions out** of the neurone, but the membrane **isn't permeable** to **sodium ions**, so they **can't diffuse back in**. This creates a **sodium ion electrochemical gradient** (a **concentration gradient** of **ions**) because there are **more** positive sodium ions **outside** the cell than inside.
5) The sodium-potassium pumps also move **potassium ions in** to the neurone, but the membrane **is permeable** to **potassium ions** so they **diffuse back out** through potassium ion channels.
6) This makes the **outside** of the cell **positively charged** compared to the inside.

Sodium-potassium pump — These pumps use **active transport** to move **three sodium ions** (Na^+) **out** of the neurone for every **two potassium ions** (K^+) moved in. ATP is needed to do this.

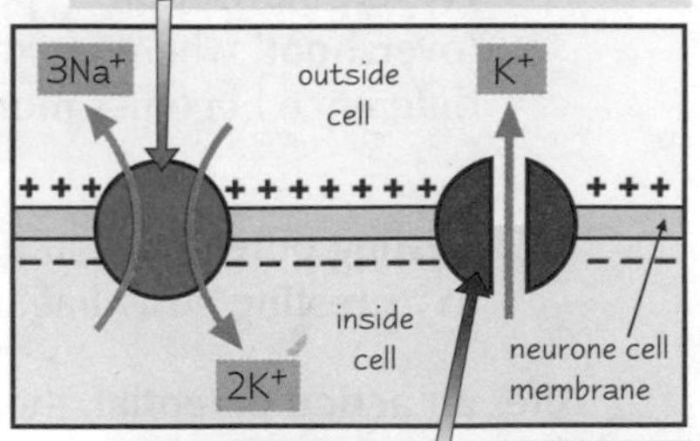

Potassium ion channel — These channels allow **facilitated diffusion** of **potassium ions** (K^+) **out** of the neurone, down their **concentration gradient**.

Practice Questions

Q1 Describe the structures of sensory, motor and relay neurones.

Q2 Describe how resting potential is maintained in a neurone.

Exam Question

Q1 Sensory neurones play a key role in the function of Pacinian corpuscles.

a) Explain why Pacinian corpuscles can be described as transducers. [1 mark]

b) Explain how a generator potential is created when a Pacinian corpuscle is stimulated. [4 marks]

c) Describe the pathway of communication from a Pacinian corpuscle to effector cells via the CNS if the generator potential reaches the threshold level. [2 marks]

Sunday afternoons — all resting potential and no action potential...

Blimey, there's a lot on these pages. All the stuff about sensory receptors and resting potentials can be a bit tricky to get your head around. Just take your time and try scribbling it all down a few times till it starts to make some kind of sense.

Action Potentials

Electrical impulses, nerve impulses, action potentials... call them what you will, you need to know how they work.

Neurone **Cell Membranes** Become **Depolarised** when They're **Stimulated**

A **stimulus** triggers **sodium ion channels** in the cell membrane to **open**. If the stimulus is big enough, it'll trigger a **rapid change** in **potential difference**. The sequence of events that happen are known as an **action potential**:

① **Stimulus** — this **excites** the neurone cell membrane, causing **sodium ion channels** to **open**. The membrane becomes **more permeable** to sodium, so **sodium ions diffuse into** the neurone down the sodium ion electrochemical gradient. This makes the **inside** of the neurone **less negative**.

② **Depolarisation** — if the potential difference reaches the **threshold** (around **–55 mV**), **voltage-gated sodium ion channels open**. **More sodium ions diffuse into** the neurone. This is **positive** feedback (see p. 3).

Voltage-gated ion channels open at a certain voltage.

③ **Repolarisation** — at a potential difference of around **+30 mV** the **sodium ion channels close** and **voltage-gated potassium ion channels open**. The membrane is **more permeable** to potassium so **potassium ions diffuse out** of the neurone down the potassium ion concentration gradient. This starts to get the membrane **back** to its **resting potential**. This is **negative** feedback (see p. 3).

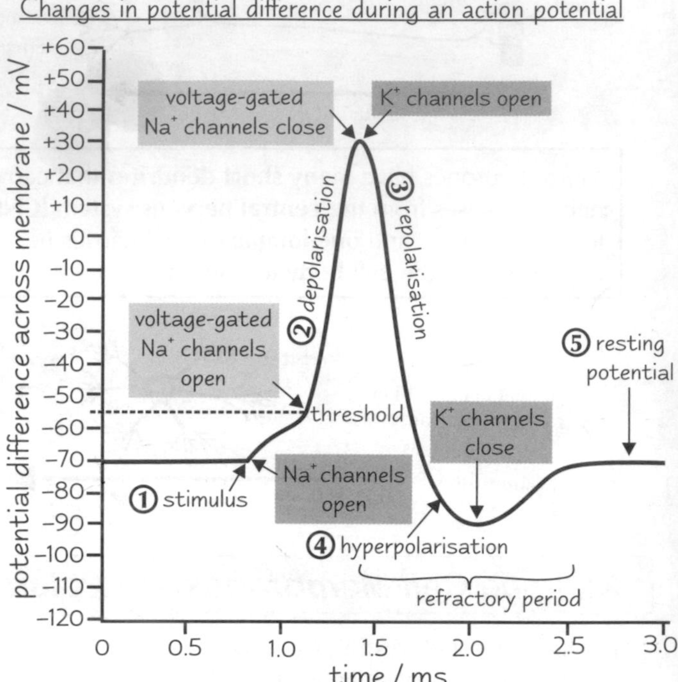

④ **Hyperpolarisation** — **potassium ion channels** are **slow to close** so there's a slight '**overshoot**' where too many potassium ions diffuse out of the neurone. The potential difference becomes **more negative** than the **resting potential** (i.e. less than –70 mV).

⑤ **Resting potential** — the ion channels are **reset**. The **sodium-potassium pump** returns the membrane to its **resting potential** and maintains it until the membrane's excited by another stimulus.

After an **action potential**, the neurone cell membrane **can't** be **excited** again straight away. This is because the ion channels are **recovering** and they **can't** be made to **open** — **sodium ion channels** are **closed** during repolarisation and **potassium ion channels** are **closed** during hyperpolarisation. This period of recovery is called the **refractory period**.

The **Action Potential** Moves **Along** the **Neurone** as a **Wave** of **Depolarisation**

1) When an **action potential** happens, some of the **sodium ions** that enter the neurone **diffuse sideways**.
2) This causes **sodium ion channels** in the **next region** of the neurone to **open** and **sodium ions diffuse into** that part.
3) This causes a **wave of depolarisation** to travel along the neurone.
4) The **wave** moves **away** from the parts of the membrane in the **refractory period** because these parts **can't fire** an action potential.

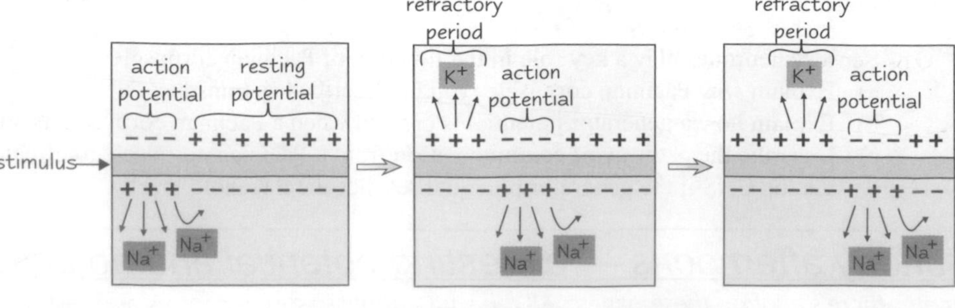

Action Potentials

A Bigger Stimulus Causes More Frequent Impulses

1) Once the threshold is reached, an action potential will **always fire** with the **same change in voltage**, no matter how big the stimulus is.
2) If the **threshold isn't reached**, an action potential **won't fire**. This is the **all-or-nothing** nature of action potentials.
3) A **bigger stimulus** won't cause a bigger action potential, but it will cause them to fire **more frequently** (so if the brain receives a **high frequency** of action potentials, it interprets this as a **big stimulus** and **responds** accordingly).

small stimulus

big stimulus

Action Potentials Go Faster in Myelinated Neurones

1) Some neurones are **myelinated** — they have a **myelin sheath**.
2) The myelin sheath is an **electrical insulator**.
3) In the peripheral nervous system (see p. 28), the myelin sheath is made of a type of cell called a **Schwann cell**.
4) Between the Schwann cells are tiny patches of **bare membrane** called the **nodes of Ranvier**. **Sodium ion channels** are **concentrated** at the nodes.
5) In a **myelinated** neurone, **depolarisation** only happens at the **nodes of Ranvier** (where sodium ions can get through the membrane).
6) The neurone's **cytoplasm conducts** enough electrical charge to **depolarise** the **next node**, so the impulse '**jumps**' from node to node.
7) This is called **saltatory conduction** and it's **really fast**.
8) In a **non-myelinated** neurone, the impulse travels as a **wave** along the **whole length** of the **axon membrane**.
9) This is **slower** than saltatory conduction (although it's still pretty quick).

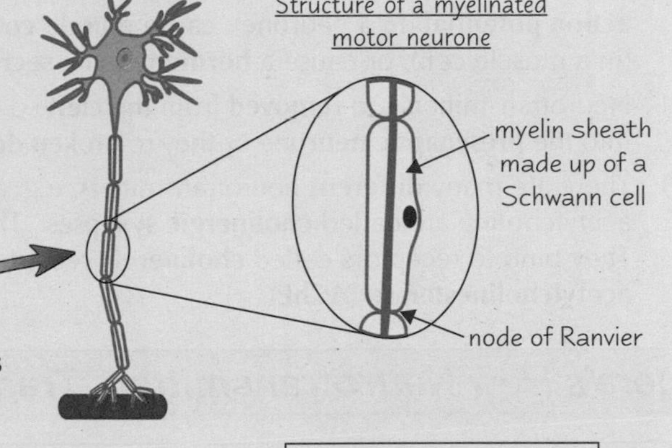
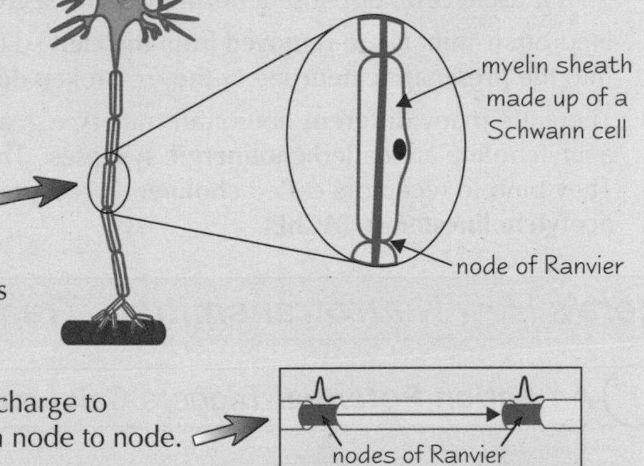

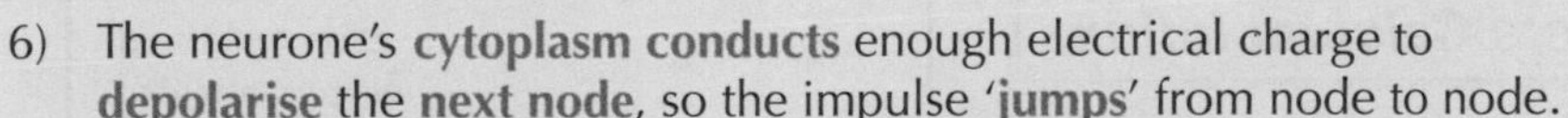

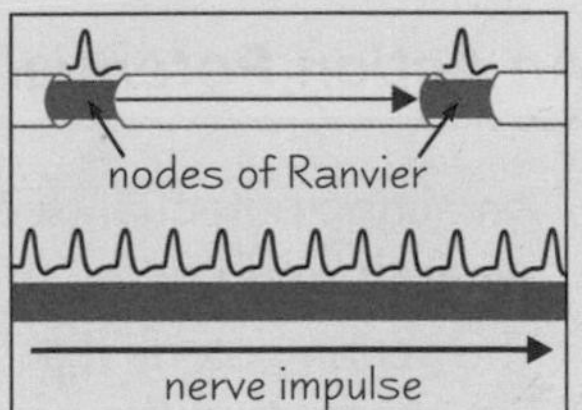

Practice Questions

Q1 Briefly describe how an action potential moves along a non-myelinated neurone.

Q2 What are nodes of Ranvier?

Exam Questions

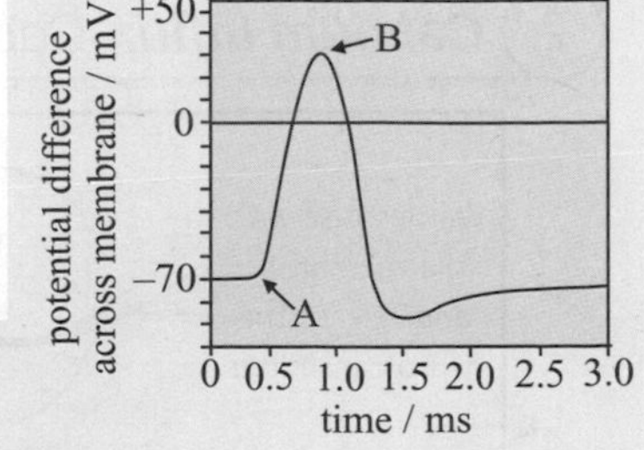

Q1 The graph shows an action potential across an axon membrane following the application of a stimulus.

a) Explain what causes the change in potential difference between point A and point B. [2 marks]

b) The same stimulus was applied consistently for over one hour. The next action potential fired at 4.5 ms. Calculate how many action potentials fired in one hour. Give your answer in standard form. [2 marks]

c) The strength of the stimulus was increased by 50%. Give the maximum potential difference across the membrane that would be experienced with this stronger stimulus. [1 mark]

Q2 Multiple sclerosis is a disease of the nervous system characterised by damage to the myelin sheaths of neurones. Explain how this will affect the transmission of action potentials. [3 marks]

I'm feeling a bit depolarised after all that...

Action potentials are potentially confusing. Just remember that polarisation is the difference in charge across the cell's membrane — during depolarisation that difference becomes smaller and during repolarisation it gets bigger again.

Synapses

When an action potential arrives at the end of a neurone the information has to be passed on to the next cell — this could be another neurone, a muscle cell or a gland cell.

A *Synapse* is a *Junction* Between a *Neurone* and the *Next Cell*

Typical structure of a synapse

1) A **synapse** is the junction between a **neurone** and another **neurone**, or between a **neurone** and an **effector cell**, e.g. a muscle or gland cell.
2) The **tiny gap** between the cells at a synapse is called the **synaptic cleft**.
3) The **presynaptic neurone** (the one before the synapse) has a **swelling** called a **synaptic knob**. This contains **synaptic vesicles** filled with **chemicals** called **neurotransmitters**.
4) When an **action potential** reaches the end of a neurone it causes **neurotransmitters** to be **released** into the synaptic cleft. They **diffuse across** to the **postsynaptic membrane** (the one after the synapse) and **bind** to **specific receptors**.
5) When neurotransmitters bind to receptors they might **trigger** an **action potential** (in a neurone), cause **muscle contraction** (in a muscle cell), or cause a **hormone** to be **secreted** (from a gland cell).
6) Neurotransmitters are **removed** from the **cleft** so the **response** doesn't keep happening, e.g. they're taken back into the **presynaptic neurone** or they're **broken down** by **enzymes** (and the products are taken into the neurone).
7) There are many **different** neurotransmitters, e.g. **acetylcholine** (**ACh**) and **noradrenaline**. Synapses that use acetylcholine are called **cholinergic synapses**. Their structure is exactly the **same** as in the diagram above. They bind to receptors called **cholinergic receptors**, and they're broken down by an enzyme called **acetylcholinesterase** (**AChE**).

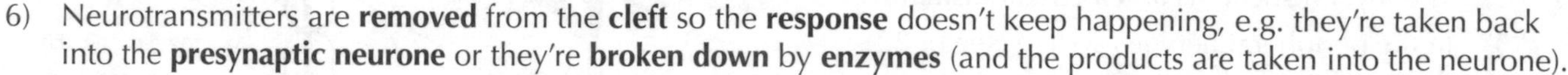

Here's How *Neurotransmitters Transmit Nerve Impulses Between Neurones*

1) An *Action Potential* Triggers *Calcium Influx*

1) An action potential (see p. 6) arrives at the **synaptic knob** of the **presynaptic neurone**.
2) The action potential stimulates **voltage-gated calcium ion channels** in the **presynaptic neurone** to **open**.
3) **Calcium ions diffuse into** the synaptic knob. (They're pumped out afterwards by active transport.)

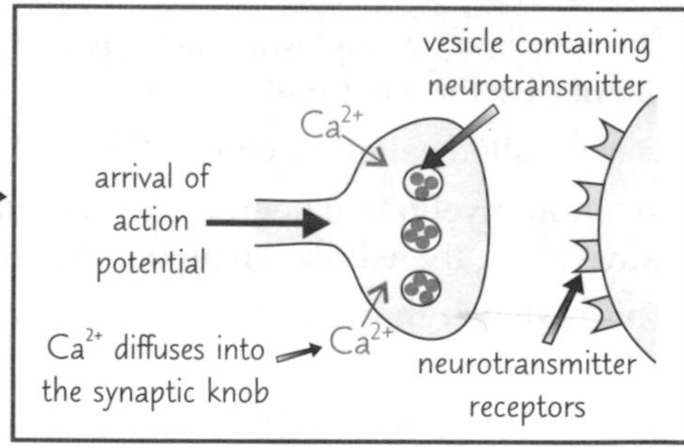

2) *Calcium Influx* Causes *Neurotransmitter Release*

1) The influx of **calcium ions** into the synaptic knob causes the **synaptic vesicles** to **move** to the **presynaptic membrane**. They then **fuse** with the presynaptic membrane.
2) The **vesicles release** the neurotransmitter into the **synaptic cleft** by **exocytosis**.

3) The *Neurotransmitter Triggers* an *Action Potential* in the *Postsynaptic Neurone*

1) The neurotransmitter **diffuses** across the **synaptic cleft** and **binds** to specific **receptors** on the **postsynaptic membrane**.
2) This causes **sodium ion channels** in the **postsynaptic neurone** to **open**. The **influx** of **sodium ions** into the postsynaptic membrane causes **depolarisation**. An **action potential** on the **postsynaptic membrane** is generated if the **threshold** is reached.
3) The **neurotransmitter** is **removed** from the **synaptic cleft** so the **response** doesn't keep happening.

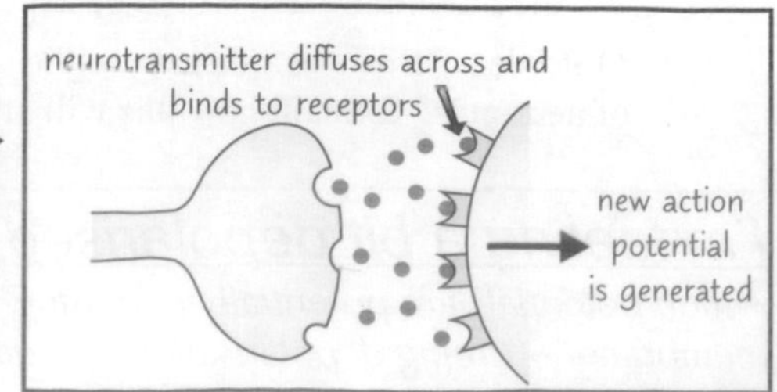

Synapses

Synapses Play Vital Roles in the Nervous System

Synapses allow Information to be Dispersed or Amplified

1) When **one** neurone **connects** to **many** neurones information can be **dispersed** to **different parts** of the body. This is called **synaptic divergence.**
2) When **many** neurones **connect** to **one** neurone information can be **amplified** (made stronger). This is called **synaptic convergence.**

Summation at Synapses Finely Tunes the Nervous Response

If a stimulus is **weak**, only a **small amount** of **neurotransmitter** will be released from a neurone into the synaptic cleft. This might not be enough to **excite** the postsynaptic membrane to the **threshold** level and stimulate an action potential. **Summation** is where the effect of neurotransmitters can be **combined**. There are two types:

Spatial summation

1) When neurones converge (see above), the small amount of **neurotransmitter** released from **each** neurone can be enough **altogether** to **reach** the **threshold** in the postsynaptic neurone and **trigger** an **action potential.**
2) Stimuli might arrive from **different sources.** Spatial summation allows signals from **multiple stimuli** to be **coordinated** into a **single response.**

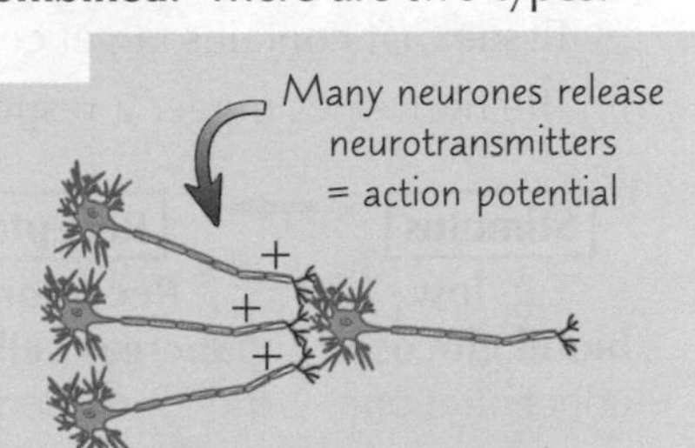

Temporal summation

Temporal summation is where **two or more** nerve impulses arrive in **quick succession** from the **same presynaptic neurone**. This makes an action potential **more likely** because **more neurotransmitter** is released into the **synaptic cleft.**

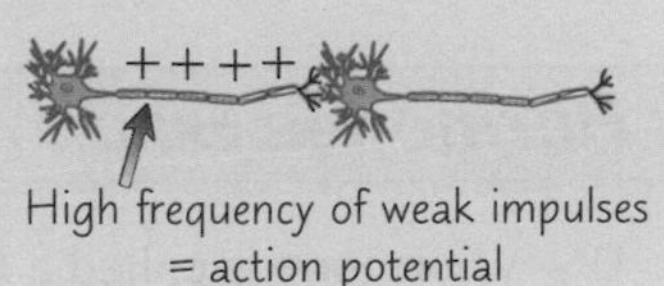

Both types of **summation** mean synapses **accurately process information, finely tuning** the response.

Synapses Make Sure Impulses are Transmitted One Way

Receptors for neurotransmitters are **only** on the **postsynaptic** membranes, so synapses make sure **impulses** can only travel in **one direction.**

Practice Questions

Q1 Give one way that neurotransmitters are removed from the synaptic cleft.
Q2 What neurotransmitter do you find at cholinergic synapses?

Exam Questions

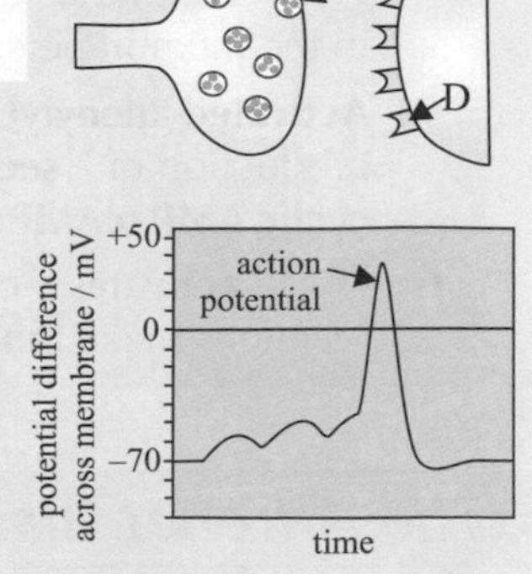

Q1 The diagram on the right shows a synapse. Describe the event that happens at each labelled point following the arrival of an action potential. [4 marks]

Q2 The graph on the right shows the potential difference across a postsynaptic membrane against time.
a) Suggest why a potential difference of –45 mV is significant for this postsynaptic membrane. [1 mark]
b) The action potential shown on the graph was fired as a result of temporal summation. Explain how the action potential was created. [4 marks]

You might need to look back at p. 6 for a quick recap on action potentials.

Synaptic knobs and clefts — will you stop giggling at the back...

Some more pretty tough pages here — lovely. And lots more diagrams to have a go at drawing and re-drawing. Don't worry if you're not the world's best artist, just make sure you add labels to your drawings to explain what's happening.

The Hormonal System and Glands

Now you've seen how the nervous system helps us respond to our environment, it's on to the hormonal system...

*The **Hormonal System** Sends Information as **Chemical Signals***

1) The **hormonal system** is made up of **glands** (called **endocrine glands**) and **hormones**:
   - **Endocrine glands** are groups of cells that are specialised to **secrete hormones**. E.g. the **pancreas** secretes **insulin**.
   - **Hormones** are '**chemical messengers**'. Many hormones are **proteins** or **peptides**, e.g. **insulin**. Some hormones are **steroids**, e.g. **progesterone**.

The hormonal system is also called the endocrine system.

2) **Hormones** are **secreted** when an **endocrine gland** is **stimulated**:
   - Glands can be **stimulated** by a **change** in **concentration** of a specific **substance** (sometimes **another hormone**).
   - They can also be **stimulated** by **electrical impulses**.
3) Hormones **diffuse directly into** the **blood**, then they're **taken** around the body by the **circulatory system**.
4) They **diffuse out** of the blood **all over** the **body** but each hormone will only **bind** to **specific receptors** for that hormone, found on the membranes of some cells, called **target cells**. Tissue that contains target cells is called **target tissue**.
5) The hormones trigger a **response** in the **target cells** (the **effectors**).

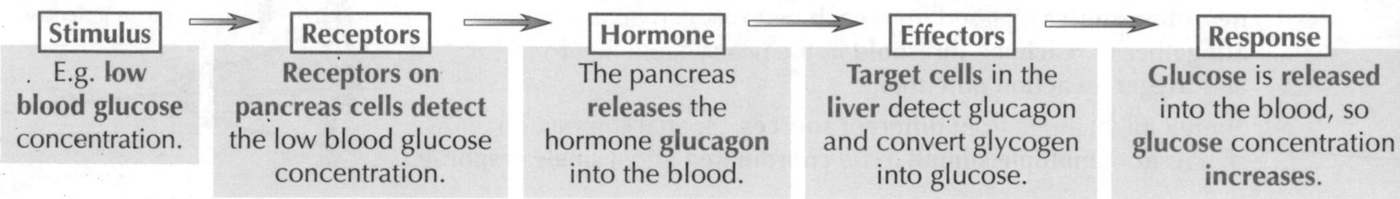

Hormones Bind to Receptors and Trigger Second Messengers

1) A **hormone** is called a **first messenger** because it carries the chemical message the **first part** of the way, from the **endocrine gland** to the **receptor** on the **target cells**.
2) When a hormone **binds** to its receptor it **activates** an **enzyme** in the **cell membrane**.
3) The enzyme catalyses the **production** of a **molecule** inside the cell called a **signalling molecule** — this molecule **signals** to **other parts** of the cell to **change** how the cell **works**.
4) The **signalling molecule** is called a **second messenger** because it carries the chemical message the **second part** of the way, from the **receptor** to **other parts** of the **cell**.
5) Second messengers **activate** a **cascade** (a chain of reactions) **inside** the cell. Here's an **example** you need to **learn**:

- The hormone **adrenaline** is a **first messenger**.
- It binds to **specific receptors** in the **cell membranes** of many cells, e.g. liver cells.
- When adrenaline binds it **activates** an **enzyme** in the membrane called **adenylyl cyclase**.
- **Activated adenylyl cyclase** catalyses the production of a **second messenger** called **cyclic AMP** (**cAMP**) from **ATP**.
- cAMP **activates** a **cascade**, e.g. a cascade of enzyme reactions make **more glucose available** to the cell by catalysing the breakdown of **glycogen** into **glucose**.

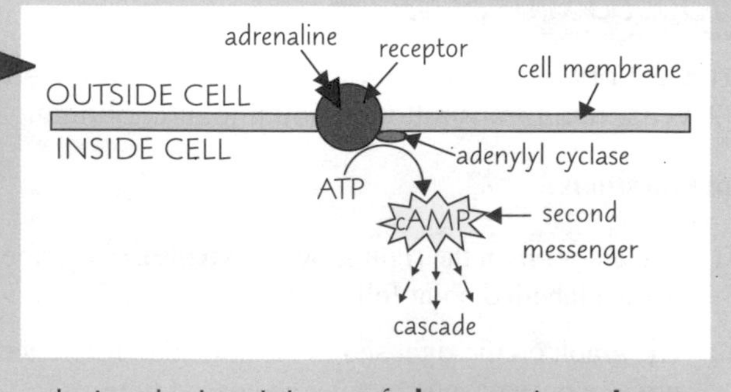

*The **Adrenal Glands** Secrete **Hormones***

1) The **adrenal glands** are **endocrine glands** that are found just **above** your **kidneys**.
2) Each adrenal gland has an **outer** part called the **cortex** and an **inner** part called the **medulla**.
3) The cortex and the medulla have **different functions** and produce different responses.

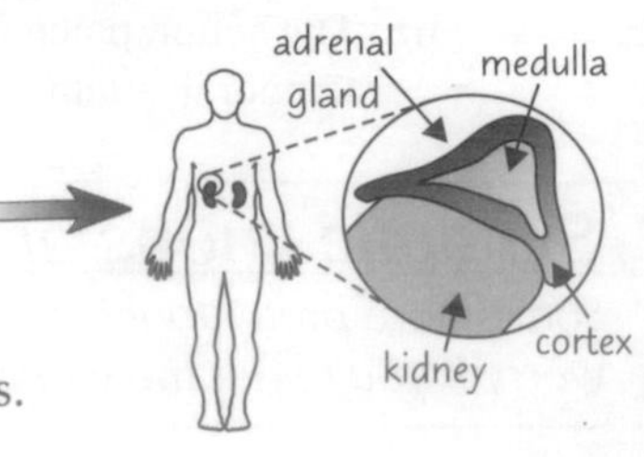

The Hormonal System and Glands

The Cortex and the Medulla are Involved in the Response to Stress

The **cortex** secretes **steroid hormones**, e.g. it secretes **cortisol** and **aldosterone** when you're **stressed**. These hormones have a role in both the **short-term** and the **long-term** responses to stress. Their effects include:

- stimulating the **breakdown** of **proteins** and **fats** into glucose. This **increases** the amount of **energy** available so the **brain** and **muscles** can **respond** to the situation.
- **increasing blood volume** and **pressure** by **increasing** the **uptake** of **sodium ions** and **water** by the kidneys.
- **suppressing** the **immune system**.

The **medulla** secretes **catecholamine hormones** (modified amino acids), e.g. it secretes **adrenaline** and **noradrenaline** when you're stressed. These act to make more **energy** available in the **short-term** by:

- **increasing heart** and **breathing** rate.
- causing cells to break down **glycogen** into **glucose**.
- **constricting** some **blood vessels** so that **blood** is diverted to the **brain** and **muscles**.

These effects help to prepare the body for the **'fight or flight'** response (see pages 30-31).

The Pancreas has a role as an Endocrine Gland

The pancreas is a gland that's found **below** the **stomach**. You need to know about its **endocrine** function:

1) The areas of the pancreas that contain **endocrine tissue** are called the **islets of Langerhans**.
2) They're found in clusters around **blood capillaries**.
3) The islets of Langerhans **secrete hormones** directly into the **blood**.
4) They're made up of **two types** of cell:
   - **Alpha** (α) **cells** secrete a **hormone** called **glucagon**.
   - **Beta** (β) **cells** secrete a **hormone** called **insulin**.
5) **Glucagon** and **insulin** help to **control blood glucose concentration** (see p. 14).

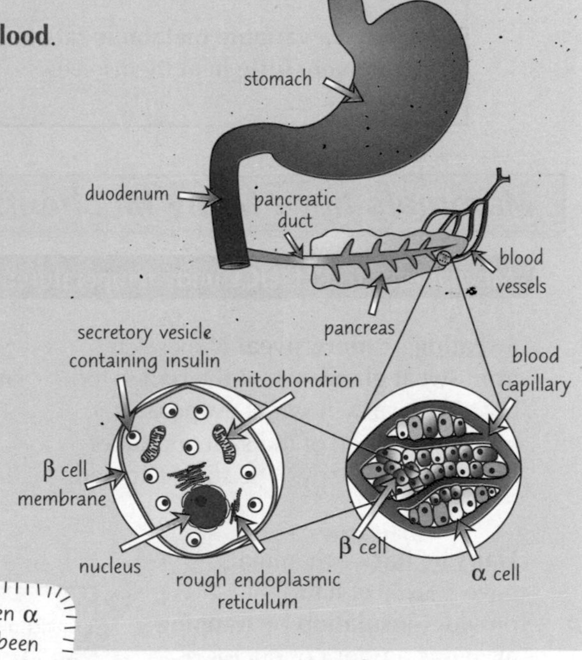

Here's what you might see if you looked at a stained section of **pancreatic tissue** under a **light microscope**:

The purple stained cells are the β cells.

If you look closely you can see pink stained cells — these are α cells.

The islets of Langerhans (endocrine tissue) appear as paler patches in amongst all the other cells.

You can only differentiate between α and β cells if a special stain has been used to make them different colours, e.g. chrome haematoxylin and phloxine.

Practice Questions

Q1 Name the two hormones secreted by the islets of Langerhans.

Q2 How would you identify endocrine tissue if you examined stained pancreatic tissue under a light microscope?

Exam Questions

Q1 Describe the role of the adrenal gland cortex in the long-term response to stress. [3 marks]

Q2 One physiological effect of the 'fight or flight' response is an increase in the conversion of glycogen to glucose. Explain how stimulation of the adrenal gland's medulla causes this effect. [3 marks]

Islets of Langerhans — sounds like an exotic beach to me...

All this talk of the "islets of Langerhans" and I can think of nothing else but sun, sea and sand... but it's secretions, second messengers and cyclic AMP for you, until your exams are over and you can start planning any holidays.

Homeostasis — Control of Body Temperature

Homeostasis is responsible for controlling body temperature in mammals like you — stopping you freezing or becoming a hot sweaty mess. Other organisms control their body temperature differently. Read on, oh chosen one, read on...

Temperature** is **Controlled Differently** in **Ectotherms** and **Endotherms

Animals are classed as either **ectotherms** or **endotherms**, depending on how they **control** their body temperature:

Ectotherms — e.g. **reptiles, fish**	**Endotherms** — e.g. **mammals, birds**
Ectotherms **can't control** their body temperature **internally** — they **control** their temperature by **changing** their **behaviour** (e.g. reptiles gain heat by basking in the sun).	Endotherms **control** their body temperature **internally** by **homeostasis**. They can also control their temperature by **behaviour** (e.g. by finding shade).
Their **internal** temperature **depends** on the **external temperature** (their surroundings).	Their internal temperature is **less affected** by the **external temperature** (within certain limits).
Their **activity** level **depends** on the external temperature — they're **more** active at **higher** temperatures and **less** active at **lower** temperatures.	Their **activity** level is largely **independent** of the **external temperature** — they can be active at any temperature (within certain limits).
They have a **variable metabolic rate** and they **generate** very **little heat** themselves.	They have a constantly **high metabolic rate** and they **generate** a **lot** of **heat** from metabolic reactions.

Mammals** have **Many Mechanisms** to **Change Body Temperature

Mechanisms to REDUCE body temperature:

Sweating — **more sweat** is secreted from **sweat glands** when the body's too hot. The water in sweat **evaporates** from the surface of the skin and **takes heat** from the body. The **skin** is **cooled**.

Hairs lie flat — mammals have a layer of **hair** that provides **insulation** by **trapping air** (air is a poor conductor of heat). When it's hot, **erector pili muscles relax** so the hairs lie flat. **Less air** is trapped, so the skin is **less insulated** and **heat** can be **lost** more easily.

Vasodilation — when it's hot, **arterioles** near the surface of the skin **dilate** (this is called **vasodilation**). **More blood** flows through the **capillaries** in the surface layers of the dermis. This means **more heat** is **lost** from the skin by **radiation** and the **temperature** is **lowered**.

Mechanisms to INCREASE body temperature:

Shivering — when it's cold, **muscles contract** in **spasms**. This makes the body **shiver** and **more heat** is **produced** from **increased respiration**.

Much less sweat — less **sweat** is secreted from sweat glands when it's cold, **reducing** the amount of **heat loss**.

Hairs stand up — **erector pili muscles contract** when it's cold, which makes the **hairs stand up**. This **traps more air** and so **prevents heat loss**.

Vasoconstriction — when it's cold, **arterioles** near the surface of the skin **constrict** (this is called **vasoconstriction**) so **less blood** flows through the **capillaries** in the surface layers of the dermis. This **reduces heat loss**.

Hormones — the body releases **adrenaline** and **thyroxine**. These **increase metabolism** and so **more heat** is **produced**.

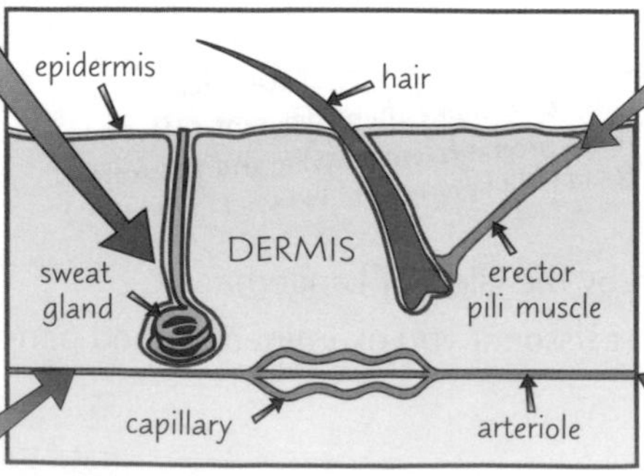

Homeostasis — Control of Body Temperature

*The **Hypothalamus Controls** Body Temperature in **Mammals***

1) **Body temperature** in mammals is **maintained** at a **constant level** by a part of the **brain** called the **hypothalamus**.
2) The hypothalamus **receives information** about **temperature** from **thermoreceptors** (temperature receptors):
   - Thermoreceptors in the **hypothalamus** detect **internal temperature** (the temperature of the blood).
   - Thermoreceptors in the **skin** (called **peripheral temperature receptors**) detect **external temperature** (the temperature of the skin).
3) Thermoreceptors send **impulses** along **sensory neurones** to the **hypothalamus**, which sends **impulses** along **motor neurones** to **effectors** (e.g. **skeletal muscles**, or **sweat glands** and **erector pili muscles** in the **skin**).
4) The effectors respond to **restore** the body temperature **back** to **normal**. Here's how it all works:

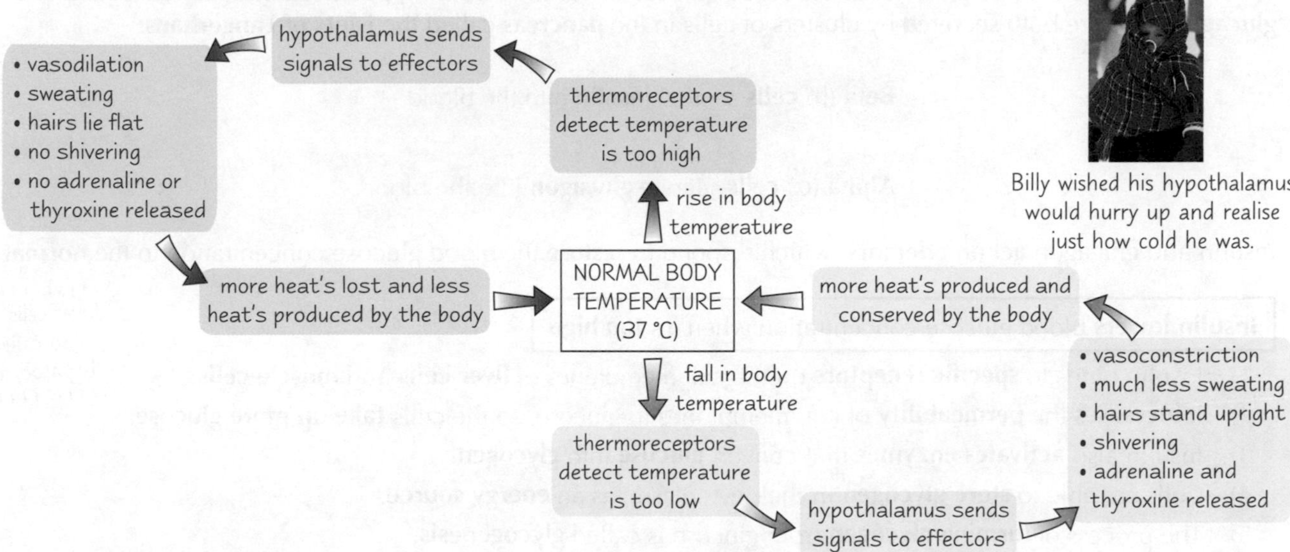

Billy wished his hypothalamus would hurry up and realise just how cold he was.

Practice Questions

Q1 Give four differences between ectotherms and endotherms.
Q2 Which type of animal has more control over their body temperature, ectotherms or endotherms?
Q3 How does sweating reduce body temperature?
Q4 How does vasodilation help the body to lose heat?
Q5 Which part of the brain is responsible for maintaining a constant body temperature in mammals?

Exam Questions

Q1 Describe and explain how the body detects a high external temperature. [2 marks]

Q2 Snakes are usually found in warm climates. Suggest why they are not usually found in cold climates. Explain your answer. [3 marks]

Q3 Mammals that live in cold climates have thick fur and layers of fat beneath their skin to keep them warm. Describe and explain two other ways they maintain a constant body temperature in cold conditions. [4 marks]

No need to sweat about this page...

The mechanisms that change body temperature are pretty good and can cope with some extreme temperatures, but I reckon I could think up some slightly less embarrassing ways of doing it, instead of getting all red-faced and stinky. Mind you, it seems like ectotherms have got it sussed with their whole sunbathing thing — now that's definitely the life...

Homeostasis — Control of Blood Glucose

These pages are all about how homeostasis helps you to not go totally hyper when you stuff your face with sweets.

Eating and *Exercise* Change the *Concentration* of *Glucose* in your *Blood*

1) **All cells** need a constant **energy supply** to work — so **blood glucose concentration** must be carefully **controlled**.
2) The **concentration** of **glucose** in the blood is **normally** around **90 mg per 100 cm³** of blood. It's **monitored** by cells in the **pancreas**.
3) Blood glucose concentration **rises** after **eating food** containing **carbohydrate**.
4) Blood glucose concentration **falls** after **exercise**, as **more glucose** is used in **respiration** to **release energy**.

Insulin and *Glucagon Control* Blood Glucose Concentration

The hormonal system (see p. 10) **controls** blood glucose concentration using **two hormones** called **insulin** and **glucagon**. They're both **secreted** by clusters of cells in the **pancreas** called the **islets of Langerhans**:

Beta (β) cells secrete **insulin** into the blood.

Alpha (α) cells secrete **glucagon** into the blood.

Insulin and glucagon act on **effectors**, which respond to **restore** the blood glucose concentration to the **normal level**:

Liver cells are also called hepatocytes.

Insulin lowers blood glucose concentration when it's **too high**

1) Insulin binds to **specific receptors** on the cell membranes of **liver cells** and **muscle cells**.
2) It **increases** the **permeability** of cell membranes to glucose, so the cells **take up more glucose**.
3) Insulin also **activates enzymes** that convert **glucose** into **glycogen**.
4) Cells are able to **store glycogen** in their cytoplasm, as an **energy source**.
5) The process of **forming glycogen** from glucose is called **glycogenesis**.

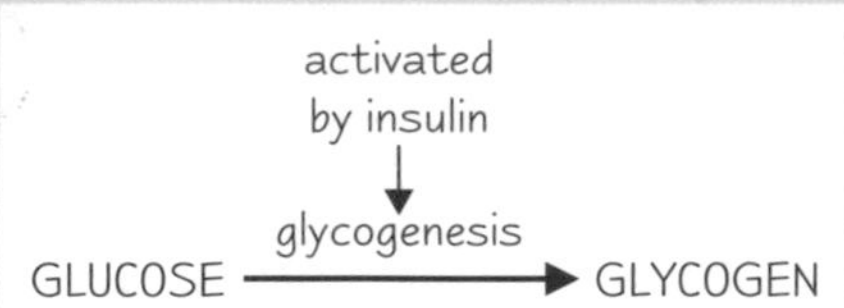

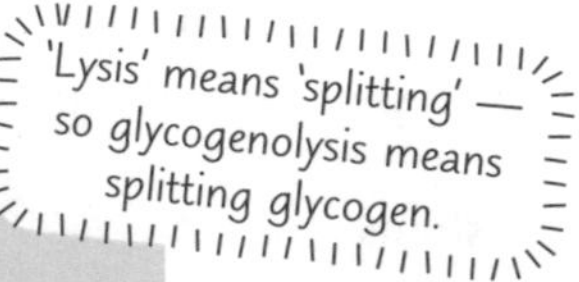

6) Insulin also **increases** the **rate** of **respiration** of glucose, especially in muscle cells.

Glucagon raises blood glucose concentration when it's **too low**

'Lysis' means 'splitting' — so glycogenolysis means splitting glycogen.

1) Glucagon binds to **specific receptors** on the cell membranes of **liver cells**.
2) Glucagon **activates enzymes** that **break down glycogen** into **glucose**.
3) The process of **breaking down glycogen** is called **glycogenolysis**.
4) Glucagon also promotes the formation of glucose from **fatty acids** and **amino acids**.
5) The process of **forming glucose** from **non-carbohydrates** is called **gluconeogenesis**.

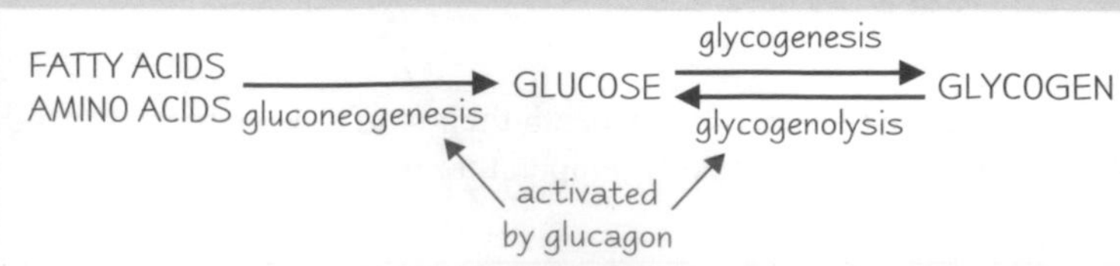

6) Glucagon **decreases** the **rate** of **respiration** of glucose in cells.

Melvin had finally mastered the ancient "chair-lysis" move.

Homeostasis — Control of Blood Glucose

Negative Feedback Mechanisms** Keep Blood Glucose Concentration **Normal

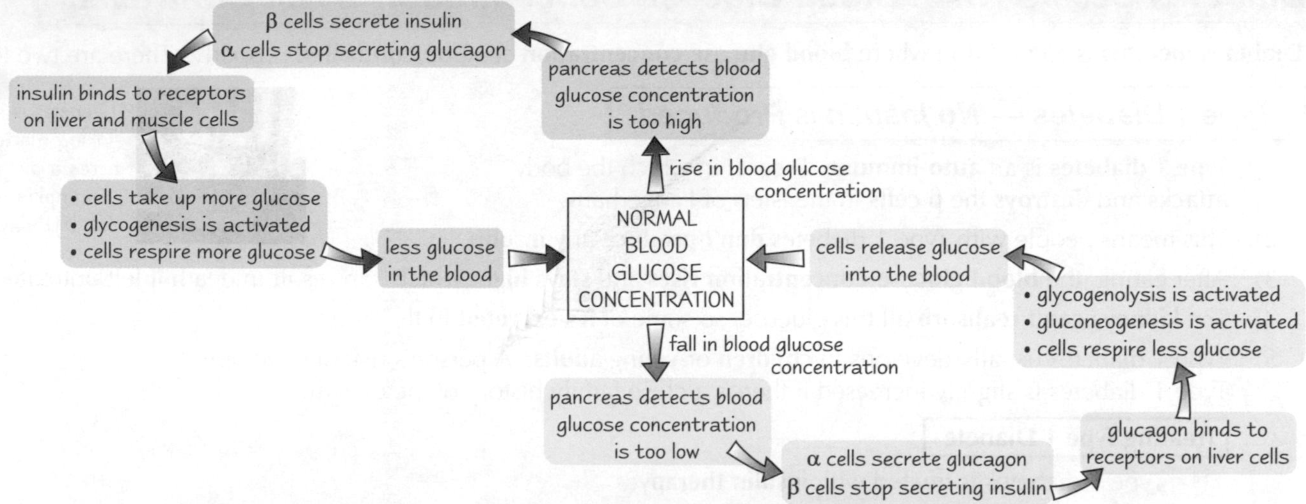

Beta (β) Cells Secrete Insulin** when they're **Depolarised

β cells **contain insulin** stored in **vesicles**. β cells **secrete insulin** when they **detect high blood glucose concentration**. Here's how it happens:

1) When blood glucose concentration is **high**, **more glucose enters** the β cells by **facilitated diffusion.**
2) **More glucose** in a β cell causes the rate of **respiration** to **increase**, making **more ATP**.
3) The **rise** in **ATP** triggers the **potassium ion channels** in the β cell plasma membrane to **close**.
4) This means **potassium ions** (K^+) **can't** get through the membrane — so they **build up inside** the cell.
5) This makes the **inside** of the β cell **less negative** because there are **more positively-charged** potassium ions **inside** the cell — so the plasma membrane of the β cell is **depolarised.**
6) Depolarisation triggers **calcium ion channels** in the membrane to **open**, so **calcium ions diffuse into** the β cell.
7) This causes the **vesicles** to **fuse** with the **β cell plasma membrane**, **releasing insulin** (by **exocytosis**).

Practice Questions

Q1 Why does your blood glucose concentration fall after exercise?

Q2 What's the process of breaking down glycogen into glucose called?

Q3 Give two effects of glucagon on liver cells.

Exam Questions

Q1 The pancreas secretes hormones that control blood glucose concentration.

a) What type of feedback mechanism is involved in the control of blood glucose concentration? Explain your answer. [1 mark]

b) Explain the role of insulin in this feedback mechanism. [4 marks]

Q2 Suggest the effect on a β cell of respiration being inhibited. [2 marks]

My α cells detect low glucose — urgent tea and biscuit break needed...

Aaaaargh there are so many stupidly complex names to learn and they all look and sound exactly the same to me. You can't even get away with sneakily misspelling them all in your exam — like writing 'glycusogen' or 'gluconesisolysis'. Nope, examiners have been around for centuries, so I'm afraid old tricks like that just won't work on them. Grrrrrrr.

Diabetes

Homeostasis really tries its best to keep everything under control. Unfortunately nothing's perfect...

Diabetes Occurs When **Blood Glucose Concentration** is **Not Controlled**

Diabetes mellitus is a condition where **blood glucose concentration** can't be **controlled** properly. There are two types:

Type 1 Diabetes — No Insulin is **Produced**

Diabetes is not a joking matter so here's a picture of a pumpkin on its birthday.

1) **Type 1 diabetes** is an **auto-immune** disease, in which the body **attacks** and **destroys** the **β cells** in the islets of Langerhans.
2) This means people with Type 1 diabetes **don't produce** any **insulin**.
3) After eating, the **blood glucose concentration rises** and **stays high**, which can result in death if left untreated.
4) The **kidneys can't reabsorb** all this glucose, so some of it's **excreted** in the urine.
5) Type 1 diabetes usually develops in **children** or **young adults**. A person's risk of developing Type 1 diabetes is slightly increased if there's a close family history of the disease.

Treating Type 1 Diabetes

1) Type 1 diabetes is treated with **insulin therapy**:
   - Most people with Type 1 diabetes need **regular insulin injections** throughout the day.
   - Some people use an **insulin pump** — this is a machine that continuously delivers insulin into the body via a tube inserted beneath the skin.
2) Some people have been successfully treated by having **islet cell transplantation** — they receive healthy islet cells from a donor so their **pancreas** can produce some insulin (although they usually still need some additional insulin therapy).
3) Whatever type of treatment they have, people with Type 1 diabetes need to regularly **monitor** their blood glucose concentration and think carefully about:
   - **Diet** — Eating a **healthy, balanced diet** reduces the amount of insulin that needs to be injected. People with Type 1 diabetes often have a **carefully planned** diet so that they can manage the amount of glucose they are taking in.
   - **Activity** — Doing **regular exercise** reduces the amount of insulin that needs to be injected by using up blood glucose.

Type 2 Diabetes — Linked to **Obesity**

1) **Type 2 diabetes** occurs when the **β cells** don't produce **enough insulin** or when the **body's cells** don't **respond properly** to insulin.
2) Cells don't respond properly because the **insulin receptors** on their membranes don't work properly, so the cells don't take up enough glucose.
3) This means the **blood glucose concentration** is **higher** than normal.
4) Type 2 diabetes is usually acquired **later in life** than Type 1, and it's often linked with **obesity**. The risk of developing Type 2 diabetes is also increased in people from certain ethnic groups, e.g. African or Asian, and in people with a close family history of the disease.

Treating Type 2 Diabetes

1) Type 2 diabetes is **initially** managed through **lifestyle** changes. Eating a **healthy, balanced diet**, getting **regular exercise** and **losing weight** if needed can help **prevent** the **onset** of Type 2 diabetes as well as **control** the **effects**.
2) If blood glucose concentration can't be controlled through lifestyle changes alone, then **medication** may be prescribed. Some examples are:
   - **Metformin** — This is usually the first medicine to be prescribed. Metformin acts on **liver cells** to **reduce** the **amount of glucose** that they **release** into the blood. It also acts to **increase** the **sensitivity** of cells to **insulin** so **more glucose** can be **taken up** with the same amount of insulin.
   - **Sulfonylureas** (e.g. gliclazide) — These stimulate the pancreas to **produce more insulin**.
   - **Thiazolidinediones** (e.g. pioglitazone) — These also make the body cells **more sensitive** to **insulin**.
3) In some people with Type 2 diabetes, these types of medication are **not enough** to control blood glucose concentration so **insulin therapy** is used in addition or instead.

Diabetes

Insulin can be *Produced* by *Genetically Modified Bacteria*

1) Insulin **used** to be **extracted** from **animal pancreases** (e.g. **pigs** and **cattle**), to treat people with **Type 1** diabetes.
2) But **nowadays**, **human insulin** can be made by **genetically modified** (**GM**) **bacteria** (see p. 100).
3) Using **GM bacteria** to produce insulin is **much better** for many reasons, for example:

- **Producing** insulin using GM bacteria is **cheaper** than extracting it from animal pancreases.
- **Larger quantities** of insulin can be produced using GM bacteria.
- GM bacteria make **human insulin**. This is **more effective** than using **pig** or **cattle insulin** (which is slightly different to human insulin) and it's **less likely** to trigger an **allergic response** or be **rejected** by the **immune system**.
- Some people **prefer** insulin from **GM bacteria** for **ethical** or **religious** reasons. E.g. some **vegetarians** may **object** to the **use** of **animals**, and some **religious people object** to using insulin from **pigs**.

Stem Cells Could be Used to *Cure Diabetes*

Look back at your notes on Module 2 if you need to remind yourself about stem cells.

1) Stem cells are **unspecialised cells** — they have the **ability** to **develop** into **any type** of cell.
2) Using stem cells could **potentially cure** diabetes — here's how:

- **Stem cells** could be **grown** into **β cells**.
- The β cells would then be **implanted** into the **pancreas** of a person with **Type 1 diabetes**.
- This means the person would be able to **make insulin** as **normal**.
- This treatment is **still being developed**. But if it's effective, it'll **cure** people with Type 1 diabetes.

Practice Questions

Q1 What is diabetes?

Q2 What is the cause of Type 1 diabetes?

Q3 Briefly describe how stem cells could be used to cure diabetes.

Exam Questions

Q1 Give two advantages of using insulin produced by genetically modified (GM) bacteria over using insulin extracted from animal pancreases. [2 marks]

Q2 A glucose tolerance test can indicate the presence of diabetes. After fasting for 12 hours, a drink containing glucose is consumed. The graph on the right shows how the blood glucose concentration of two people changed in the time after having the drink. Person A has Type 2 diabetes, person B does not have diabetes.

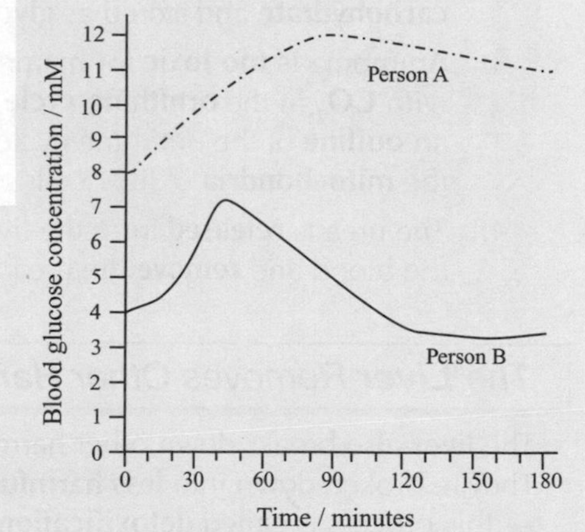

a) Give two pieces of evidence from the graph that suggest person A has diabetes. [1 mark]

b) Person A produces insulin but can't control their blood glucose concentration. Explain why. [2 marks]

c) i) Calculate the rate at which person B's blood glucose concentration is decreasing between 50 and 120 minutes. [1 mark]

ii) Explain why person A's blood glucose does not decrease at the same rate as person B's. [1 mark]

d) After the test person A started taking Metformin regularly. Explain how this would affect their blood glucose concentration if they were to do the glucose tolerance test again in the future. [3 marks]

And people used to think the pancreas was just a cushion...(true)

Sometimes the hormonal system goes wrong and causes problems, like diabetes. Luckily advances in medical technology (e.g. GM insulin and stem cells) have helped to treat these problems. A healthy diet and regular exercise help too. Congratulations, you've made it to the end of this gigantic section. Have some tea to celebrate.

The Liver and Excretion

Liver — not just what my friend Ted eats with onions. The liver has lots of functions, but the main one you need to know about is its job in excretion. It's great at breaking things down like excess amino acids and other harmful substances.

Excretion is the Removal of Waste Products from the Body

All the **chemical reactions** that happen in your cells make up your **metabolism**. Metabolism produces **waste products** — substances that **aren't needed** by the cells, such as **carbon dioxide** and **nitrogenous** (nitrogen-containing) **waste**. Many of these products are **toxic**, so if they were allowed to **build up** in the body they would cause **damage**, e.g. by affecting other metabolic reactions. This is where **excretion** comes in. Excretion is the **removal** of the **waste products of metabolism** from the body.

For example, **carbon dioxide** is a waste product of **respiration**. **Too much** in the blood is toxic, so it's removed from the body by the **lungs** (e.g. in mammals) or **gills** (e.g. in fish). The lungs and gills act as **excretory organs**.

Excreting waste products from the body **maintains normal metabolism**. It also **maintains homeostasis** by helping to keep the levels of certain substances in the blood **roughly constant**.

You Need to Know About the Functions of the Liver

The liver has important functions in **excretion** and **energy storage**:

Excess Amino Acids are Broken Down by the Liver

One of the liver's most important roles is getting rid of **excess amino acids** produced by eating and **digesting protein**. **Amino acids** contain **nitrogen** in their **amino groups**. **Nitrogenous substances can't** usually be **stored** by the body. This means **excess** amino acids can be **damaging** to the body, so they must be **used** by the body (e.g. to make proteins) or be **broken down and excreted**. Here's how excess amino acids are broken down in the **liver**:

1) First, the nitrogen-containing **amino groups** (-NH_2) are **removed** from any **excess** amino acids, forming **ammonia** (NH_3) and **organic acids** — this process is called **deamination**.
2) The organic acids can be **respired** to give **ATP** or converted to **carbohydrate** and stored as **glycogen**.
3) Ammonia is **too toxic** for mammals to excrete directly, so it's **combined** with CO_2 in the **ornithine cycle** to create **urea**. The diagram shows an **outline** of the ornithine cycle — the part in **orange** happens in the **mitochondria** of liver cells and the rest happens in the **cytoplasm**.
4) The urea is **released** from the liver into the **blood**. The **kidneys** then **filter** the blood and **remove** the urea as **urine** (see p. 21-22), which is excreted from the body.

The Liver Removes Other Harmful Substances from the Blood

The **liver** also breaks down other harmful substances, like **alcohol**, **drugs** and **unwanted hormones**. They're broken down into **less harmful compounds** that can then be **excreted** from the body — this process is called **detoxification**. Some of the harmful products broken down by the liver include:

1) **Alcohol (ethanol)** — a **toxic** substance that can **damage** cells. It's **broken down** by the liver into **ethanal**, which is then broken down into a **less harmful** substance called **acetic acid**. **Excess** alcohol over a long period can lead to **cirrhosis** of the liver — this is when the cells of the liver **die** and **scar tissue blocks blood flow**.
2) **Paracetamol** — a common painkiller that's **broken down** by the liver. **Excess** paracetamol in the blood can lead to **liver** and **kidney failure**.
3) **Insulin** — a **hormone** that controls **blood glucose concentration**. Insulin is also broken down by the liver as excess insulin can cause problems with blood sugar levels.

The Liver Stores Glycogen

The body needs **glucose** for **energy**. The liver converts **excess glucose** in the blood to **glycogen** and stores it as granules in its cells until the glucose is needed for energy.

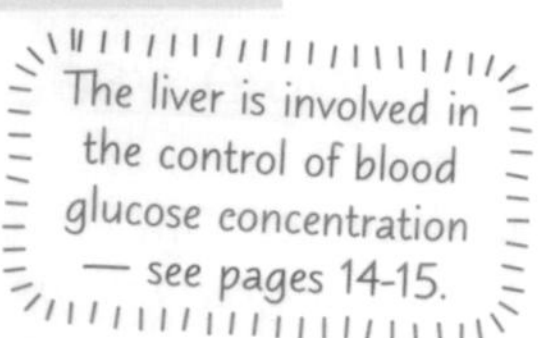

The Liver and Excretion

You Need to Know the *Structure* of the Liver

You need to learn all the different **veins**, **arteries** and **ducts** connected to the liver:

1) The **hepatic artery** supplies the liver with **oxygenated blood** from the heart, so the liver has a good supply of **oxygen** for **respiration**, providing plenty of **energy**.
2) The **hepatic vein** takes **deoxygenated blood** away from the liver.
3) The **hepatic portal vein** brings blood from the **duodenum** and **ileum** (parts of the small intestine), so it's rich in the products of **digestion**. This means any ingested harmful substances are **filtered out** and **broken down straight away**.
4) The **bile duct** takes **bile** (a substance produced by the liver to **emulsify fats**) to the **gall bladder** to be **stored**.

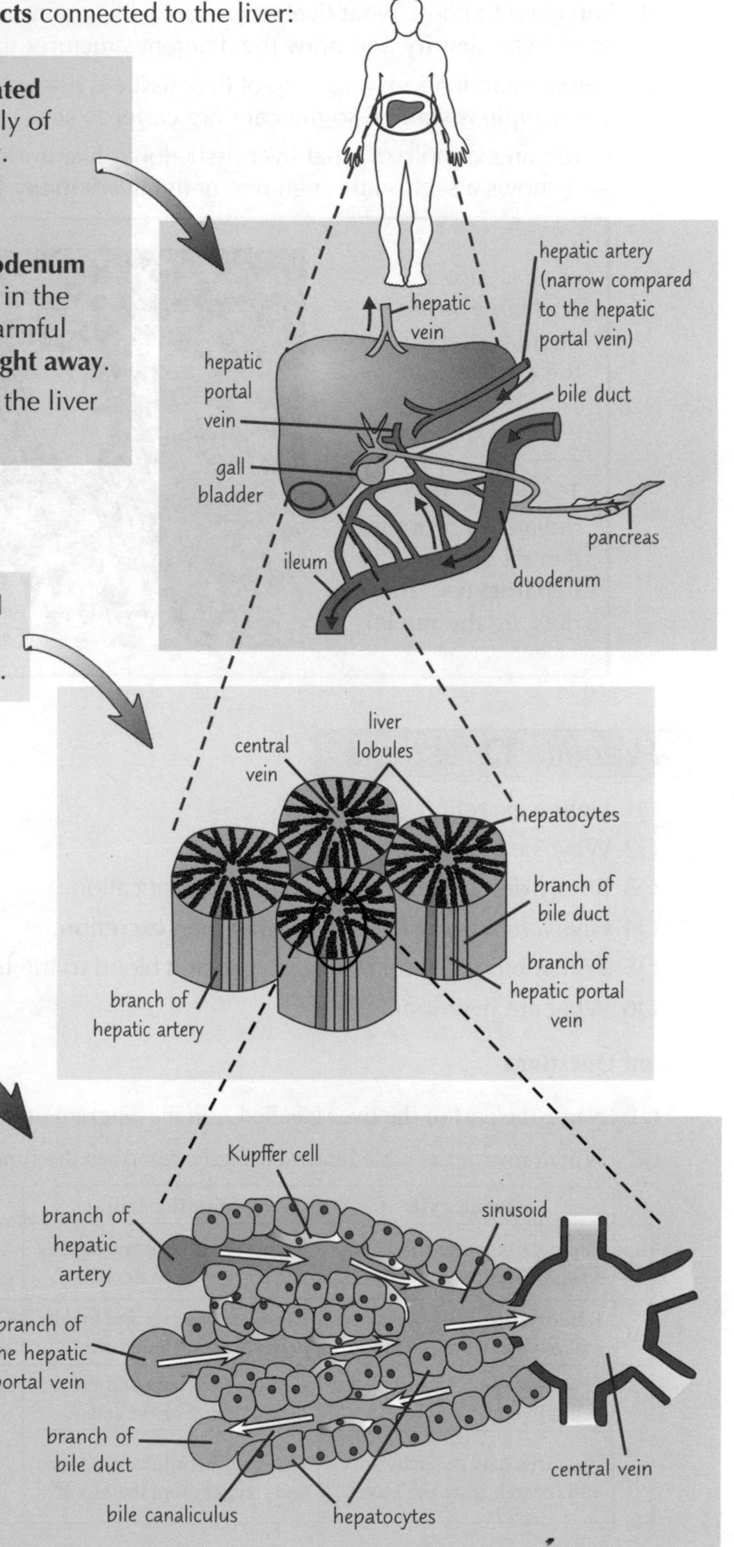

You need to learn about the **structure** of the liver too:

1) The liver is made up of **liver lobules** — **cylindrical** structures made of **cells** called **hepatocytes** that are arranged in rows **radiating** out from the centre.
2) Each lobule has a **central vein** in the middle that connects to the **hepatic vein**. **Many branches** of the **hepatic artery**, **hepatic portal vein** and **bile duct** are also found connected to each lobule (only one of each is shown in the picture).
3) The **hepatic artery** and the **hepatic portal vein** are connected to the **central vein** by **capillaries** called **sinusoids**.
4) Blood runs **through** the sinusoids, past the hepatocytes that **remove harmful substances** and **oxygen** from the blood.
5) The harmful substances are **broken down** by the hepatocytes into **less harmful** substances that then **re-enter** the blood.
6) The blood runs to the **central vein**, and the central veins from all the lobules **connect** up to form the **hepatic vein**.
7) Cells called **Kupffer cells** are also attached to the walls of the sinusoids. They **remove bacteria** and **break down** old **red blood cells**.
8) The **bile duct** is connected to the **central vein** by **tubes** called **canaliculi**.

The Liver and Excretion

You Need to be Able to Examine and Draw Sections of Liver Tissue

1) You need to know what liver tissue looks like under a **light microscope** and be able to **identify** and **draw** the different structures that you see.
2) Before examination, a sample of liver tissue is placed on a **microscope slide**. The sample is **stained** so the cells are **easier to see**.
3) Here's an example of what liver tissue looks like under a light microscope — it shows a section through **one** of the liver's many **lobules**:

Tissue samples to be viewed under a light microscope are commonly stained with haematoxylin and eosin.

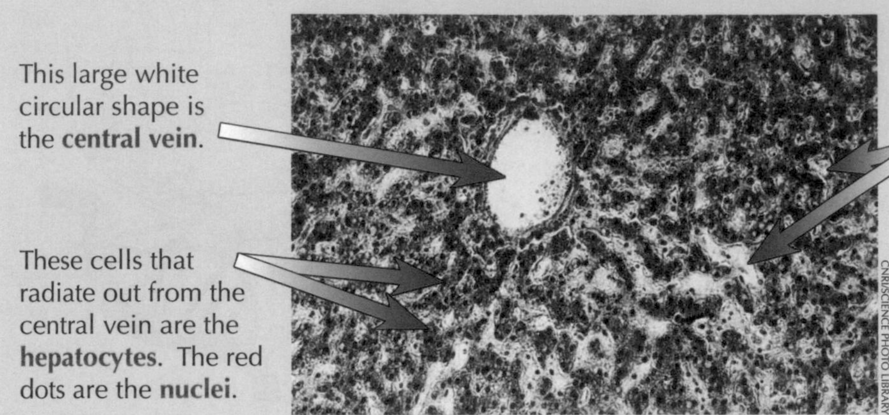

This large white circular shape is the **central vein**.

These white spaces are the **sinusoids**.

These cells that radiate out from the central vein are the **hepatocytes**. The red dots are the **nuclei**.

See the previous page for the functions of all of these structures.

Practice Questions

Q1 Define excretion.

Q2 Why is excretion needed?

Q3 Briefly describe the liver's role in detoxification.

Q4 Give a function of the liver, other than excretion.

Q5 Which blood vessel brings oxygenated blood to the liver?

Q6 What are liver lobules?

Exam Questions

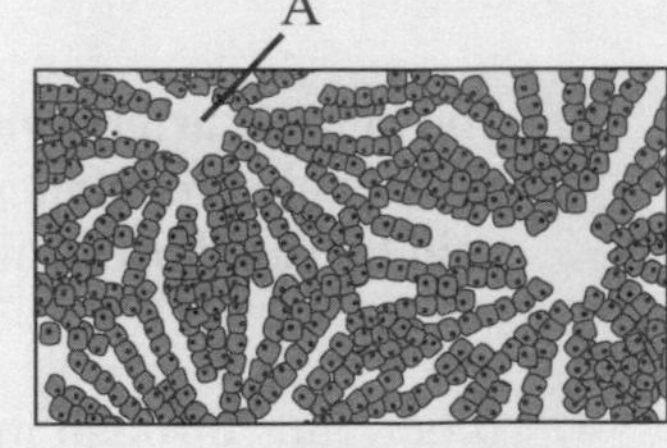

Q1 Name the part of the liver labelled A in the diagram on the right. [1 mark]

Q2 Which row in the table below correctly describes the function of each part of the liver?

	Hepatocyte	Kupffer cell	Canaliculus	Sinusoid
A	Removes bacteria and breaks down old red blood cells.	Removes harmful substances and oxygen from the blood.	Connects the bile duct to the central vein.	Connects the hepatic artery and the hepatic portal vein to the central vein.
B	Removes harmful substances and oxygen from the blood.	Removes bacteria and breaks down old red blood cells.	Connects the bile duct to the central vein.	Connects the hepatic artery and the hepatic portal vein to the central vein.
C	Connects the bile duct to the central vein.	Removes bacteria and breaks down old red blood cells.	Removes bacteria and breaks down old red blood cells.	Connects the hepatic artery and the hepatic portal vein to the central vein.
D	Removes harmful substances and oxygen from the blood.	Removes harmful substances and oxygen from the blood.	Connects the hepatic artery and the hepatic portal vein to the central vein.	Connects the bile duct to the central vein.

[1 mark]

Q3* Explain why the concentration of urea in urine might increase after eating a meal that's rich in protein. [6 marks]

* You will be assessed on the quality of your written response in this question.

Lots of important functions — can't liver without it...

Poor little amino acids, doing no harm then suddenly they're broken down and excreted. As upsetting as it is, however, you need to learn how they're broken down in the liver. It's a heart-wrenching tale of separation — the amino group and the organic acid are torn from each other's life. Right, enough of that nonsense. Learn it and learn it good.

The Kidneys and Excretion

So you've learnt about how the liver does a pretty good job at breaking down stuff for excretion. Now you get to learn that the kidneys like to play a part in this excretion malarkey too...

The **Kidneys** are **Organs** of **Excretion**

One of the main **functions** of the **kidneys** is to **excrete waste products**, e.g. **urea** produced by the **liver**. They also **regulate** the **water potential** of the blood (see p. 24-25). Here's an overview of how they excrete waste products (you need to **learn** the **structure** of the kidneys too):

1) Blood **enters** the kidney through the **renal artery** and then passes through **capillaries** in the **cortex** of the kidneys.
2) As the blood passes through the capillaries, **substances** are **filtered out of the blood** and into **long tubules** that surround the capillaries. This process is called **ultrafiltration** (see below).
3) **Useful substances** (e.g. glucose) are **reabsorbed** back into the blood from the tubules in the **medulla** and **cortex** — this is called **selective reabsorption** (see next page).
4) The remaining **unwanted substances** (e.g. urea) pass along the tubules, then along the **ureter** to the **bladder**, where they're **expelled** as **urine**.
5) The filtered blood passes out of the kidneys through the **renal vein**.

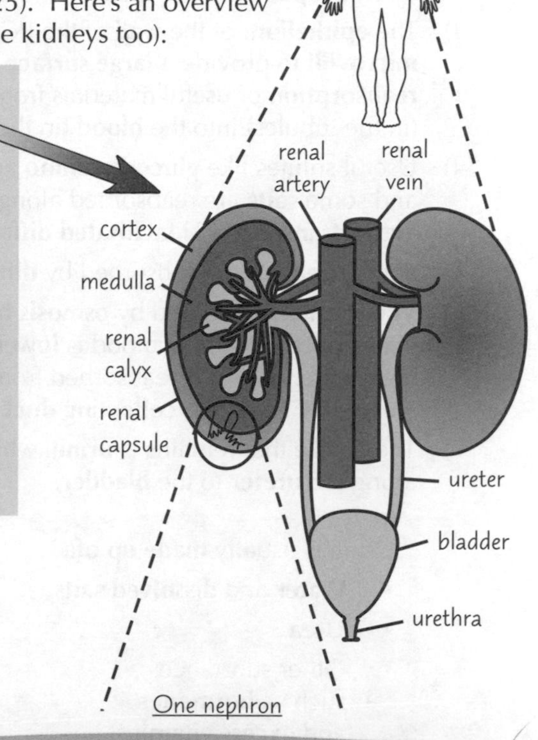

Blood is **Filtered** at the **Start** of the **Nephrons**

The **long tubules** along with the bundle of **capillaries** where the blood is **filtered** are called **nephrons** — there are around **one million** nephrons in each kidney.

1) Blood from the **renal artery** enters smaller **arterioles** in the **cortex**.
2) Each arteriole splits into a structure called a **glomerulus** — a **bundle** of **capillaries** looped inside a hollow ball called the **Bowman's capsule**.
3) This is where **ultrafiltration** takes place.
4) The **arteriole** that takes blood **into** each glomerulus is called the **afferent** arteriole, and the arteriole that takes the filtered blood **away** from the glomerulus is called the **efferent** arteriole.
5) The **efferent** arteriole is **smaller** in **diameter** than the afferent arteriole, so the blood in the glomerulus is under **high pressure**.
6) The high pressure **forces liquid** and **small molecules** in the blood **out** of the **capillary** and **into** the **Bowman's capsule**.
7) The liquid and small molecules pass through **three** layers to get into the Bowman's capsule and **enter** the nephron **tubule** — the **capillary wall**, a membrane (called the **basement membrane**) and the **epithelium** of the Bowman's capsule. Larger molecules like **proteins** and **blood cells can't pass through** and **stay** in the blood.
8) The liquid and small molecules, now called **filtrate**, pass along the rest of the nephron and **useful substances** are **reabsorbed** along the way — see next page.
9) Finally, the filtrate flows through the **collecting duct** and passes out of the kidney along the **ureter**.

One nephron

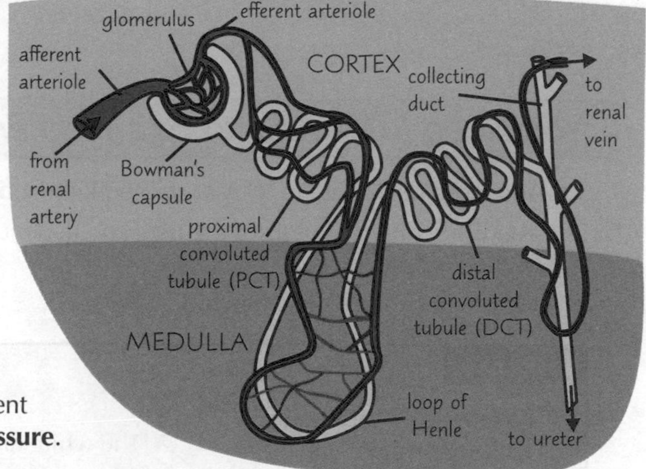

Ultrafiltration

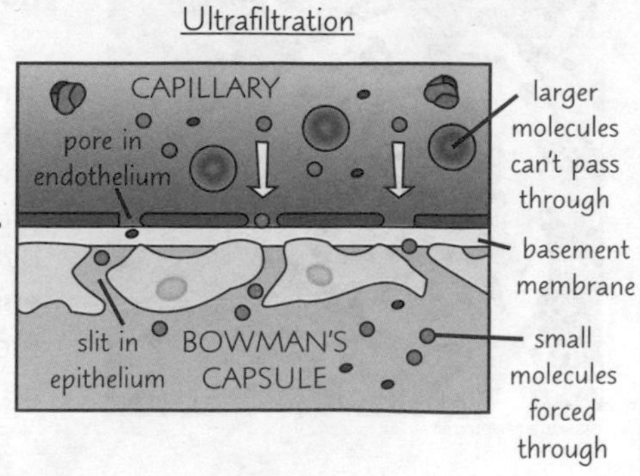

The Kidneys and Excretion

Useful *Substances are* ***Reabsorbed*** *Along the* ***Nephron Tubules***

1) **Selective reabsorption** takes place as the filtrate flows along the **proximal convoluted tubule** (**PCT**), through the **loop of Henle**, and along the **distal convoluted tubule** (**DCT**).
2) **Useful substances** leave the tubules of the nephrons and **enter** the capillary network that's **wrapped** around them (see diagram on previous page).
3) The **epithelium** of the wall of the PCT has **microvilli** to provide a **large surface area** for the **reabsorption** of useful materials from the **filtrate** (in the tubules) into the **blood** (in the capillaries).

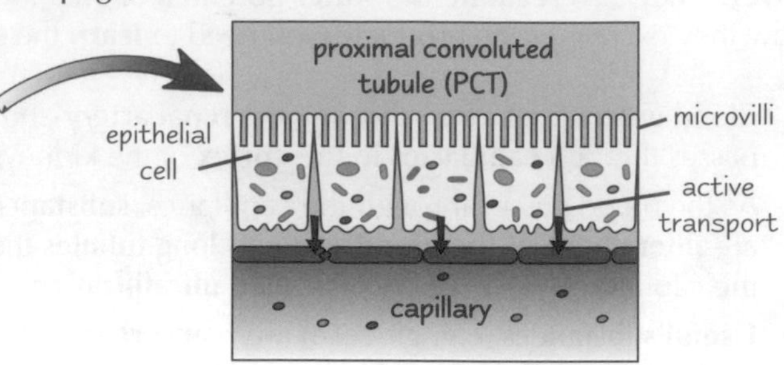

4) Useful solutes like **glucose**, **amino acids**, **vitamins** and some **salts** are reabsorbed along the PCT by **active transport** and **facilitated diffusion**.
5) Some **urea** is also reabsorbed by **diffusion**.
6) **Water** enters the blood by **osmosis** because the **water potential** of the blood is **lower** than that of the filtrate. Water is reabsorbed from the **loop of Henle**, **DCT** and the **collecting duct** (see page 24).
7) The filtrate that remains is **urine**, which passes along the **ureter** to the **bladder**.

Water potential basically describes the tendency of water to move from one area to another. Water will move from an area of higher water potential to an area of lower water potential — it moves down the water potential gradient.

Urine is usually **made up of**:
- **Water** and **dissolved salts**.
- **Urea**.
- Other substances such as **hormones** and **excess vitamins**.

Urine **doesn't** usually contain:
- **Proteins** and **blood cells** — they're **too big** to be **filtered out** of the blood.
- **Glucose**, **amino acids** and **vitamins** — they're **actively reabsorbed** back into the blood (see above).

The volume of water in urine varies depending on how much you've drunk (see p. 24). The amount of urea also varies depending on how much protein you've eaten (see p. 18).

You Need to be Able to ***Examine*** *and* ***Draw Nephrons***

1) You need to be able to look at stained **kidney tissue** under a **light microscope** and **identify** and **draw** what you see.
2) You'll see different parts of the nephron depending on whether you're looking at the **cortex** or the **medulla** region of the kidney.
3) Here's an example of what you might see:

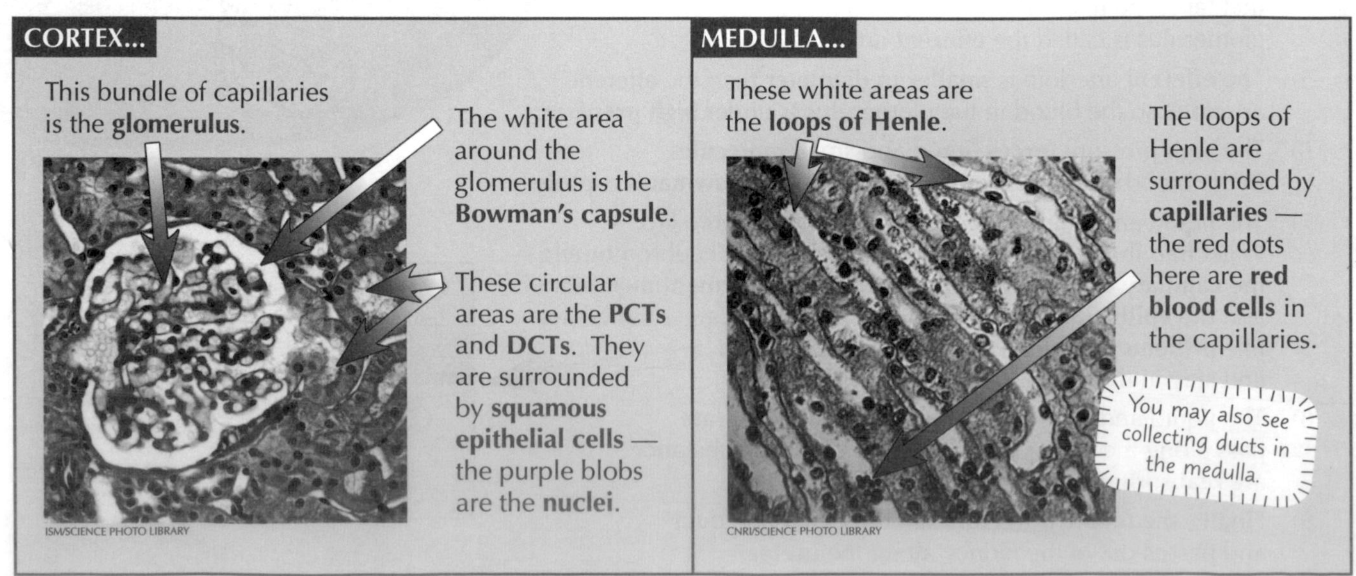

The Kidneys and Excretion

You Need to be Able to do a **Kidney Dissection**

A **kidney dissection** is great for really getting to know the **structure** of the kidney.

Equipment you'll need:

A **mammal's kidney** (e.g. from a sheep, pig or cow), a **dissecting tray**, a **scalpel**, an **apron** and **lab gloves**.

External examination:

1) Look at the outside of the kidney — it's covered with a thin, strong membrane called the **renal capsule**.
2) Beneath the renal capsule is the outside of the **cortex**.
3) You'll notice that part of the kidney is **indented** — this is the **renal hilum** and you'll probably see **tubes** coming from here.
4) Have a look at the tubes and see if you can identify them as the **renal vein**, **renal artery** and **ureter**. You might need to **look inside** the blood vessels to identify them — the wall of the artery will be thicker than the wall of the vein. The ureter is likely to have the most **adipose** (fatty) **tissue** around it.
5) Draw a **sketch** of the outside of the kidney and add clear **labels**.

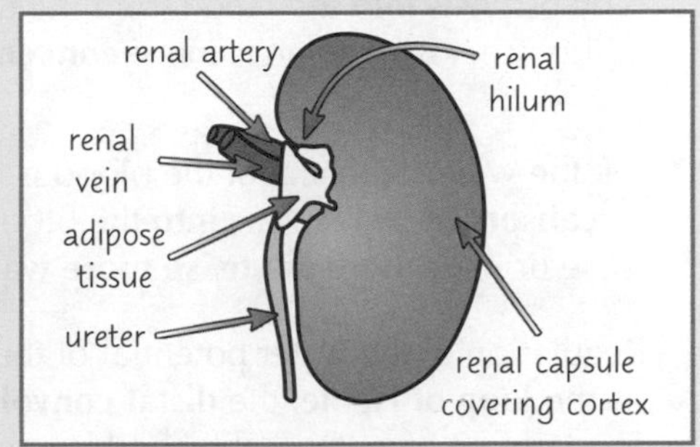

Internal examination:

1) Cut the kidney in half **lengthways** from one side. Split it open and have a look at the structures inside.
2) You should notice that the **cortex** appears **dense** and **grainy** and is a **lighter shade** than the medulla.
3) In the **medulla** you will find many **cone-shaped** structures — these are **renal pyramids**. They appear **stripy** because they contain straight sections of nephrons (loops of Henle and collecting ducts).
4) In-between the pyramids are **renal columns**.
5) You may see **hollow cavities** leading from the base of the renal pyramids — these are the **renal calyces** (singular is a **renal calyx**).
6) These lead to a larger hollow structure called the **renal pelvis**, which connects to the **ureter**.
7) Draw a **sketch** to show the structures you see inside the kidney. Don't forget to add **labels**.

Practice Questions

Q1 Which blood vessel supplies the kidney with blood?

Q2 What are the bundles of capillaries found in the cortex of the kidneys called?

Q3 What is selective reabsorption?

Q4 Why aren't proteins normally found in urine?

Q5 Describe the internal structures you'd expect to see during a kidney dissection.

Exam Question

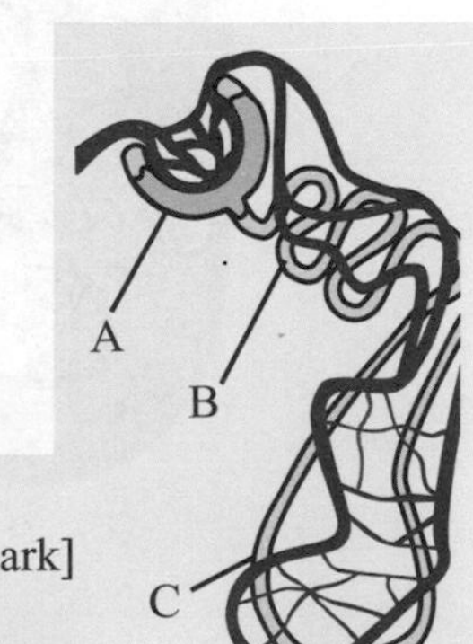

Q1 The diagram on the right shows part of a nephron in a kidney.

a) From which structure (A-C) is water reabsorbed into the blood? [1 mark]

b) Would you expect the concentration of glucose to be lower at point B or point C on the diagram? Explain your answer. [1 mark]

c) Describe and explain the process that occurs at point A on the diagram. [5 marks]

Mmm — it's steak and excretion organ pie for dinner...

Excretion is a pretty horrible sounding word I know, but it's gotta be done. Mind you, I've never been able to eat kidney ever since I learnt all about this urine production business. Shame really — I used to love kidney sarnies for lunch.

Controlling Water Potential

More lovely kidney to gobble up on these pages — this time it's their role in controlling the water potential of the blood. Busy things, these kidneys.

*The **Kidneys** Regulate the **Water Potential** of the **Blood***

Water is **essential** to keep the body **functioning**, so the **amount** of water in the **blood** (and so the **water potential** of the blood) needs to be kept **constant**. Mammals excrete **urea** (and other waste products) in **solution**, which means **water** is **lost** during excretion. Water is also lost in **sweat**. The kidneys **regulate** the water potential of the blood (and urine), so the body has just the **right amount** of water:

If the water potential of the blood is too **low** (the body is **dehydrated**), **more** water is **reabsorbed** by osmosis **into** the blood from the tubules of the nephrons (see p. 21-22 for more). This means the urine is **more concentrated**, so **less** water is **lost** during excretion.

Brad liked his urine to be dilute.

If the water potential of the blood is too **high** (the body is too **hydrated**), **less** water is **reabsorbed** by osmosis **into** the blood from the tubules of the nephrons. This means the urine is **more dilute**, so **more** water is **lost** during excretion (see next page).

Regulation of the water potential of the blood takes place in the **middle** and **last parts** of the nephron — the **loop of Henle**, the **distal convoluted tubule** (DCT) and the **collecting duct** (see below). The **volume** of water reabsorbed is controlled by **hormones** (see next page).

*The **Loop of Henle** has a **Countercurrent Multiplier Mechanism***

The **loop of Henle** is made up of two **'limbs'** — the **descending** limb and the **ascending** limb. They help set up a mechanism called the **countercurrent multiplier mechanism**. It's this mechanism that helps to **reabsorb water** back into the blood. Here's how it **works**:

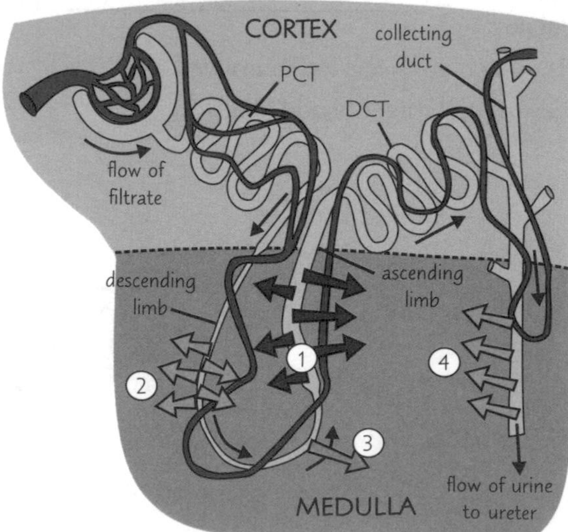

1. Near the **top** of the **ascending** limb, Na^+ and Cl^- ions are **actively pumped out** into the **medulla**. The ascending limb is **impermeable** to **water**, so the water **stays inside** the tubule. This creates a **low water potential** in the **medulla**, because there's a **high concentration** of ions.

2. Because there's a **lower** water potential in the **medulla** than in the descending limb, **water** moves **out** of the **descending limb into** the **medulla** by **osmosis**. This makes the **filtrate more concentrated** (the ions can't diffuse out — the descending limb isn't permeable to them). The water in the medulla is **reabsorbed** into the **blood** through the **capillary network**.

3. Near the **bottom** of the **ascending** limb Na^+ and Cl^- ions **diffuse out** into the **medulla**, further **lowering** the **water potential** in the medulla. (The ascending limb is **impermeable** to **water**, so it **stays in the tubule**.)

4. The first three stages massively **increase** the **ion concentration** in the **medulla**, which **lowers** the **water potential**. This causes **water** to **move out** of the **collecting duct** by **osmosis**. As before, the water in the medulla is **reabsorbed** into the **blood** through the **capillary network**.

The **volume** of water **reabsorbed** from the collecting duct into the capillaries is **controlled** by **changing the permeability** of the **collecting duct** (see next page).

Different animals have **different length loops of Henle**. The **longer** an animal's loop of Henle, the **more water they can reabsorb** from the filtrate. When there's a longer ascending limb, **more ions** are **actively pumped out** into the medulla, which creates a **really low water potential** in the medulla. This means **more water** moves **out** of the nephron and collecting duct **into** the **capillaries**, giving very **concentrated urine**. Animals that live in areas where there's **little water** usually have **long loops** to **save** as much **water** as possible.

Controlling Water Potential

Water Reabsorption is Controlled by Hormones

It's called antidiuretic hormone because diuresis is when lots of dilute urine is produced, so anti means a small amount of concentrated urine is produced.

1) The water potential of the blood is **monitored** by cells called **osmoreceptors** in a part of the **brain** called the **hypothalamus**.
2) When the osmoreceptors are **stimulated** by **low** water potential in the blood, the hypothalamus sends **nerve impulses** to the **posterior pituitary gland** to release a **hormone** called **antidiuretic hormone** (ADH) into the blood.
3) ADH makes the walls of the DCT and collecting duct **more permeable** to **water**.
4) This means **more water** is **reabsorbed** from these tubules **into** the medulla and into the blood by osmosis. A **small** amount of **concentrated urine** is produced, which means **less water** is **lost** from the body.

Here's how ADH changes the **water content** of the **blood** when it's too **low** or too **high**:

1) Blood ADH Level Rises When You're Dehydrated

Dehydration is what happens when you **lose water**, e.g. by sweating during exercise, so the **water content** of the blood needs to be **increased:**

1) The **water content** of the blood **drops**, so its **water potential drops**.
2) This is detected by **osmoreceptors** in the **hypothalamus**.
3) The **posterior pituitary gland** is stimulated to release **more ADH** into the blood.
4) **More ADH** means that the DCT and collecting duct are **more permeable**, so **more water** is **reabsorbed** into the blood by osmosis.
5) A **small amount** of **highly concentrated** urine is produced and **less water** is **lost**.

Dehydrated? Me? As if...

2) Blood ADH Level Falls When You're Hydrated

If you're **hydrated**, you've taken in **lots of water**, so the **water content** of the blood needs to be **reduced**:

1) The **water content** of the blood **rises**, so its **water potential rises**.
2) This is detected by the **osmoreceptors** in the **hypothalamus**.
3) The **posterior pituitary gland** releases **less ADH** into the blood.
4) **Less ADH** means that the DCT and collecting duct are **less permeable**, so **less water** is **reabsorbed** into the blood by osmosis.
5) A **large amount** of **dilute** urine is produced and **more water** is **lost**.

Practice Questions

Q1 In which parts of the nephron does water reabsorption take place?

Q2 Describe what happens along the descending limb of the loop of Henle.

Q3 Which cells monitor the water potential of the blood?

Q4 Which gland releases ADH?

Exam Questions

Q1 The level of ADH in the blood rises during strenuous exercise.
a) Explain the cause of the increase in ADH level. [3 marks]
b) Explain the effect the increased ADH level has on kidney function. [2 marks]

Q2 Gerbils are small rodents. They produce relatively little urine in comparison to other rodents of a similar size, such as mice or rats. Suggest and explain how the nephrons of gerbils differ from those of mice or rats. [4 marks]

If you don't understand what ADH does, ur-ine trouble...

There are two main things to learn here — how water is reabsorbed from the kidney tubules, and how the water potential of the blood is regulated by osmoreceptors, the hypothalamus and the posterior pituitary gland. Now I need a wee.

Kidney Failure and Detecting Chemicals

Everything's fine while the kidneys are working well, but when they get damaged things don't run quite so smoothly.

Kidney Failure is When the Kidneys **Stop Working Properly**

Kidney failure is also called renal failure.

Kidney failure is when the kidneys **can't** carry out their **normal functions** because they **don't work properly**. Kidney failure can be **detected** by measuring the **glomerular filtration rate** (**GFR**) — this is the rate at which blood is filtered from the glomerulus into the Bowman's capsule. A rate **lower** than the normal range indicates the kidneys aren't working properly. Kidney failure can be **caused** by many things including:

1) **Kidney infections** — these can cause **inflammation** (swelling) of the kidneys, which can **damage** the cells. This **interferes** with **filtering** in the Bowman's capsules, or with **reabsorption** in the other parts of the nephrons.
2) **High blood pressure** — this can damage the **glomeruli**. The blood in the glomeruli is already under **high pressure** but the **capillaries** can be **damaged** if the blood pressure gets **too high**. This means **larger** molecules like **proteins** can get through the capillary walls and into the **urine**.

Kidney failure causes **lots of problems**, for example:

1) **Waste products** that the kidneys would normally **remove** (e.g. **urea**) begin to **build up** in the blood. **Too much** urea in the blood causes **weight loss** and **vomiting**.
2) **Fluid** starts to **accumulate** in the tissues because the kidneys **can't remove excess water** from the blood. This causes **parts of the body** to **swell**, e.g. the person's legs, face and abdomen can swell up.
3) The balance of **electrolytes** (ions) in the body becomes, well, unbalanced. The blood may become **too acidic**, and an imbalance of calcium and phosphate can lead to **brittle bones**. **Salt build-up** may cause more **water retention**.
4) **Long-term** kidney failure causes **anaemia** — a **lack** of **haemoglobin** in the blood.

If the problems caused by kidney failure **can't be controlled**, it can eventually lead to **death**.

Renal Dialysis and **Kidney Transplants** can be used to **Treat** Kidney Failure

When the kidneys can no longer **function** (i.e. they've **totally failed**), a person is unable to **survive** without **treatment**. There are **two** main treatment options:

Renal dialysis

1) **Renal dialysis** is where a **machine** is used to **filter** a patient's blood.
   - The patient's blood is passed through a **dialysis machine** — the **blood** flows on one side of a **partially permeable membrane** and **dialysis fluid** flows on the other side.
   - **Waste products** and **excess water** and **ions** diffuse across the membrane into the dialysis fluid, **removing** them from the blood.
   - **Blood cells** and **larger** molecules like **proteins** are **prevented** from **leaving** the blood.
2) Patients can feel increasingly **unwell** between dialysis sessions because **waste products** and **fluid** start to build up in their **blood**.
3) Each dialysis session takes **three to five hours**, and patients need **two or three sessions a week**, usually in **hospital**. This is **quite expensive** and is pretty **inconvenient** for the patient.
4) But dialysis can keep a person **alive** until a **transplant** is available (see below), and it's a lot **less risky** than having the **major surgery** involved in a transplant.

Kidney transplant

1) A **kidney transplant** is where a **new kidney** is implanted into a patient's body to **replace** a damaged kidney.
2) The new kidney has to be from a person with the **same blood** and **tissue type**. They're often donated from a **living relative**, as people can survive with **only one** kidney. They can also come from **other people** who've recently **died** — organ donors.
3) Transplants have a lot of **advantages** over dialysis:
   - It's **cheaper** to give a person a transplant than keep them on dialysis for a **long time**.
   - It's **more convenient** for a person than regular dialysis sessions.
   - Patients don't have the problem of feeling **unwell** between dialysis sessions.
4) But there are also **disadvantages** to having a kidney transplant:
   - The patient will have to undergo a **major operation**, which is **risky**.
   - The **immune system** may **reject** the transplant, so the patient has to take **drugs** to **suppress it**.

Kidney Failure and Detecting Chemicals

Urine is used to Test for Pregnancy and Drug Use

Urine is made by **filtering** the **blood**, so you can have a look at what's in a person's blood by **testing** their **urine**. Urine samples can be used to test for **medical problems** such as diabetes, as well as **pregnancy** and **drug use**.

PREGNANCY: Pregnancy tests detect the hormone **human chorionic gonadotropin (hCG)** that's only found in the **urine** of **pregnant women**:

1) A **stick** is used with an **application area** that contains **monoclonal antibodies for hCG** bound to a **coloured bead** (**blue**). Monoclonal antibodies are all **identical** to each other.
2) When urine is applied to the application area any hCG will **bind** to the antibody on the beads.
3) The urine **moves** up to the **test strip**, **carrying** the **beads** with it.
4) The test strip has **antibodies to hCG** stuck in place (**immobilised**).
5) If there **is hCG present** the test strip turns **blue** because the **immobilised** antibody binds to any **hCG** attached to the **blue** beads, concentrating the **blue beads** in that area. If **no hCG** is present, the beads will **pass through** the test area **without** binding to anything, and so it **won't** go blue.

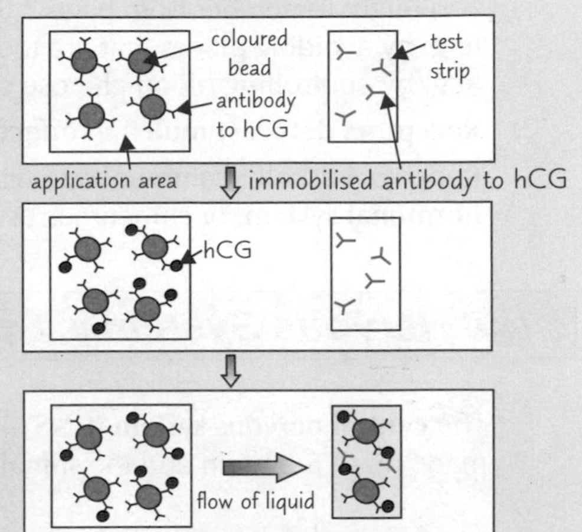

STEROIDS:

1) **Anabolic steroids** (e.g. **testosterone**, **Nandrolone**) are **drugs** that **build up muscle tissue**.
2) Some **athletes** are **banned** from taking anabolic steroids. This is to try to stop the misuse of steroids that can have **dangerous side-effects**, such as **liver damage**. Also, it's considered **unfair** for some athletes to use steroids.
3) Athletes regularly have their **urine tested** for steroids (or the **products** made when they're **broken down**) by a technique called **gas chromatography/mass spectrometry (GC/MS)**.
4) In gas chromatography the urine sample is **vaporised** (turned into a **gas**) and passed through a column containing a **polymer**. **Different substances** move through the column at **different speeds**, so substances in the urine sample **separate out**. Once the substances have separated out, a **mass spectrometer** converts them into **ions**, then **separates** them depending on their **mass** and **charge**. The results are **analysed** by a computer and by comparing them with the results of **known substances** it's possible to tell which substances were in the urine sample.

RECREATIONAL DRUGS:

1) Sometimes people have their urine tested to see if they've been using **recreational drugs** such as **cannabis**, **ecstasy** or **cocaine**. For example, some **employers** can carry out **drug tests** on their employees.
2) Testing for these drugs usually starts with **test strips**, which contain **antibodies** that the drug being tested for will **bind to** (or the products made when it's broken down) A sample of urine is applied to the test strip and if a **certain amount** of the drug (or its products) is present a **colour change** will occur, indicating a **positive result**.
3) If this first test shows a positive result, a sample of the urine is usually sent for **further testing** to confirm **which drugs** have been used. This second test uses **GC/MS** (just like the test for steroids).

Practice Questions

Q1 Give one effect of kidney failure on the body.

Q2 What substance does a pregnancy test detect in a urine sample?

Q3 Briefly describe how use of recreational drugs, such as cannabis, can be tested for.

Exam Question

Q1 Describe two advantages and two disadvantages of kidney transplants over renal dialysis. [4 marks]

Kidney failure, kidney infections, kidney transplants, kidney beans...

So you can either treat kidney failure with a kidney transplant or you can use kidney dialysis to filter the blood a few times a week. Both treatments come with their advantages and disadvantages, so make sure you can sum them both up.

The Nervous System

The nervous system is so clever that lots of stuff happens without you even having to think about it — digestion, breathing, blinking, yawning... aaaawaaaaawh...

Responding to their Environment Helps Animals Survive

1) You might remember from page 2 that animals need to **respond** to changes in their **external** environment, (e.g. by avoiding places that are too hot or too cold) as well as changes in their **internal** environment, (e.g. by controlling blood glucose concentration). This **increases** their chance of **survival**.
2) **Receptors detect stimuli** and **effectors** bring about a **response** to a **stimulus**.
3) Receptors usually **communicate** with effectors via the **nervous system** or the **hormonal system**, or sometimes using **both**.

A stimulus is any change in the internal or external environment.

The Nervous System is Split into Two Main Structural Systems

The **central nervous system** (**CNS**) — made up of the **brain** and the **spinal cord**.

The **peripheral nervous system** — made up of the neurones that connect the CNS to the **rest** of the **body**. It also has two different functional systems:

The **somatic nervous system** controls **conscious** activities, e.g. running and playing video games.

The **autonomic nervous system** controls **unconscious** activities, e.g. digestion. It's got two divisions that have **opposite effects** on the body:

The **sympathetic** nervous system gets the body **ready for action**. It's the **'fight or flight'** system. Sympathetic neurones release the neurotransmitter **noradrenaline**.

The **parasympathetic** nervous system **calms** the body down. It's the **'rest and digest'** system. Parasympathetic neurones release the neurotransmitter **acetylcholine**.

The Brain is Part of the Central Nervous System

You need to know the **location** and **function** of these **five brain structures**:

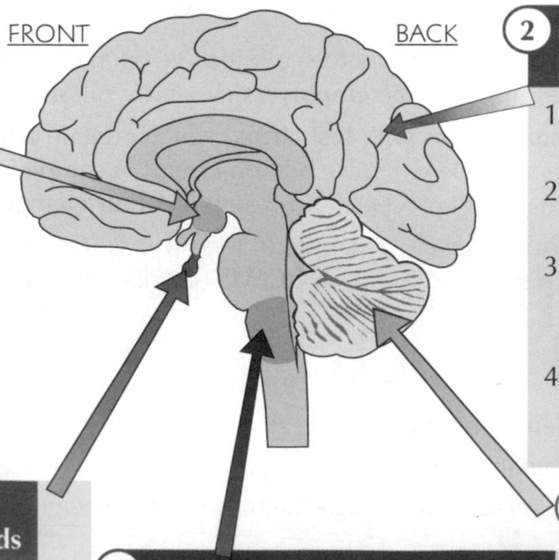

FRONT BACK

1 Hypothalamus — Controls Body Temperature

1) The hypothalamus is found just **beneath** the **middle part** of the brain.
2) The hypothalamus automatically **maintains body temperature** at the normal level (see p. 13).
3) The hypothalamus produces **hormones** that **control** the **pituitary gland**.

2 Cerebrum — Allows You to See, Hear, Learn and Think

1) The **cerebrum** is the **largest** part of the brain.
2) It's divided into **two halves** called **cerebral hemispheres**.
3) The cerebrum has a thin **outer layer** called the **cerebral cortex**, which is highly **folded**.
4) The cerebrum is involved in **vision**, **hearing**, **learning** and **thinking**.

3 Pituitary Gland — Controls Hormone Release by Body Glands

1) The **pituitary gland** is found beneath the **hypothalamus**
2) It is controlled by the **hypothalamus**. It releases **hormones** and **stimulates** other **glands**, e.g. the **adrenal** glands (see p. 10), to release their hormones.

4 Medulla Oblongata — Controls Breathing Rate and Heart Rate

1) The **medulla oblongata** is at the **base** of the **brain**, at the top of the spinal cord.
2) It automatically controls **breathing rate** and **heart rate**.

5 Cerebellum — Coordinates Muscles, Balance and Posture

1) The **cerebellum** is **underneath** the **cerebrum** and it also has a **folded cortex**.
2) It's important for **muscle coordination**, **posture** and **coordination of balance**.

The Nervous System

Reflexes are Rapid, Automatic Responses to Stimuli

1) A **reflex** is where the body **responds** to a stimulus **without** making a **conscious decision** to respond. This is because the **pathway** of **communication** doesn't involve **conscious** parts of the **brain**.
2) Because you don't have to **spend time deciding** how to respond, information travels **really fast** from **receptors** to **effectors**.
3) So simple reflexes help organisms to **avoid damage** to the body because they're **rapid**.
4) You need to know about two particular reflexes — the **blinking reflex** and the **knee-jerk reflex**.

The Blinking Reflex

When your body detects something that could **damage** your **eye**, you automatically **blink** — you quickly **close** your **eyelid** to protect your eye, then **open** your eyelid again. For example, you **blink** if your eye is **touched:**

- **Sensory nerve endings** in the cornea (front part of the eye) are stimulated by **touch.**
- A nerve impulse is sent along the **sensory neurone** to a **relay neurone** in the **CNS.**
- The impulse is then passed from the relay neurone to **motor neurones.**
- The **motor neurones** send impulses to the **effectors** — the **orbicularis oculi muscles** that move your eyelids. These muscles **contract** causing your eyelids to **close quickly** and **prevent** your eye from being **damaged.**

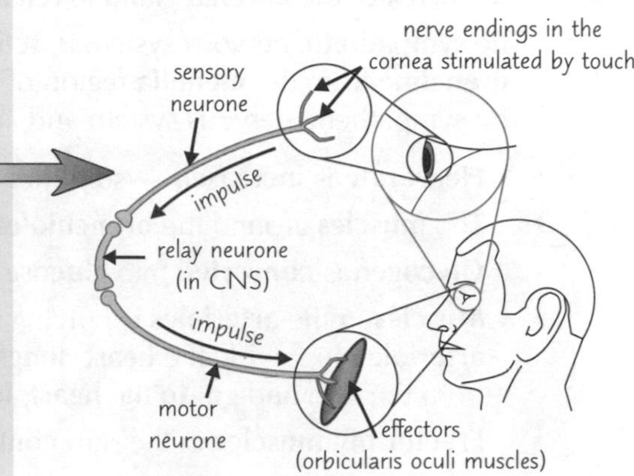

See page 5 for more about the structure and function of the different types of neurone.

The Knee-jerk Reflex

The **knee-jerk reflex** works to quickly straighten your leg if the body detects your quadriceps is suddenly stretched. It helps to maintain **posture** and **balance**. For example, if your knees **buckle** after landing from a jump, the reflex causes your quadriceps to **contract** to keep you **upright**. This is how it works:

- **Stretch receptors** in the **quadriceps muscle** detect that the muscle is being **stretched.**
- A nerve impulse is passed along a **sensory neurone**, which communicates directly with a **motor neurone** in the **spinal cord** (there is no relay neurone involved).
- The **motor neurone** carries the nerve impulse to the **effector** (the **quadriceps muscle**) causing it to **contract** so the lower leg **moves forward** quickly.

You can test your knee-jerk reflex by quickly hitting your patellar tendon (just below your kneecap) when your leg is bent.

Practice Questions

Q1 Which part of the nervous system controls unconscious activities?

Q2 What does the sympathetic nervous system do?

Q3 Which part of the brain controls body temperature?

Exam Questions

Q1 The diagram on the right shows a cross-section of the brain from front to back.

a) Name structure A on the diagram of the brain. [1 mark]

b) Give two roles of structure B. [1 mark]

c) What effect might damage to structure C have on the body? [1 mark]

Q2 a) State why the knee-jerk reflex is beneficial for humans. [1 mark]

b) Explain how the knee-jerk reflex is coordinated by the body. [4 marks]

A
B
C

AAAAAAAAAAAAAAAAAAAAAAARGH — the reflex response to revision...

You covered a bit about the nervous system at the start of this module. Now you need to learn about how the nervous system is organised and the structure of that big squelchy mess in your skull. Reflexes are automatic responses that keep your body out of all sorts of trouble — make sure you know how the blinking and knee-jerk reflexes work.

'Fight or Flight' Response and Heart Rate

Woah there. I know this looks scary, but don't run away. There are hormones, racing hearts, exercise... it's gripping stuff.

The **Nervous** and **Hormonal** Systems **Coordinate 'Fight or Flight'**

1) When an organism is **threatened** (e.g. by a predator) it responds by **preparing the body for action** (e.g. for fighting or running away). This **response** is called the '**fight or flight**' response.
2) **Nerve impulses** from **sensory** neurones arrive at the **hypothalamus** (see page 28), activating both the **hormonal system** and the **sympathetic nervous system**.
    - The **pituitary gland** is stimulated to release a **hormone** called **ACTH**. This causes the **cortex** of the **adrenal gland** to release **steroidal hormones** (see page 11).
    - The **sympathetic** nervous system is **activated**, **triggering** the **release** of **adrenaline** from the **medulla** region of the **adrenal gland** (see page 11).

    The sympathetic nervous system and adrenaline have the following effects:

Harold thought it was about time his sympathetic nervous system took over.

- **Heart rate** is **increased** — so **blood** is **pumped** around the body **faster** (see below).
- The **muscles** around the **bronchioles relax** — so **breathing is deeper**.
- **Glycogen** is **converted** into **glucose** — so **more glucose** is **available** for **muscles** to **respire**.
- **Muscles** in the **arterioles** supplying the **skin** and **gut constrict**, and muscles in the **arterioles** supplying the **heart**, **lungs** and **skeletal muscles dilate** — so **blood** is **diverted** from the skin and gut **to** the **heart**, **lungs** and **skeletal muscles**.
- **Erector pili muscles** in the skin **contract** — this makes **hairs stand on end** so the animal looks **bigger**.

The conversion of glycogen to glucose is called glycogenolysis (see page 14).

The **Control** of **Heart Rate** Involves **Both** the **Nervous** and **Hormonal Systems**

The **nervous system** helps to control heart rate in these ways:

1) The **sinoatrial node** (**SAN**) generates **electrical impulses** that cause the **cardiac muscles** to **contract**.
2) The **rate** at which the SAN fires (i.e. heart rate) is **unconsciously controlled** by a part of the **brain** called the **medulla**.
3) Animals need to **alter** their **heart rate** to **respond** to **internal stimuli**, e.g. to prevent fainting due to low blood pressure or to make sure the heart rate is high enough to supply the body with enough oxygen.
4) **Stimuli** are **detected** by **pressure receptors** and **chemical receptors**:
    - There are **pressure receptors** called **baroreceptors** in the **aorta** and the **vena cava**. They're stimulated by **high** and **low blood pressure**.
    - There are **chemical receptors** called **chemoreceptors** in the **aorta**, the **carotid artery** (a major artery in the neck) and in the **medulla**. They **monitor** the **oxygen** level in the **blood** and also **carbon dioxide** and **pH** (which are indicators of O_2 level).
5) Electrical impulses from receptors are sent **to the medulla** along **sensory** neurones. The medulla processes the information and sends impulses to the SAN along **motor** neurones. Here's how it all works:

STIMULUS	RECEPTOR	NEURONE	EFFECTOR	RESPONSE
High blood pressure.	Baroreceptors detect high blood pressure.	Impulses are sent to the medulla, which sends impulses along the vagus nerve. This secretes acetylcholine, which binds to receptors on the SAN.	Cardiac muscles	Heart rate slows down to reduce blood pressure back to normal.
Low blood pressure.	Baroreceptors detect low blood pressure.	Impulses are sent to the medulla, which sends impulses along the accelerator nerve. This secretes noradrenaline, which binds to receptors on the SAN.	Cardiac muscles	Heart rate speeds up to increase blood pressure back to normal.
High blood O_2, low CO_2 or high pH levels.	Chemoreceptors detect chemical changes in the blood.	Impulses are sent to the medulla, which sends impulses along the vagus nerve. This secretes acetylcholine, which binds to receptors on the SAN.	Cardiac muscles	Heart rate decreases to return O_2, CO_2 and pH levels back to normal.
Low blood O_2, high CO_2 or low pH levels.	Chemoreceptors detect chemical changes in the blood.	Impulses are sent to the medulla, which sends impulses along the accelerator nerve. This secretes noradrenaline, which binds to receptors on the SAN.	Cardiac muscles	Heart rate increases to return O_2, CO_2 and pH levels back to normal.

The **hormonal system** also helps to control heart rate by releasing adrenaline, e.g. when the 'fight or flight' response is activated. Adrenaline **binds** to **specific receptors** in the **heart**. This causes the cardiac muscle to **contract more frequently** and with **more force**, so **heart rate increases** and the heart **pumps more blood**.

'Fight or Flight' Response and Heart Rate

You Can Investigate The Effect of Exercise on Heart Rate

Before you start, make sure you know how to measure your **heart rate**. Find your **pulse** in your wrist by placing your index and middle finger where the base of your thumb meets your forearm. Count the **number** of **beats** in **15 seconds** and then **multiply by four** to get the number of **beats per minute**. Then:

1) Measure your heart rate at **rest** and record it in a table.
2) Do some **gentle exercise**, such as stepping on and off a step for about 5 minutes. **Immediately** afterwards, measure your heart rate again.
3) Return to a **resting position**. Measure your heart rate **every minute** until it returns to the starting rate. Record **how long** it takes to return to normal.

You could use an electrical heart rate monitor instead — these contain sensors which measure your heart rate.

You could also measure other effects on heart rate in a similar way. For example, you could test the effect of a loud noise or the effect of anxiety (by doing something that makes you nervous).

Analyse the Effect of Exercise on Heart Rate Using Student's t-Test

You can test whether **regular, intense exercise** has a **significant** effect on **resting heart rate** by using **Student's t-test**. You need **two sets of data** — the example below uses two groups of 8 people. One group received **six months** of **endurance training** (Set 1) and the other group **did not** (Set 2). The **resting heart rates** of both groups were then **measured**.

Student's t-test is used to find out whether there is a **significant difference** in the **means** of the two data sets. The value obtained is compared to a **critical value**, which helps you decide how **likely** it is that the results or 'differences in the means' were due to **chance**.

$$t = \frac{\bar{x}_1 - \bar{x}_2}{\sqrt{(s_1^2 / n_1) + (s_2^2 / n_2)}}$$

$\bar{x}$ = mean
s = standard deviation
n = number of values in group
$_1$ or $_2$ = group being referred to

There is a different equation that you can use for paired data (data that includes two measurements for each person, e.g. before and after endurance training).

To carry out the t-test, follow these steps:

1) **Identify the null hypothesis**. This is always that the **means** for the two sets of data are going to be **exactly** the **same**, i.e. there is no significant difference between them.
2) **Calculate the mean and standard deviation** for each data set.
3) **Use the formula** in the pink box above to calculate t.
4) **Calculate the degrees of freedom** by doing $(n_1 + n_2) - 2$. (Look at the key next to the formula above to help you here).
5) **Look up the values for t** in a table of **critical values**. If the value obtained from the t-test is **greater** than the **critical value** at a probability (or P value) of **5% or less** (≤ 0.05), then you can be **95% confident** that the difference is **significant** and not due to chance. So you'd **reject** the null hypothesis.

If the result of your t-test is greater than the critical value at a P value of less than 2% (< 0.02), or even 1%, you can be even more confident that the difference is significant.

Example

① **Null hypothesis** — there is **no significant difference** between the mean resting heart rate of people who received endurance training and those who did not.

Resting heart rate at end of test period (beats min^{-1})	
Set 1	Set 2
67	89
72	68
65	78
61	70
75	67
78	82
65	94
69	76

② $\bar{x}_1 = 69$, $\bar{x}_2 = 78$
$s_1 = 5.7$, $s_2 = 9.9$

③ $$t = \frac{69 - 78}{\sqrt{(5.7^2 / 8) + (9.9^2 / 8)}}$$

$t = -2.2$ (to 1 decimal place) (You can ignore the minus sign.)

④ Degrees of freedom = (8 + 8) – 2 = 14

⑤ **Critical value** is **2.145**. The t value of **2.2** is **greater** — this means that the mean resting heart rate for the group that received endurance training was **significantly lower** after 6 months than for the group that did not receive training.

degrees of freedom	critical t values			
12	1.356	1.782	2.179	2.681
13	1.350	1.771	2.160	2.650
14	1.345	1.761	2.145	2.624
15	1.341	1.753	2.131	2.602
probability that result is due to chance only	0.2 (20%)	0.1 (10%)	0.05 (5%)	0.02 (2%)

Abridged from Statistical Tables for Biological Agricultural and Medical Research (6th ed.) © 1963 R.A Fisher and F. Yates. Reprinted with permission of Pearson Education Limited.

You'll be given a table of critical values in the exam.

Practice Question

Q1 Describe how the hormonal and nervous systems coordinate the 'fight or flight' response.

Exam Questions

Q1 a) Explain how high blood pressure in the aorta causes the heart rate to slow down. [5 marks]
b) What would be the effect of severing the nerves from the medulla to the sinoatrial node (SAN)? [2 marks]

My heart rate seems to be controlled by the boy next door...

It's also rising rapidly at the sight of so much to learn. You've got to properly learn it though — it's no good just having a rough idea. SANs, baroreceptors, chemoreceptors — get it learnt then try to reproduce the table from the previous page.

Muscle Contraction

Muscles are effectors — they contract so you can respond to your environment. You need to know how they contract, but first you need to know a bit more about them.

The Central Nervous System (CNS) Coordinates Muscular Movement

1) The **CNS** (**brain** and **spinal cord**) receives **sensory information** and **decides** what kind of **response** is needed.
2) If the response needed is **movement**, the CNS sends signals along **neurones** to tell **skeletal muscles** to **contract**.
3) Skeletal muscle (also called striated, striped or voluntary muscle) is the type of muscle you use to **move**, e.g. the biceps and triceps move the lower arm.

Skeletal Muscle is made up of Long Muscle Fibres

1) Skeletal muscle is made up of **large bundles** of **long cells**, called **muscle fibres**.
2) The cell membrane of muscle fibre cells is called the **sarcolemma**.
3) Bits of the sarcolemma **fold inwards** across the muscle fibre and stick into the **sarcoplasm** (a muscle cell's cytoplasm). These folds are called **transverse (T) tubules** and they help to **spread electrical impulses** throughout the sarcoplasm so they **reach** all parts of the **muscle fibre**.
4) A network of **internal membranes** called the **sarcoplasmic reticulum** runs through the sarcoplasm. The sarcoplasmic reticulum **stores** and **releases calcium ions** that are needed for muscle contraction (see p. 33-34).
5) Muscle fibres have lots of **mitochondria** to **provide** the **ATP** that's needed for **muscle contraction**.
6) They are **multinucleate** (contain many nuclei).
7) Muscle fibres have lots of **long**, **cylindrical organelles** called **myofibrils**. They're made up of proteins and are **highly specialised** for **contraction**.

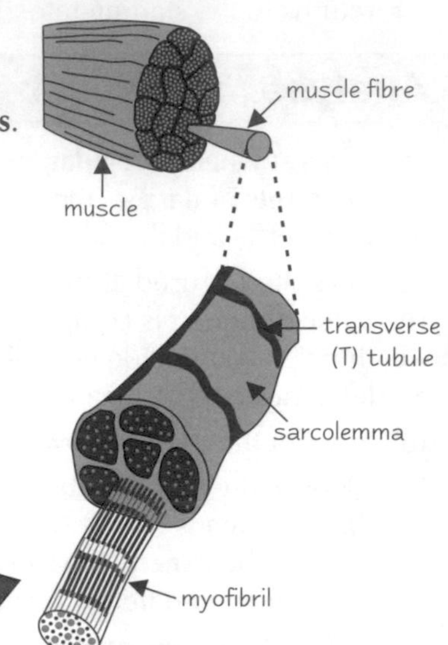

Myofibrils Contain Thick Myosin Filaments and Thin Actin Filaments

1) Myofibrils contain bundles of **thick** and **thin myofilaments** that **move past each other** to make muscles **contract**.
   - **Thick myofilaments** are made of the protein **myosin**.
   - **Thin myofilaments** are made of the protein **actin**.
2) If you look at a **myofibril** under a **microscope**, you'll see a pattern of alternating **dark** and **light bands**:
   - **Dark** bands contain the **thick myosin filaments** and some overlapping thin actin filaments — these are called **A-bands**.
   - **Light** bands contain **thin actin filaments** only — these are called **I-bands**.
3) A myofibril is made up of many short units called **sarcomeres**.
4) The **ends** of each **sarcomere** are marked with a **Z-line**.
5) In the **middle** of each sarcomere is an **M-line**. The M-line is the **middle** of the **myosin** filaments.
6) **Around** the M-line is the **H-zone**. The H-zone **only** contains **myosin** filaments.

There's more detail on actin and myosin on pages 33-34.

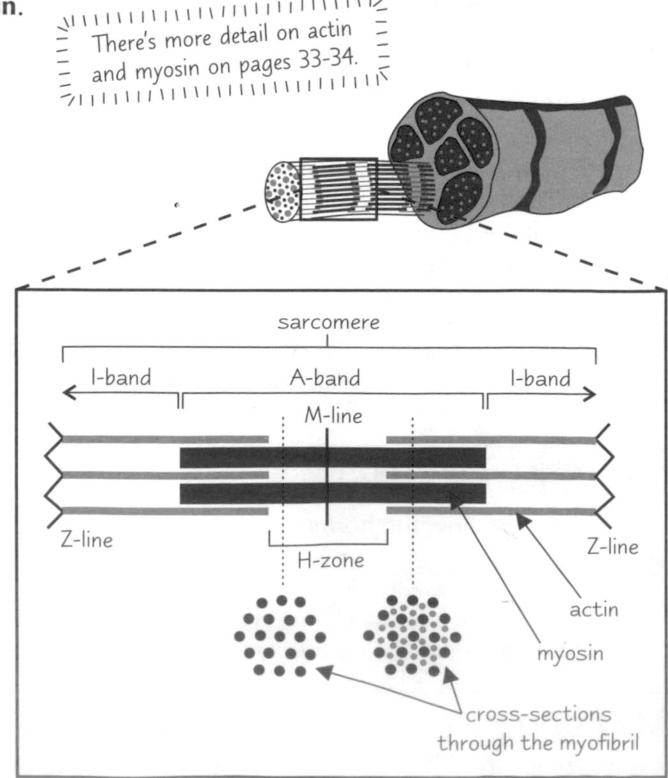

Eric and Susan just loved working their myofibrils. Oh yeah.

Muscle Contraction

Muscle Contraction is Explained by the Sliding Filament Theory

1) **Myosin** and **actin** filaments **slide** over one another to make the **sarcomeres contract** — the myofilaments themselves **don't** contract.
2) The **simultaneous contraction** of lots of **sarcomeres** means the **myofibrils** and **muscle fibres contract**.
3) Sarcomeres return to their **original length** as the muscle **relaxes**.

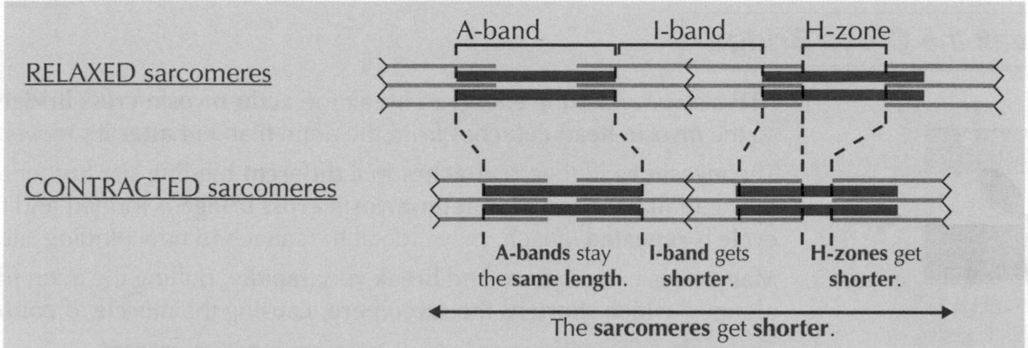

Myosin Filaments Have Globular Heads and Binding Sites

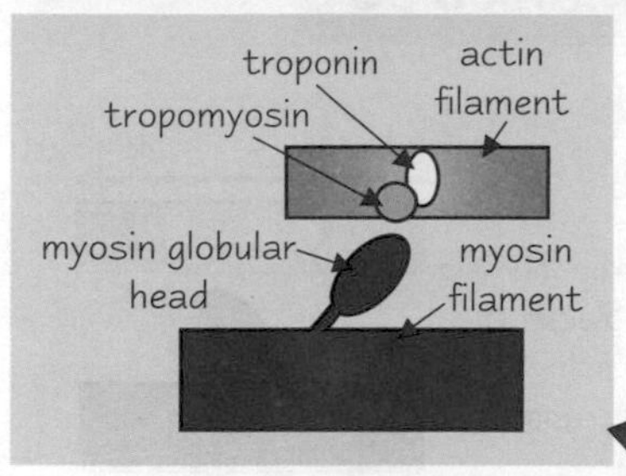

1) **Myosin filaments** have **globular heads** that are **hinged**, so they can move **back** and **forth**.
2) Each myosin head has a **binding site** for **actin** and a **binding site** for **ATP**.
3) **Actin filaments** have **binding sites** for **myosin heads**, called **actin-myosin** binding sites.
4) Two other **proteins** called **tropomyosin** and **troponin** are found between actin filaments. These proteins are **attached** to **each other** and they **help** myofilaments **move** past each other.

Binding Sites in Resting Muscles are Blocked by Tropomyosin

1) In a **resting** (unstimulated) muscle the **actin-myosin binding site** is **blocked** by **tropomyosin**, which is held in place by **troponin**.
2) So **myofilaments can't slide** past each other because the **myosin heads can't bind** to the actin-myosin binding site on the actin filaments.

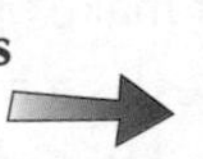

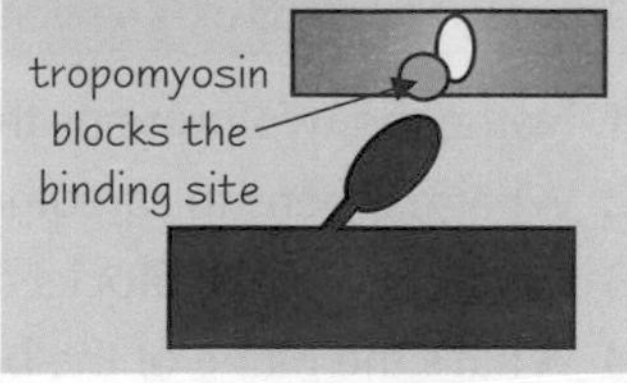

Muscle Contraction is Triggered by an Action Potential

1 The Action Potential Triggers an Influx of Calcium Ions

1) When an action potential from a motor neurone **stimulates** a muscle cell, it **depolarises** the **sarcolemma**. Depolarisation **spreads** down the **T-tubules** to the **sarcoplasmic reticulum** (see previous page).
2) This causes the **sarcoplasmic reticulum** to **release** stored **calcium ions** (Ca^{2+}) into the **sarcoplasm**.

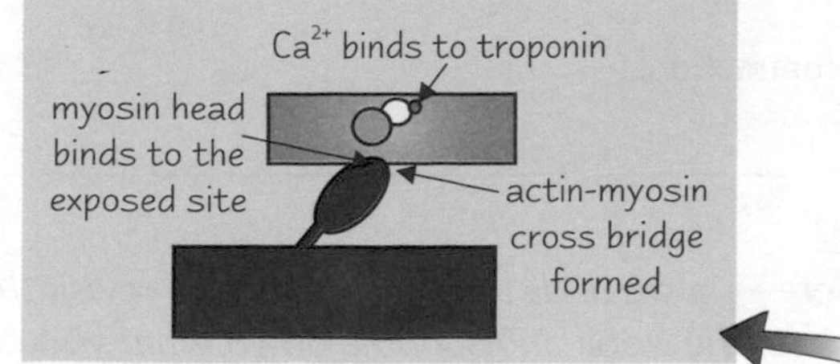

3) Calcium ions **bind** to **troponin**, causing it to **change shape**. This **pulls** the attached **tropomyosin out** of the **actin-myosin binding site** on the actin filament.
4) This **exposes** the **binding site**, which allows the **myosin head** to **bind**.
5) The bond formed when a **myosin head** binds to an **actin filament** is called an **actin-myosin cross bridge**.

Muscle Contraction

2) ATP Provides the Energy Needed to Move the Myosin Head...

1) **Calcium** ions also **activate** the enzyme **ATPase**, which **breaks down ATP** (into ADP + P_i) to **provide** the **energy** needed for muscle contraction.
2) The **energy** released from ATP **moves** the **myosin head**, which **pulls** the **actin filament** along in a kind of **rowing action**.

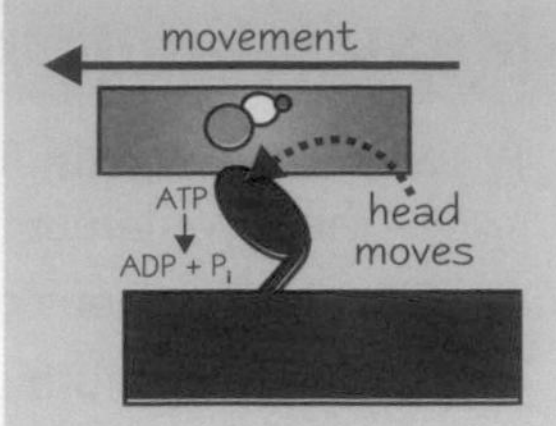

3) ...and to Break the Cross Bridge

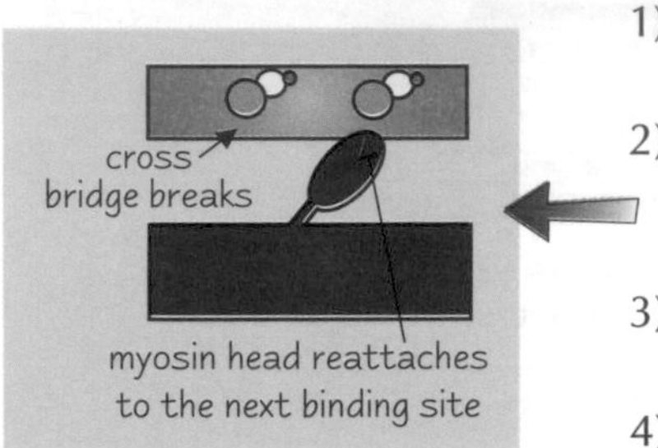

1) **ATP** also provides the **energy** to **break** the **actin-myosin cross bridge**, so the **myosin head detaches** from the actin filament **after** it's moved.
2) The **myosin head** then **reattaches** to a **different binding site** further along the actin filament. A **new actin-myosin cross bridge** is formed and the **cycle** is **repeated** (attach, move, detach, reattach to new binding site...).
3) **Many** cross bridges **form** and **break** very **rapidly**, pulling the actin filament along — which **shortens** the **sarcomere**, causing the **muscle** to **contract**.
4) The cycle will **continue** as long as **calcium ions** are **present** and **bound** to **troponin**.

When Excitation Stops, Calcium Ions Leave Troponin Molecules

1) When the muscle **stops** being **stimulated**, **calcium ions leave** their **binding sites** on the **troponin** molecules and are moved by **active transport** back into the **sarcoplasmic reticulum** (this needs **ATP** too).
2) The **troponin** molecules return to their **original shape**, pulling the attached **tropomyosin** molecules with them. This means the **tropomyosin** molecules **block** the actin-myosin **binding sites** again.
3) Muscles **aren't contracted** because **no myosin heads** are **attached** to **actin** filaments (so there are no actin-myosin cross bridges).
4) The **actin** filaments **slide back** to their **relaxed** position, which **lengthens** the **sarcomere**.

Practice Questions

Q1 Name the two proteins that make up myofibrils.

Q2 What happens to sarcomeres as a muscle relaxes?

Q3 Which molecule blocks the actin-myosin binding site in resting muscles?

Q4 What's the name of the bond that's formed when a myosin head binds to an actin filament?

Exam Questions

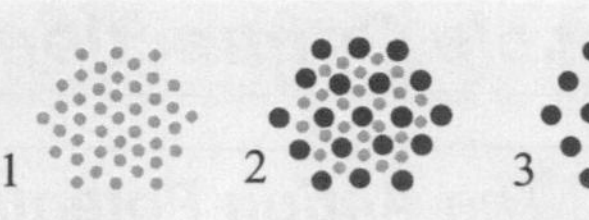

Q1 A muscle myofibril was cut through the M-line and then examined under an electron microscope. State which of the cross-section drawings (1-3) you would expect to see and explain why. [3 marks]

Q2 Describe how the lengths of the different bands in a myofibril change during muscle contraction. [2 marks]

Q3 Rigor mortis is the stiffening of muscles in the body after death. It happens when ATP reserves are exhausted. Explain why a lack of ATP leads to muscles being unable to relax. [3 marks]

Q4 Bepridil is a drug that blocks calcium ion channels. Describe and explain the effect this drug will have on muscle contraction. [3 marks]

What does muscle contraction cost? 80p...

Sorry, that's my favourite sciencey joke so I had to fit it in somewhere — a small distraction before you revisit this page. It's tough stuff but you know the best way to learn it. That's right, shut the book and scribble down what you can remember — if you can't remember much, read it again till you can (then read it again anyway, just to be sure).

Muscle Contraction

Keep going, you've almost got muscles done and dusted — just a few more bits and pieces to learn about them.

ATP and *CP* Provide the *Energy* for *Muscle Contraction*

So much **energy** is **needed** when muscles contract that **ATP** gets **used up very quickly**.
ATP has to be **continually generated** so exercise can continue — this happens in **three main ways:**

① Aerobic respiration

- **Most ATP** is generated via **oxidative phosphorylation** in the cell's **mitochondria**.
- **Aerobic** respiration only works when there's **oxygen** so it's good for **long periods** of **low-intensity exercise**, e.g. walking or jogging.

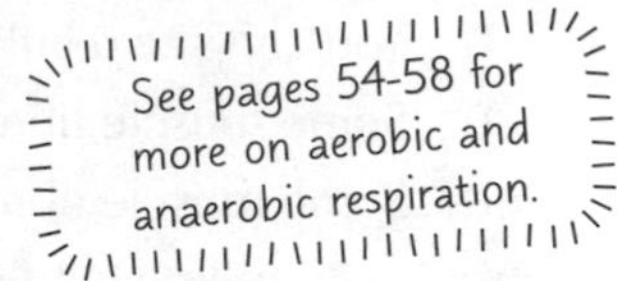

② Anaerobic respiration

- ATP is made **rapidly** by **glycolysis.**
- The **end product** of glycolysis is **pyruvate**, which is converted to **lactate** by **lactate fermentation.**
- Lactate can **quickly build up** in the muscles and cause **muscle fatigue** (where the muscles can't contract as forcefully as they could do previously).
- Anaerobic respiration is good for **short periods of hard exercise**, e.g. a **400 m sprint**.

Many activities use a combination of these systems.

③ ATP-Creatine Phosphate (CP) System

- **ATP** is made by **phosphorylating ADP** — adding a phosphate group taken from **creatine phosphate (CP)**.
- **CP is stored** inside cells and the ATP-CP system **generates ATP** very **quickly**.

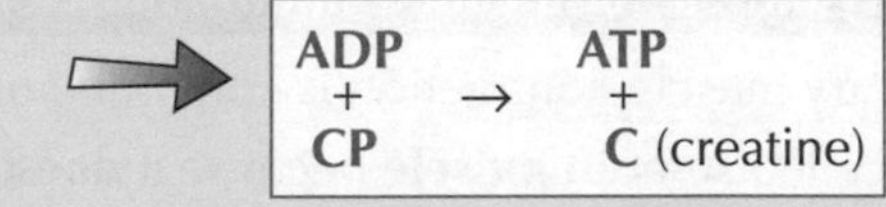

- **CP runs out** after a few seconds so it's used during **short bursts** of **vigorous exercise**, e.g. a tennis serve.
- The ATP-CP system is **anaerobic** (it doesn't need oxygen) and it's **alactic** (it doesn't form any lactate).

Neuromuscular Junctions are *Synapses* Between *Neurones* and *Muscles*

1) A **neuromuscular junction** is a **synapse** between a **motor neurone** and a **muscle cell.**
2) Neuromuscular junctions use the neurotransmitter **acetylcholine (ACh)**, which binds to receptors called **nicotinic cholinergic receptors.**
3) Neuromuscular junctions **work** in the **same way** as **synapses between neurones** — they **release neurotransmitter**, which triggers **depolarisation** in the **postsynaptic cell** (see pages 8-9).
4) Depolarisation of a muscle cell always causes it to **contract** (if the **threshold level** is reached).
5) **Acetylcholinesterase (AChE)** stored in clefts on the postsynaptic membrane is released to **break down** acetylcholine after use.

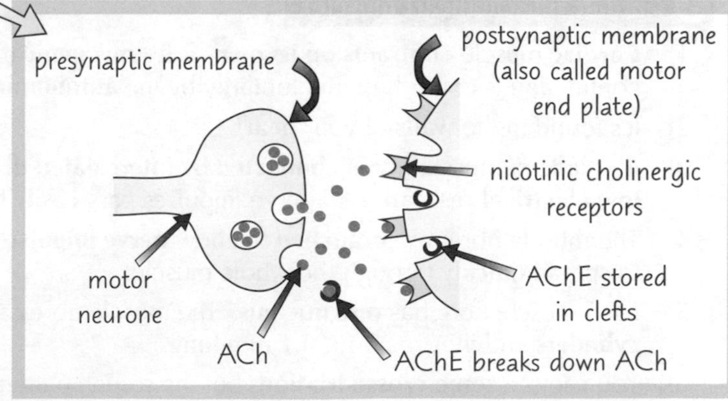

- Sometimes a chemical (e.g. a drug) may **block** the **release** of the **neurotransmitter** or affect the way it **binds** to the **receptors** on the **postsynaptic membrane**. This may prevent the **action potential** from being passed on to the **muscle,** so the **muscle won't contract.**
- This can be **fatal** if it affects the muscles involved in **breathing**, e.g. the **diaphragm** and **intercostal muscles**. If they can't contract, **ventilation** can't take place and the organism can't **respire aerobically**.

Muscle Contraction

There are Three Types of Muscle

You need to learn the differences between the **structure** and **function** of each different muscle type.

1 Skeletal muscle (also called voluntary muscle)

1) **Skeletal** muscle contraction is controlled **consciously** (you have to voluntarily decide to contract it).
2) It's made up of **many muscle fibres** that have **many nuclei**. The muscle fibres can be **many centimetres long**.
3) You can see regular **cross-striations** (a **striped pattern**) under a **microscope** (see below).
4) Some muscle fibres **contract very quickly** — they're used for **speed** and **strength** but **fatigue** (get tired) **quickly**.
5) Some muscle fibres **contract slowly** and **fatigue slowly** — they're used for **endurance** and **posture**.

You need to know how to examine a **stained** section of skeletal muscle under a **light microscope** or examine a **photomicrograph** of one. Here's an example of what you might see:

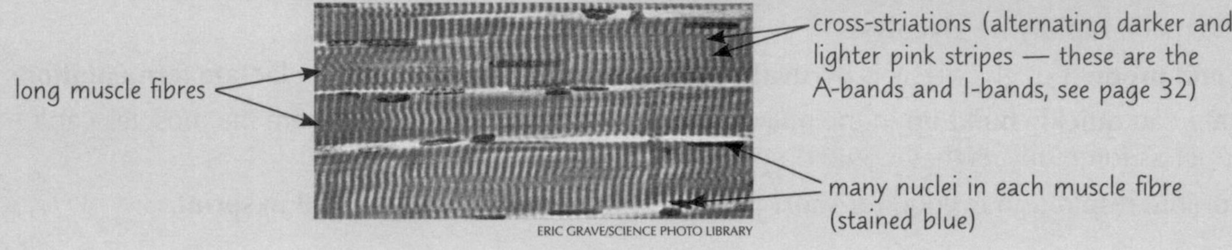

2 Involuntary muscle (also called smooth muscle)

1) **Involuntary** muscle contraction is controlled **unconsciously** (it'll contract automatically without you deciding).
2) It's also called **smooth muscle** because it **doesn't** have the **striped appearance** of voluntary muscle.
3) It's found in the **walls** of your **hollow internal organs**, e.g. the **gut**, the **blood vessels**. Your **gut smooth muscles contract** to **move food along** (**peristalsis**) and your **blood vessel smooth muscles contract** to **reduce** the **flow** of **blood**.
4) Each muscle fibre has **one nucleus**. The muscle fibres are **spindle-shaped** with **pointed ends**, and they're only about **0.2 mm long**.
5) The muscle fibres **contract slowly** and **don't fatigue**.

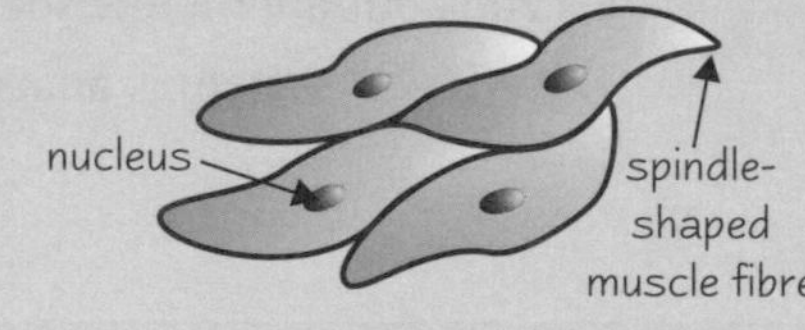

3 Cardiac muscle (heart muscle)

1) **Cardiac** muscle **contracts** on its **own** — it's **myogenic** (but the **rate** of contraction is controlled involuntarily by the **autonomic nervous system**).
2) It's found in the **walls** of your **heart**.
3) It's made of muscle fibres **connected** by **intercalated discs**, which have **low electrical resistance** so nerve impulses pass **easily** between cells.
4) The muscle fibres are **branched** to allow **nerve impulses** to **spread quickly** through the whole muscle.
5) Each muscle fibre has **one nucleus**. The muscle fibres are shaped like **cylinders** and they're about **0.1 mm long**.
6) You can see **some cross-striations** but the striped pattern **isn't** as **strong** as it is in voluntary muscle.
7) The muscle fibres **contract rhythmically** and **don't fatigue**.

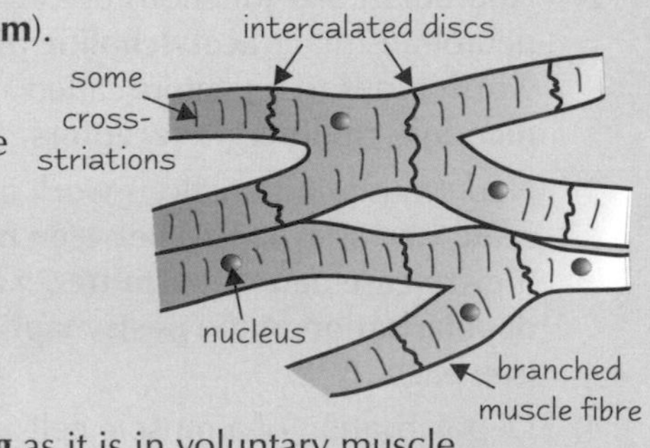

John liked to put his skeletal muscle to the test by holding up ancient monuments.

Muscle Contraction

Electrical Signals Can be Used to Monitor Muscle Fatigue

If you have access to specialist equipment you may be able to investigate **muscle contraction** and **fatigue** by **monitoring** the **electrical activity** that occurs.

1) Muscles **contract** in **response** to nervous impulses — these are **electrical signals**.
2) Electrical signals in muscles can be **detected** by **electrodes** (sensors) placed on the **skin**. The electrodes are connected to a **computer** to allow the electrical signals to be monitored. The procedure is called **electromyography** and the reading it generates is called an **electromyogram**.

Bill and Bob felt they were perfect candidates for the experiment.

To carry out the procedure:

1) First of all you need to **attach** two **electrodes** to places on the **muscle** that you want to record from — in this example we will use the **biceps** muscle in the arm. A third electrode goes on an **inactive** point (such as the bony wrist area) to act as a **control**.
2) Switch off any other **electrical** equipment that you don't need as this generates '**noise**' that **interferes** with the **electrical signal** from the **muscle**.
3) **Connect** the electrodes to an **amplifier** and a **computer**. (An amplifier increases the strength of the electrical signals from the muscle.)
4) Keep the muscle **relaxed**. You should see a **straight line** on the electromyogram.
5) Then **contract** the **muscle** by bending your arm. You should see **spikes** in the graph as **motor units** are activated to contract the muscle.
6) If you then **lift** a weight, the **amplitude** of the trace on the graph will **increase** — there are more electrical signals because **more motor units** are required to lift the weight.
7) If you **continue** to **hold** the **weight**, your muscle will begin to **fatigue**. On the electromyogram you will see the **amplitude** of the trace **increase** further. This is because your brain is trying to activate **more motor units** to generate the **force** needed to hold the weight up.

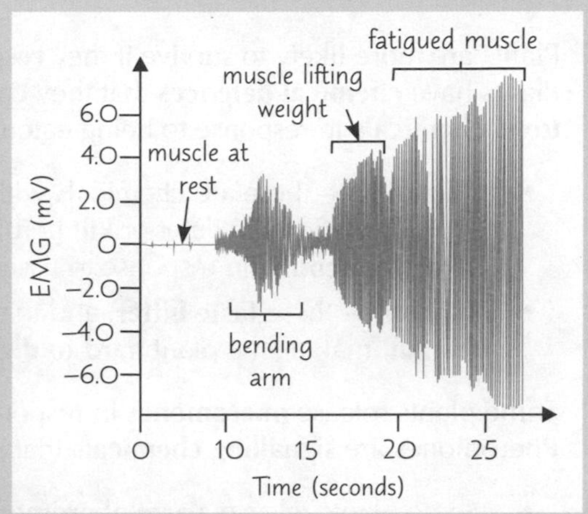

A motor unit is made up of a motor neurone and all the muscle fibres that it connects to.

Practice Questions

Q1 What is a neuromuscular junction?

Q2 Describe the role of AChE at a neuromuscular junction.

Q3 How does the function of involuntary muscle differ from skeletal muscle?

Q4 Describe the structure of cardiac muscle.

Q5 Briefly describe how you could use electrical signals to monitor muscle fatigue.

Exam Questions

Q1 During exercise the supply of ATP stored in the body is very quickly used up.

a) How does creatine phosphate maintain the supply of ATP so that exercise can continue? [2 marks]

b) What type of exercise does the ATP-creatine phosphate system provide energy for? Give a reason for your answer. [2 marks]

Q2 Myasthenia gravis is a neuromuscular disease in which antibodies can damage or block the nicotinic cholinergic receptors at neuromuscular junctions. A symptom of myasthenia gravis is muscle fatigue. Suggest why this is the case. [4 marks]

Smooth muscle — it has a way with the ladies...

Blimey, what a section. Neuromuscular junctions are synapses that are specific to muscle cells so make sure you learn the names of the neurotransmitters and the receptors involved here. You also need to learn the structure and function of the three different types of muscle so cover and scribble 'til you're sure you've got it. Then that's it for muscles. Happy days.

Plant Responses

You might not think that plants do much, but they respond to stimuli just like us. OK, not just like us (I can't picture a daisy boogying to cheesy music), but their responses are important all the same.

Plants Need to Respond to Stimuli

1) Plants, like animals, **increase** their chances of **survival** by **responding** to changes in their **environment**, e.g.

- They sense the direction of **light** and **grow** towards it to **maximise** light absorption for **photosynthesis**.
- They can sense **gravity**, so their roots and shoots **grow** in the **right direction**.
- **Climbing** plants have a sense of **touch**, so they can find things to climb and **reach** the **sunlight**.

2) Plants are more likely to survive if they **respond** to **herbivory** — **being eaten** by **animals** (including insects). Plants have **chemical defences** that they can use against herbivory. For example, they can produce **toxic chemicals** in response to being eaten. Examples of these chemicals include:

Herbivores are animals that eat plants.

- **Alkaloids** — these are chemicals with **bitter tastes**, **noxious smells** or **poisonous characteristics** that deter or kill herbivores, e.g. **tobacco plants** produce the alkaloid **nicotine** in response to tissue damage. Nicotine is **highly poisonous** to many insects.
- **Tannins** — these **taste bitter**, and in some herbivores (e.g. cattle, sheep) they can **bind to proteins** in the **gut**, making the plant **hard to digest**. Both of these things **deter animals** from eating the plant.

Some plants release **pheromones** in response to herbivory.
Pheromones are **signalling chemicals** that produce a **response** in other **organisms**, e.g.

- Some plants release **alarm pheromones** into the air in response to herbivore grazing. This can cause **nearby plants** that detect these chemicals to start making chemical defences such as **tannins**.
- When **corn plants** are being eaten by **caterpillars**, they can produce **pheromones** which **attract parasitic wasps**. These wasps then lay their eggs in the caterpillars (eww), which eventually kills them.

Other plants are able to **fold up** in response to being **touched**, e.g.

If a single leaflet (a mini leaf-shaped structure that makes up part of a leaf) of the plant *Mimosa pudica* is touched, a signal spreads through the whole leaf, causing it to quickly fold up. It's thought that this could help **protect** *Mimosa pudica* **against herbivory** in a variety of ways, e.g. it may help to **knock off** any **small insects** feeding on the plant. It may also **scare off** animals trying to eat it (I'd certainly be scared if my dinner moved mid-meal).

3) Plants are more likely to survive if they **respond** to **abiotic stress** — anything **harmful** that's **natural** but **non-living**, like a **drought**. E.g. some plants respond to **extreme cold** by **producing** their own form of **antifreeze**:

Carrots produce **antifreeze proteins** at low temperatures — the proteins **bind** to **ice crystals** and **lower** the **temperature** that water **freezes** at, **stopping** more ice crystals from **growing**.

A Tropism is a Plant's Growth Response to an External Stimulus

1) A **tropism** is the **response** of a plant to a **directional stimulus** (a stimulus coming from a particular direction).
2) Plants respond to stimuli by **regulating** their **growth**.
3) A **positive tropism** is growth **towards** the stimulus.
4) A **negative tropism** is growth **away** from the stimulus.

Unidirectional light
Shoots
Unidirectional light
Roots

Phototropism is the growth of a plant in response to **light**.
- **Shoots** are **positively phototropic** and grow **towards** light.
- **Roots** are **negatively phototropic** and grow **away** from light.

Geotropism is the growth of a plant in response to **gravity**.
- **Shoots** are **negatively geotropic** and grow **upwards**.
- **Roots** are **positively geotropic** and grow **downwards**.

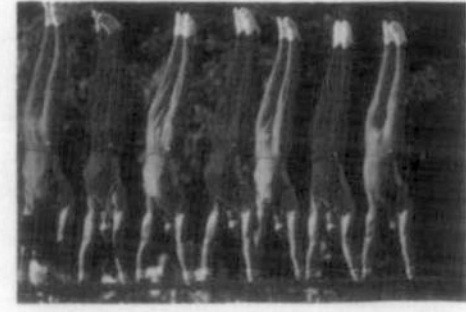
The men's gymnastics team were positively phototropic.

Plant Responses

Other tropisms you might come across include:

- **Hydrotropism** — plant growth in response to **water**. **Roots** are **positively hydrotropic**.
- **Thermotropism** — plant growth in response to **temperature**.
- **Thigmotropism** — plant growth in response to **contact with an object**.

Responses are *Brought About* by *Growth Hormones*

1) Plants **respond** to some stimuli using **growth hormones** — chemicals that **speed up** or **slow down** plant **growth**.
2) Growth hormones are **produced** in the **growing regions** of the plant (e.g. shoot tips, leaves) and they **move** to where they're needed in the **other parts** of the plant.
3) A growth hormone called **gibberellin** stimulates **seed germination**, **stem elongation**, **side shoot formation** and **flowering**.
4) Growth hormones called **auxins** stimulate the **growth** of shoots by **cell elongation** — this is where **cell walls** become **loose** and **stretchy**, so the cells get **longer**.
5) **High** concentrations of auxins **inhibit growth** in **roots** though.

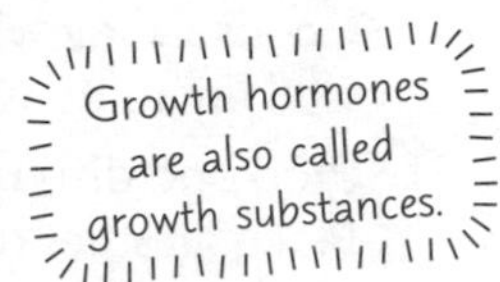

Indoleacetic Acid (IAA) is an Important Auxin

1) **Auxins** are produced in the **tips** of **shoots** in flowering plants (see p. 41). One important example of an auxin is **indoleacetic acid** (**IAA**) which, like other auxins, works by stimulating **cell elongation**.
2) IAA is **moved** around the plant to **control tropisms** — it moves by **diffusion** and **active transport** over short distances, and via the **phloem** over long distances.
3) This results in **different parts** of the plants having **different amounts** of IAA. The **uneven distribution** of IAA means there's **uneven growth** of the plant, e.g.:

Phototropism — IAA moves to the more **shaded** parts of the **shoots** and **roots**, so there's uneven growth.

shoot — IAA moves to this side — cells elongate and the shoot bends towards the light

root — IAA moves to this side — growth is inhibited so the root bends away from the light

Geotropism — IAA moves to the **underside** of **shoots** and **roots**, so there's uneven growth.

shoot — IAA moves to this side — cells elongate so the shoot grows upwards

root — IAA moves to this side — growth is inhibited so the root grows downwards

You Can Carry Out Practical Investigations *into* Phototropism

This investigation can be done to show how **plant shoots** respond to **light**.

1) Take **nine wheat shoots**. The shoots should be planted in **individual pots** in the **same type** of **soil**. The shoots should be roughly **equal in height**.
2) Cover the **tips** of **three shoots** with a **foil cap**. Leave **three shoots without foil**. Wrap the **base** of the final **three shoots** with **foil**, leaving only the tip exposed.
3) Set up the shoots in front of a **light source** and **leave them for two days**. The shoots should all be the **same distance** from the light source and experience the **same intensity** of light. **All other variables**, including **temperature** and **exposure to moisture**, should be **controlled**.
4) By the end of the experiment, the plants should look a bit like this. The shoots with **exposed tips** should have **grown towards the light source** (positive phototropism). **Covering the tip** with a foil cap **prevents growth towards the light** — it's the **tip** (where IAA is produced) that's **most sensitive** to light and because it's covered the shoot should have continued to grow straight up. **Covering the base** of the shoot with foil should still **allow** the **tip** to **grow towards the light**.
5) Recording the **amount** of **growth** (in mm), as well as the **direction** of growth, will give you quantitative results.

foil, light, foil, A B C
Experimental set-up

light, A B C
Results

Plant Responses

You Can Carry Out *Practical Investigations* into *Geotropism* too

There are lots of ways you could investigate geotropism. Here's one of them:

1) Line **three Petri dishes** with **moist** (but not soaking wet) **cotton wool**. You should use the **same volume** of **water** and the same amount of cotton wool in each dish.
2) Space out **10 cress seeds** on the surface of the cotton wool in each dish, then push each one into the wool.
3) Tape a **lid** onto each dish and **wrap** each one in **foil** (this will prevent any light reaching the seeds and affecting your results).
4) Choose somewhere you can leave the dishes where the **temperature** is likely to be **warmish** and **pretty constant**, e.g. a cupboard.
5) Prop one dish **upright**, at a **90° angle** — **label it** and mark which way is '**up**' (or down). Place another dish on a **slope** at a **45° angle**. Place the third dish on a **flat, horizontal surface**. You need to **label** the dishes **carefully**, so you know **which way up** each one was when you come to unwrap the dishes at the end of the experiment.
6) Leave the seeds for **4 days**. Then take a look at their **shoot** and **root growth**.
7) You should find that **whatever** the **angle** the dishes were placed at, the **shoots** have all **grown away** from **gravity** (negative geotropism) and the **roots** have grown **towards gravity** (positive geotropism).
8) To get quantitative results, **measure** the **amount** of growth of the shoots and roots and the **angle** of growth.

UP

Practice Questions

Q1 Why is it important for plants to respond to stimuli?

Q2 Give two examples of chemical defences produced by plants in response to herbivory.

Q3 What is a tropism?

Q4 What is hydrotropism?

Q5 How does the movement of IAA control geotropism in roots?

Exam Question

Q1 An experiment was carried out to investigate the role of auxin in shoot growth. Eight shoots, equal in height and mass, had their tips removed. Sponges soaked in glucose and either auxin or water were then placed where the tip should be. This is shown in the diagram on the right.

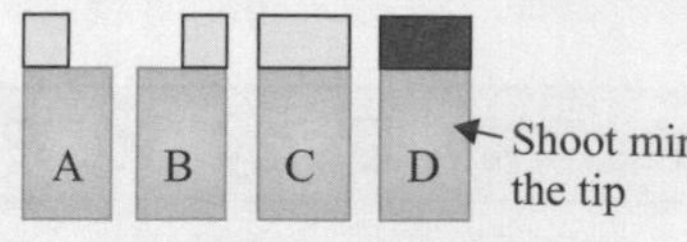

Four shoots were then placed in the dark (experiment A) and the other four shoots were exposed to a light source directed at them from the right (experiment B).

After two days, the amount of growth (in mm) and direction of growth was recorded. The results are shown in the table.

	Growth			
	Shoot A	**Shoot B**	**Shoot C**	**Shoot D**
Experiment A (dark)	6 mm, right	6 mm, left	6 mm, straight	1 mm, straight
Experiment B (light)	8 mm, right	8 mm, right	8 mm, right	3 mm, straight

a) Why were the tips of the shoots removed before the experiment began? [1 mark]

b) Suggest why glucose was added to the sponges. [1 mark]

c) Explain why two of the sponges were soaked in water and glucose rather than auxin and glucose. [2 marks]

d)* Explain the results for shoots A-C in each experiment. [6 marks]

* You will be assessed on the quality of your written response in this question.

IAA Productions — do you have the growth factor — with Simon Trowel...

Remember a tropism is a plant growth response to a directional stimulus — the bit before 'tropism' gives you a clue as to what that stimulus is, e.g. 'photo' = light, 'hydro' = water, 'thermo' = temperature, etc. Tropisms increase a plant's chances of survival, e.g. shoots need light to photosynthesise, so they grow towards light to help the plant survive.

The Effects of Plant Hormones

Plant hormones are responsible for all sorts — like your roses getting the hump and not keeping their pot tidy.

Auxins are Involved in *Apical Dominance*

1) The **shoot tip** at the top of a flowering plant is called the **apical bud**.
2) Auxins **stimulate** the **growth** of the **apical bud** and **inhibit** the **growth** of **side shoots** from **lateral buds**. This is called **apical dominance** — the apical bud is **dominant** over the lateral buds.

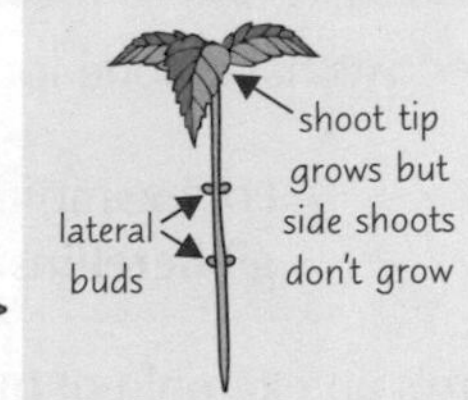

3) Apical dominance prevents side shoots from growing — this **saves energy** and prevents side shoots from the same plant **competing** with the shoot tip for light.
4) Because energy **isn't** being used to grow side shoots, apical dominance allows a **plant** in an area where there are **loads of other plants** to **grow tall very fast**, past the smaller plants, to **reach** the **sunlight**.
5) If you **remove** the apical bud then the plant **won't produce auxins**, so the **side shoots** will **start growing** by **cell division** and **cell elongation**.
6) However, if you replace the tip with a **source of auxin**, side shoot development is **inhibited**. This demonstrates that apical dominance is **controlled by auxin**.
7) Auxins become **less concentrated** as they **move away** from the apical bud to the rest of the plant. If a plant grows **very tall**, the bottom of the plant will have a **low auxin concentration** so side shoots will start to grow near the bottom.

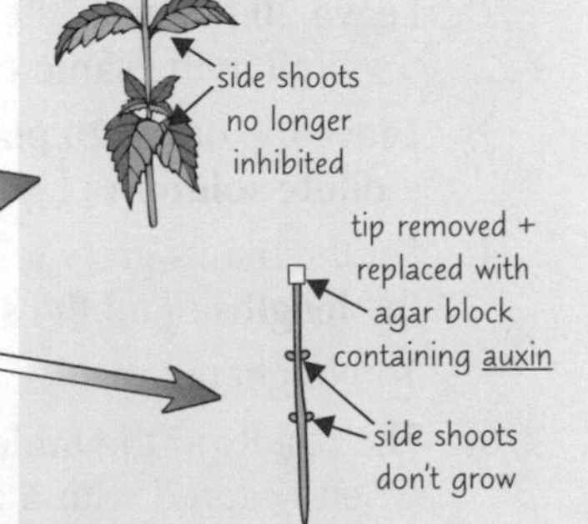

The Role of *Auxins* in *Apical Dominance* Can be *Investigated*

Scientists have **demonstrated** the **role of auxins** in **apical dominance** in **experiments** like the one below. You could also do this experiment yourself:

1) Plant **30 plants** (e.g. **pea plants**) that are a **similar age**, **height** and **weight** in pots.
2) **Count** and **record** the number of **side shoots** growing from the main stem of **each plant**.
3) For **10 plants**, **remove** the **tip** of the **shoot** and apply a **paste containing auxins** to the **top** of the **stem**.
4) For another 10 plants, remove the tip of the shoot and apply a **paste without auxins** to the top of the stem.
5) Leave the final 10 plants as they are — these are your untreated **controls**. These are needed for **comparison** so that you know the **effect** you see is **likely** to be due to the **hormone** and **not any other factor**.
6) Let each group **grow** for **six days**. You need to keep all the plants in the **same conditions** — the same **light intensity**, **water**, etc. This makes sure any **variables** that may affect your results are **controlled**, which makes your experiment **valid**.
7) After six days, **count** the number of **side shoots** growing from the main stem of **each** of your **plants**.
8) The results in the **table** show that **removing** the **tips** of shoots caused **extra side shoots** to **grow**, but removing tips **and** applying **auxins prevented** extra side shoots from growing.
9) The results suggest auxins **inhibit** the **growth** of side shoots — suggesting that auxins are involved in **apical dominance**.

	average no. of side shoots per plant	
	start of experiment	end of experiment
untreated plants (control group)	4	5
tips removed, auxin paste applied	4	5
tips removed, paste without auxins applied	4	9

Gibberellins are Another Type of *Plant Hormone*

1) **Gibberellins** are produced in **young leaves** and in **seeds**. They stimulate **seed germination**, **stem elongation**, **side shoot formation** and **flowering**.
2) Gibberellins **stimulate** the **stems** of plants to **grow** by **stem elongation** — this helps plants to grow **very tall**. If a **dwarf variety** of a plant is treated with gibberellin, it will grow to the **same height** as the **tall variety**. Unlike auxins, gibberellins **don't inhibit** plant growth in any way.
3) Gibberellins stimulate **seed germination** by triggering the **breakdown** of **starch** into **glucose** in the seed. The **plant embryo** in the seed can then use the glucose to begin **respiring** and **release** the **energy** it needs to **grow**. Gibberellins are **inhibited** (and so seed germination is prevented) by the hormone **abscisic acid**.

The Effects of Plant Hormones

The Role of Gibberellins can be Investigated

Scientists have done lots of experiments to provide **evidence** for the role of **gibberellins** in plant growth.

For example, scientists have produced **genetically altered** seeds that are **unable** to **produce gibberellins**. These seeds are **unable to germinate** unless they are given gibberellins.

Here's an example of how you could investigate the role of gibberellins in **stem elongation:**

1) Plant **40 plants** (e.g. dwarf pea plants) that are a similar **age**, **height** and **mass** in pots.
2) **Leave 20** plants as they are to grow, **watering** them **all** in the **same way** and keeping them **all** in the **same conditions** — these are your **controls**.
3) **Leave** the **other 20 plants** to grow in the **same conditions**, **except** water them with a **dilute solution** of **gibberellin** (e.g. **100 mg dm^{-3}** gibberellin).
4) Let the plants grow for about **28 days** and **measure** the **lengths** of all the **stems once each week.**
5) You might get **results** a bit like these:

time / days	average stem length / cm	
	plants watered normally	plants watered with gibberellin
0	14	14
7	15	17
14	18	27
21	19	38
28	23	46

6) The results in the **table** show that stems **grow more** when watered with a dilute solution of **gibberellin**.
7) The results suggest **gibberellin stimulates stem elongation.**
8) You might have to **calculate** the **rate of growth** of the plants in your exam, e.g:
   - In **28 days** the plants **watered normally** grew an **average** of **9 cm** (23 cm – 14 cm), so they grew at an average **rate** of 9 ÷ 28 = **0.32 cm/day** or **0.32 cm day^{-1}**.
   - In **28 days** the plants **watered with gibberellin** grew an **average** of **32 cm** (46 cm – 14 cm), so they grew at an average **rate** of 32 ÷ 28 = **1.14 cm day^{-1}**.

Gibberellins and Auxins can Work Together to Affect Plant Growth

Auxins and gibberellins are often **synergistic** — this means that they **work together** to have a really **big effect**. E.g. auxins and gibberellins work together to help plants grow **very tall**.

Auxins and gibberellins are sometimes **antagonistic** — this means they **oppose** each other's actions. E.g. **gibberellins stimulate** the growth of **side shoots** but **auxins inhibit** the growth of side shoots.

Hormones are Involved in Leaf Loss in Deciduous Plants

1) **Deciduous plants** are plants that **lose** their **leaves** in **winter**.
2) Losing their leaves helps plants to **conserve water** (lost from leaves) during the cold part of the year, when it might be **difficult** to **absorb water** from the **soil** (the soil water may be **frozen**), and when there's **less light** for **photosynthesis**.
3) Leaf loss is **triggered** by the **shortening day length** in the autumn.
4) Leaf loss is **controlled** by **hormones**:

The technical term for leaf loss is abscission.

- **Auxins inhibit** leaf loss — auxins are produced by **young leaves.** As the leaf gets **older**, **less auxin** is produced, leading to **leaf loss.**
- **Ethene stimulates** leaf loss — ethene is produced by **ageing leaves**. As the leaves get **older, more ethene** is produced. A **layer** of **cells** (called the **abscission layer**) develops at the **bottom** of the **leaf stalk** (where the leaf joins the stem). The abscission layer **separates** the leaf from the rest of the plant. Ethene **stimulates** the cells in the abscission layer to **expand**, **breaking** the **cell walls** and causing the **leaf** to **fall off**.

Auxins are antagonistic to ethene.

The Effects of Plant Hormones

Hormones are Involved in Stomatal Closure

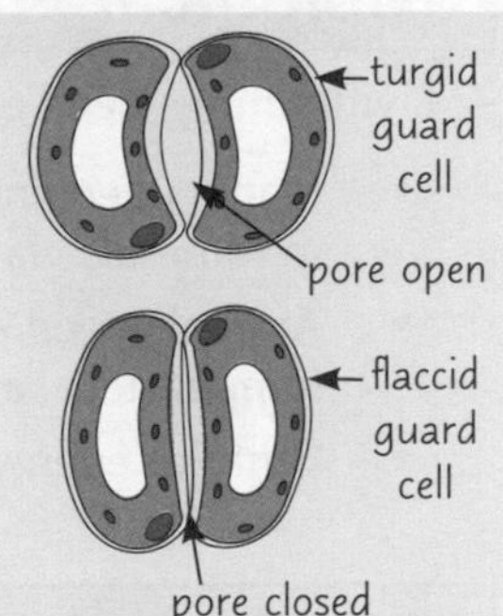

1) Plants need to be able to close their **stomata** in order to **reduce water loss** through **transpiration.**
2) They do this using **guard cells**. Guard cells are found either side of a stomatal pore. When the guard cells are **full of water**, they are plump and **turgid** and the pore is **open**. When the guard cells **lose water**, they become **flaccid**, making the pore **close.**
3) The plant hormone **abscisic acid** (ABA) is able to **trigger stomatal closure.**
4) ABA **binds** to receptors on the **guard cell membranes**. This causes specific **ion channels** to **open**, which allows **calcium ions** to enter the **cytosol** from the vacuole. The increased concentration of calcium ions in the cytosol causes **other ion channels** to **open**. These ion channels allow ions (such as potassium ions) to **leave** the guard cells, **raising** the **water potential** of the cells. **Water** then **leaves** the guard cells by **osmosis**. The guard cells become **flaccid** and the **stomata close**.

Plant Hormones have Many Commercial Uses

1) The **fruit industry** uses different **plant hormones** to **control** how different fruits develop, e.g.

Ethene stimulates enzymes that **break down cell walls**, **break down chlorophyll** and convert **starch** into **sugars**. This makes the fruit **soft**, **ripe** and **ready to eat**. E.g. **bananas** are harvested and transported **before** they're **ripe** because they're **less likely** to be **damaged** this way. They're then **exposed** to **ethene** on arrival so they **all ripen** at the **same time** on the **shelves** and in people's **homes**.

2) **Auxins** are also used **commercially** by **farmers** and **gardeners**, for example:

Auxins are used in **selective weedkillers** (**herbicides**) — auxins make **weeds** produce **long stems** instead of lots of **leaves**. This makes the weeds **grow too fast**, so they **can't** get enough **water** or **nutrients**, so they **die**.

Auxins are used as **rooting hormones** (e.g. in **rooting powder**) — auxins make a **cutting** (part of the plant, e.g. a stem cutting) **grow roots**. The **cutting** can then be **planted** and **grown** into a new plant. **Many cuttings** can be taken from **just one original plant** and **treated** with **rooting hormones**, so **lots** of the same plant can be grown **quickly** and **cheaply** from just one plant.

Practice Questions

Q1 Name the type of plant hormone that controls apical dominance.

Q2 Apart from controlling seed germination, give one function of gibberellins in a plant.

Exam Questions

Q1 Which of the following hormones inhibits leaf loss in deciduous plants?

A auxins B gibberellins C ethene D abscisic acid [1 mark]

Q2 A tomato grower wants all her tomatoes to ripen at the same time, just before she sells them at a market.

a) Name a plant hormone she could use to make the tomatoes ripen. [1 mark]

b) Explain how the hormone you named in part a) makes tomatoes ripen. [1 mark]

c) Suggest a commercial advantage of being able to pick and transport tomatoes before they're ripe. [1 mark]

Q3 Drought conditions stimulate plants to produce the hormone abscisic acid (ABA). Suggest how this helps plants to survive when there is little or no water available. [2 marks]

The weeping willow — yep, that plant definitely has hormones...

Just wait till the next time you're in a supermarket — I bet you can't get round the whole shop without commenting on why the bananas are ripe. And you're going to be great fun when all the leaves start dropping off the trees in autumn. Make sure you know the roles of all the plant hormones mentioned on pages 41-43 or there'll be trouble.

Photosynthesis and Respiration

OK, this isn't the easiest topic in the world, but 'cos I'm feeling nice today we'll take it slowly, one bit at a time...

Biological Processes Need Energy

Living things **need energy** for biological processes to occur:

- **Plants** need energy for things like **photosynthesis**, **active transport** (e.g. to take in minerals via their roots), **DNA replication**, **cell division** and **protein synthesis**.
- **Animals** need energy for things like **muscle contraction**, maintenance of **body temperature**, **active transport**, **DNA replication**, **cell division** and **protein synthesis**.
- Without energy, these biological processes would **stop** and the plant or animal would **die**.

Microorganisms need energy for things like DNA replication, cell division, protein synthesis and sometimes motility (movement).

Photosynthesis Stores Energy in Glucose

1) **Plants** can **make** their **own food** (**glucose**). They do this using **photosynthesis**.
2) **Photosynthesis** is the process where **energy** from **light** is used to **make glucose** from H_2O and CO_2 (the light energy is **converted** to **chemical energy** in the form of glucose).
3) Photosynthesis occurs in a **series** of **reactions**, but the overall equation is:

$$6CO_2 + 6H_2O + \text{Energy} \longrightarrow C_6H_{12}O_6 \text{ (glucose)} + 6O_2$$

4) So, energy is **stored** in the **glucose** until the plants **release** it by **respiration**.
5) **Animals can't make** their **own food**. So, they obtain glucose by **eating plants** (or **other animals**), then respire the glucose to release energy.

Cells Release Energy from Glucose by Respiration

1) **Living** cells **release energy** from **glucose** — this process is called **respiration**.
2) This energy is used to power all the **biological processes** in a cell.
3) There are two types of respiration:
   - **Aerobic respiration** — respiration **using oxygen**.
   - **Anaerobic respiration** — respiration **without oxygen**.
4) Aerobic respiration produces **carbon dioxide** and **water**, and releases **energy**.

The overall equation is: $$C_6H_{12}O_6 \text{ (glucose)} + 6O_2 \longrightarrow 6CO_2 + 6H_2O + \text{Energy}$$

The glucose made in photosynthesis by plants is needed for use in respiration in both plants and animals.

You Need to Know Some Basics Before You Start

There are some pretty confusing terms in this section (and the next) that you need to get your head around:

- **Metabolic pathway** — a **series** of **small reactions** controlled by **enzymes**, e.g. **respiration** and **photosynthesis**.
- **Phosphorylation** — **adding phosphate** to a molecule, e.g. **ADP** is phosphorylated to **ATP**.
- **Photophosphorylation** — **adding phosphate** to a molecule using **light**.
- **Photolysis** — the **splitting** (lysis) of a molecule using **light** (photo) energy.
- **Hydrolysis** — the **splitting** (lysis) of a molecule using **water** (hydro).
- **Decarboxylation** — the **removal** of **carbon dioxide** from a molecule.
- **Dehydrogenation** — the **removal** of **hydrogen** from a molecule.
- **Redox reactions** — reactions that involve **oxidation** and **reduction**.

Remember redox reactions:

1) If something is **reduced** it has **gained electrons** (e^-), and may have **gained hydrogen** or lost oxygen.
2) If something is **oxidised** it has **lost electrons**, and may have **lost hydrogen** or gained oxygen.
3) Oxidation of one molecule **always** involves reduction of another molecule.

One way to remember electron and hydrogen movement is OILRIG. Oxidation Is Loss, Reduction Is Gain.

Photosynthesis and Respiration

Photosynthesis and *Respiration* Involve *Coenzymes*

1) As you know from Module 2, a **coenzyme** is a molecule that **aids** the **function** of an **enzyme**.
2) They usually work by **transferring** a **chemical group** from one molecule to another.
3) A coenzyme used in **photosynthesis** is **NADP**. NADP transfers **hydrogen** from one molecule to another — this means it can **reduce** (give hydrogen to) or **oxidise** (take hydrogen from) a molecule.
4) Examples of coenzymes used in **respiration** are: **NAD**, **coenzyme A** and **FAD**.
   - NAD and FAD transfer **hydrogen** from one molecule to another — this means they can **reduce** (give hydrogen to) or **oxidise** (take hydrogen from) a molecule.
   - **Coenzyme A** transfers **acetate** between molecules (see page 55).

When hydrogen is transferred between molecules, electrons are transferred too.

Photosynthesis Takes Place in the *Chloroplasts* of *Plant Cells*

1) **Chloroplasts** are **small**, **flattened organelles** found in **plant cells**. They're the **location** for **photosynthesis** in plant cells.
2) They have a **double membrane** called the **chloroplast envelope**.
3) **Thylakoids** (fluid-filled sacs) are **stacked up** in the chloroplast into structures called **grana** (singular = **granum**). The grana are **linked** together by bits of thylakoid membrane called **lamellae** (singular = **lamella**).
4) Chloroplasts contain **photosynthetic pigments** (e.g. **chlorophyll a**, **chlorophyll b** and **carotene**). These are **coloured substances** that **absorb** the **light energy** needed for photosynthesis. The pigments are found in the **thylakoid membranes** — they're attached to **proteins**. The protein and pigment is called a **photosystem**.
5) A photosystem contains **two types** of photosynthetic pigments — **primary** pigments and **accessory** pigments. Primary pigments are **reaction centres**, where **electrons** are **excited** during the light-dependent reaction (see pages 46-47). **Accessory pigments** make up **light-harvesting systems**. These **surround** reaction centres and **transfer light energy** to them to boost the energy available for electron excitement to take place.

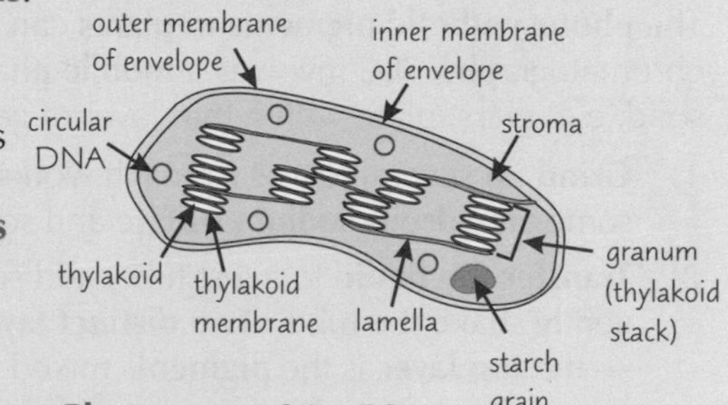

6) There are **two photosystems** used by plants to capture light energy. **Photosystem I** (or PSI) absorbs light best at a wavelength of **700 nm** and **photosystem II** (PSII) absorbs light best at **680 nm**.
7) Contained within the inner membrane of the chloroplast and **surrounding** the thylakoids is a gel-like substance called the **stroma**. It contains **enzymes**, **sugars** and **organic acids**.
8) Chloroplasts have their own **DNA**. It's found in the **stroma** and is often **circular**. There can be **multiple copies** in **each** chloroplast.
9) Carbohydrates produced by photosynthesis and not used straight away are stored as **starch grains** in the **stroma**.

Practice Questions

Q1 Write down three biological processes in animals that need energy.

Q2 Give the name of a coenzyme involved in respiration.

Q3 What are photosynthetic pigments?

Exam Question

Q1 Which one of these statements about chloroplasts is correct?
- A The thylakoids are stacked up into structures called lamellae.
- B The photosynthetic pigments are located in the chloroplast envelope.
- C The stroma is a gel-like substance that contains enzymes, sugars and organic acids.
- D Chloroplasts don't contain any DNA.

[1 mark]

Oh dear, I've used up all my energy on these two pages...

Well, I won't beat about the bush, this stuff is pretty tricky... nearly as hard as a cross between Hugh Jackman and concrete. With a little patience and perseverance (and plenty of [chocolate] [coffee] [marshmallows] — delete as you wish), you'll get there. Once you've got these pages straight in your head, the next ones will be easier to understand.

Photosynthesis

Right, pen at the ready. Check. Brain switched on. Check. Cuppa piping hot. Check. Sweets on standby. Check. Okay, I think you're all sorted to look at the light-dependent stage of photosynthesis. Here we go...

Photosynthesis can be Split into Two Stages

See p. 48 for loads more information on the Calvin cycle.

There are actually **two stages** that make up **photosynthesis**:

1) The Light-Dependent Reaction

1) As the name suggests, this reaction **needs light energy**.
2) It takes place in the **thylakoid membranes** of the chloroplasts.
3) Here, light energy is absorbed by **photosynthetic pigments** in the **photosystems** and converted to **chemical energy**.
4) The light energy is used to add a phosphate group to ADP to form **ATP**, and to reduce NADP to form **reduced NADP**. (Reduced NADP is an **energy-rich molecule** because it can transfer hydrogen, and so electrons, to other molecules.) **ATP transfers energy** and reduced **NADP transfers hydrogen** to the light-independent reaction.
5) During the process $\mathbf{H_2O}$ is **oxidised** to $\mathbf{O_2}$.

2) The Light-Independent Reaction

1) This is also called the **Calvin cycle** and as the name suggests it **doesn't use light energy** directly. (But it does **rely** on the **products** of the light-dependent reaction).
2) It takes place in the **stroma** of the chloroplasts.
3) Here, the **ATP** and **reduced NADP** from the light-dependent reaction supply the **energy** and **hydrogen** to make **glucose** from $\mathbf{CO_2}$.

Thin Layer Chromatography can Separate Photosynthetic Pigments

The **photosynthetic pigments** in plants can be **separated** using **thin layer chromatography** (**TLC**). Like all types of chromatography, TLC involves a **mobile phase** (in this case a liquid solvent) and a **stationary phase** (in this case a solid, e.g. glass, plate with a thin layer of gel, e.g. silica gel, on top — called a **chromatography plate**).

It's best to do steps 2 and 5 in a fume cupboard as the chemicals used are volatile (evaporate easily) and the vapours are hazardous.

1) **Grind** up several leaves (spinach works nicely) with some **anhydrous sodium sulfate** and some **propanone**.
2) **Transfer** the **liquid** to a test tube, add some **petroleum ether** and gently shake the tube. **Two distinct layers** will form in the liquid — the **top layer** is the **pigments** mixed in with the petroleum ether.
3) Transfer some of the liquid from the **top layer** into a second test tube with some **anhydrous sodium sulfate**.
4) Draw a horizontal **pencil line** near the bottom of a **chromatography plate**. Build up a single **concentrated spot** of the liquid from step 3) on the line by applying several drops and ensuring each one is **dry** before the next is added. This is the **point of origin**.
5) Once the point of origin is completely dry, put the plate into a glass beaker with some prepared **solvent** (e.g. a mixture of **propanone**, **cyclohexane** and **petroleum ether**) — just enough so that the **point of origin** is a little bit **above** the solvent. Put a **lid** on the beaker and leave the plate to develop. As the solvent spreads up the plate, the different **pigments** move with it, but at **different rates** — so they **separate**.

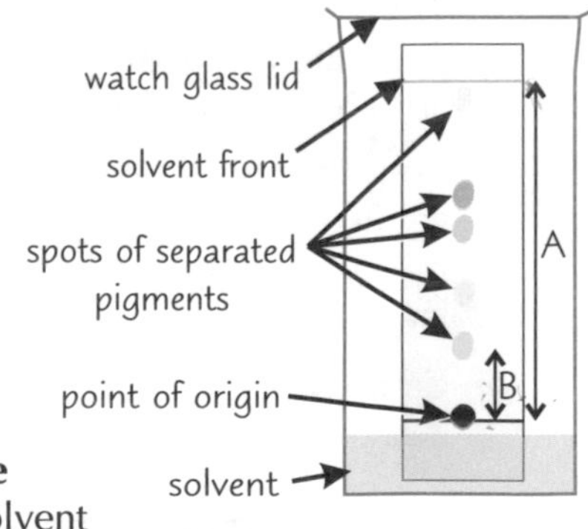

6) When the solvent has **nearly** reached the top, take the plate out and **mark** the **solvent front** (the furthest point the solvent has reached) with a **pencil** and leave the plate to dry in a well-ventilated place.
7) There should be **several** new coloured spots on the chromatography plate between the **point of origin** and the **solvent front**. These are the separated **pigments**. You can calculate their $\mathbf{R_f}$ **values** and look them up in a database to **identify** what the pigments are.

$$R_f \text{ value} = \frac{B}{A} = \frac{\text{distance travelled by spot}}{\text{distance travelled by solvent}}$$

In the Light-Dependent Reaction, ATP is Made by Photophosphorylation

In the light-dependent reaction, the **light energy** absorbed by the photosystems is used for **three** things:

1) Making **ATP** from **ADP** and **inorganic phosphate**. This reaction is called **photophosphorylation** (see p. 44).
2) Making **reduced NADP** from **NADP**.
3) Splitting **water** into **protons** (H^+ ions), **electrons** and **oxygen**. This is called **photolysis** (see p. 44).

The light-dependent reaction actually includes **two types** of **photophosphorylation** — **non-cyclic** and **cyclic**. Each of these processes has **different products**.

Photosynthesis

Non-cyclic Photophosphorylation Produces ATP, Reduced NADP and O_2

To understand the process you need to know that the photosystems (in the thylakoid membranes) are **linked** by **electron carriers**. Electron carriers are **proteins** that **transfer electrons**. The photosystems and electron carriers form an **electron transport chain** — a **chain** of **proteins** through which **excited electrons flow**. All the processes in the diagrams are happening together — I've just split them up to make it easier to understand.

1) Light energy excites electrons in chlorophyll

- **Light energy** is absorbed by **PSII**.
- The light energy **excites electrons** in **chlorophyll**.
- The electrons move to a **higher energy level** (i.e. they have more energy).
- These high-energy electrons **move along** the **electron transport chain** to **PSI**.

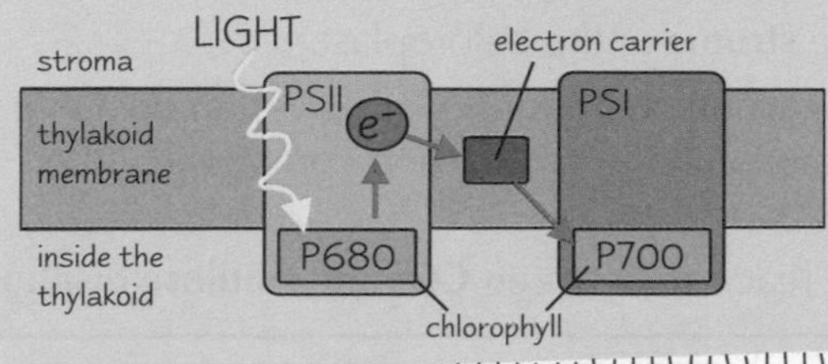

If too much light energy has been absorbed, plants release some of the excess energy by emitting fluorescent light. This is called chlorophyll fluorescence.

2) Photolysis of water produces protons (H^+ ions), electrons and O_2

- As the excited electrons **from chlorophyll leave PSII** to **move along** the electron transport chain, they must be **replaced**.
- **Light** energy splits **water** into **protons** (H^+ ions), **electrons** and **oxygen**. (So the O_2 in photosynthesis comes from water.)
- The reaction is: $H_2O \rightarrow 2H^+ + \frac{1}{2}O_2$

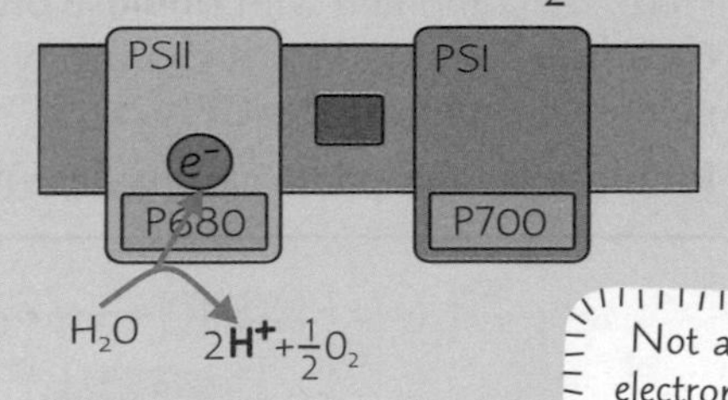

Not all of the electron carriers are shown in these diagrams.

3) Energy from the excited electrons makes ATP...

- The excited electrons **lose energy** as they **move along** the **electron transport chain**.
- This energy is used to **transport protons into** the **thylakoid**, via membrane proteins called **proton pumps**, so that the thylakoid has a **higher concentration** of protons than the stroma. This forms a **proton gradient** across the membrane.
- Protons move **down** their concentration gradient, into the stroma, **via** an enzyme called **ATP synthase**. The energy from this movement combines **ADP** and **inorganic phosphate** (P_i) to form **ATP**.

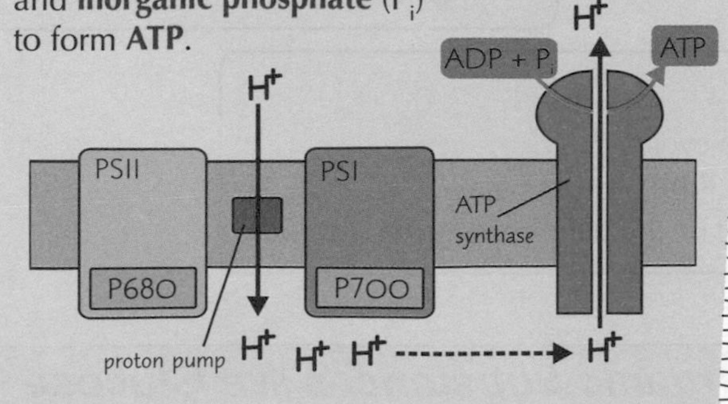

The process of electrons flowing down the electron transport chain and creating a proton gradient across the membrane to drive ATP synthesis is called chemiosmosis. It's described by the chemiosmotic theory.

4) ...and generates reduced NADP.

- Light energy is **absorbed** by PSI, which excites the electrons again to an **even higher** energy level.
- Finally, the electrons are **transferred** to **NADP**, along with a **proton** (H^+ ion) from the **stroma**, to form **reduced NADP**.

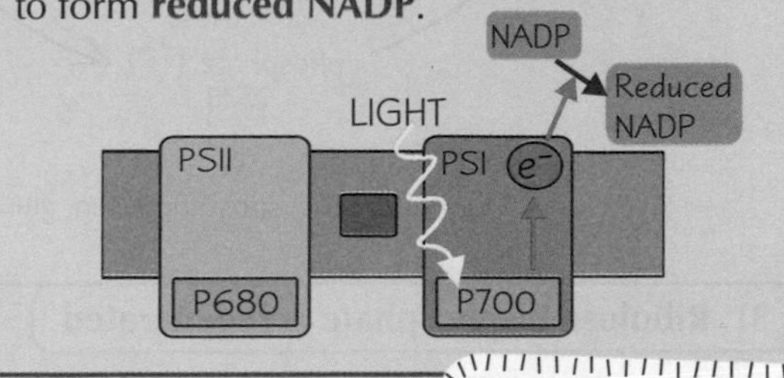

Remember a 'proton' is just another word for a hydrogen ion (H^+).

Cyclic Photophosphorylation Only Produces ATP

Cyclic photophosphorylation **only uses PSI**. It's called 'cyclic' because the electrons from the chlorophyll molecule **aren't** passed onto NADP, but are **passed back** to PSI via electron carriers. This means the electrons are **recycled** and can repeatedly flow through PSI. This process doesn't produce any reduced NADP or O_2 — it **only produces** small amounts of **ATP**.

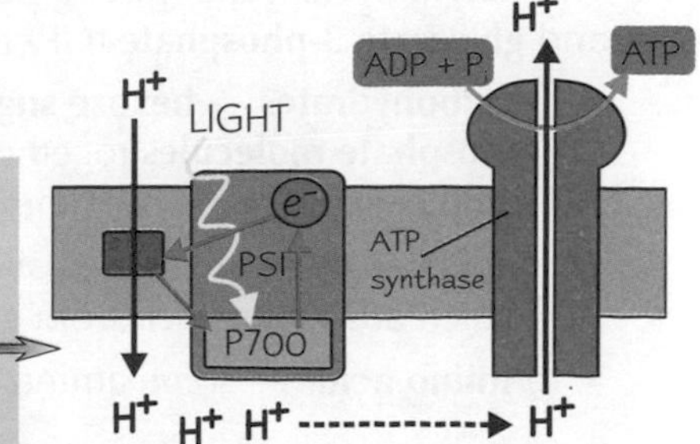

Photosynthesis

Don't worry, you're over the worst of photosynthesis now. Instead of electrons flying around, there's a nice cycle of reactions to learn. What more could you want from life? Money, fast cars and nice clothes have nothing on this...

The **Light-Independent** Reaction is also called the **Calvin Cycle**

1) **The Calvin cycle** takes place in the **stroma** of the chloroplasts. (The Calvin cycle is also known as **carbon dioxide fixation** because **carbon** from CO_2 is '**fixed**' into an **organic molecule**.)
2) It makes a molecule called **triose phosphate** from CO_2 and **ribulose bisphosphate** (a 5-carbon compound). Triose phosphate can be used to make **glucose** and other **useful organic substances** (see below).
3) There are a few steps in the cycle, and it needs **ATP** and **H^+ ions** to keep it going.
4) The reactions are linked in a **cycle**, which means the starting compound, **ribulose bisphosphate**, is **regenerated**.

Here's what happens at each stage in the cycle:

1) Carbon dioxide is combined with ribulose bisphosphate to form two molecules of glycerate 3-phosphate

- CO_2 enters the leaf through the **stomata** and diffuses into the **stroma** of the chloroplast.
- Here, it's combined with **ribulose bisphosphate** (**RuBP**), a **5-carbon** compound. This gives an **unstable 6-carbon** compound, which quickly breaks down into **two** molecules of a **3-carbon** compound called **glycerate 3-phosphate** (**GP**).
- **Ribulose bisphosphate carboxylase** (**RuBisCO**) catalyses the reaction between CO_2 and **ribulose bisphosphate**.

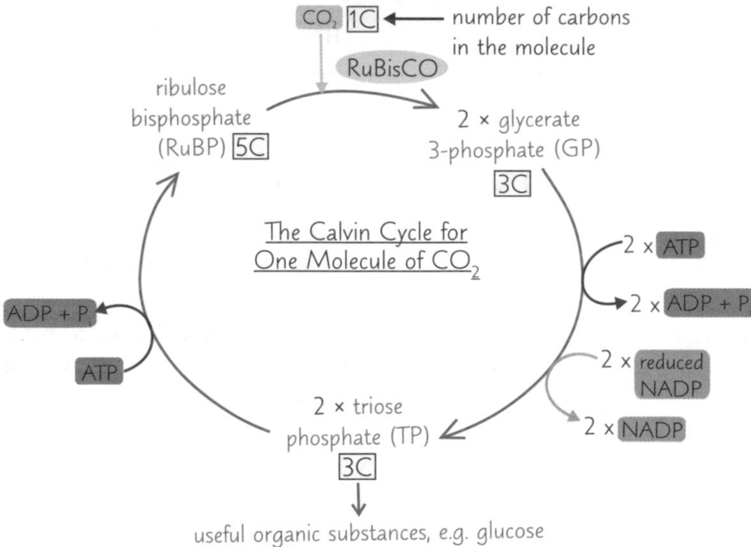

2) ATP and reduced NADP are required for the reduction of GP to triose phosphate

- Now **ATP**, from the **light-dependent** reaction, **provides energy** to turn the **3-carbon** compound, **GP**, into a **different** 3-carbon compound called **triose phosphate** (**TP**).
- This reaction also requires **H^+ ions**, which come from **reduced NADP** (also from the **light-dependent reaction**). Reduced NADP is **recycled** to **NADP** (for use in the light-dependent reaction again).
- **Triose phosphate** is then converted into many **useful organic compounds**, e.g. glucose (see below).

3) Ribulose bisphosphate is regenerated

- **Five** out of every **six** molecules of **TP** produced in the cycle aren't used to make hexose sugars, but to **regenerate RuBP**.
- Regenerating RuBP uses the **rest** of the **ATP** produced by the **light-dependent reaction**.

TP and **GP** are **Converted** into **Useful Organic Substances** like **Glucose**

The **Calvin cycle** is the starting point for making **all** the organic substances a plant needs. **Triose phosphate** (TP) and **glycerate 3-phosphate** (GP) molecules are used to make **carbohydrates**, **lipids** and **amino acids**:

- **Carbohydrates** — **hexose sugars** (e.g. glucose) are made by joining **two triose phosphate molecules** together and **larger** carbohydrates (e.g. sucrose, starch, cellulose) are made by joining **hexose sugars** together in **different ways**.
- **Lipids** — these are made using **glycerol**, which is synthesised from **triose phosphate**, and **fatty acids**, which are synthesised from **glycerate 3-phosphate**.
- **Amino acids** — some amino acids are made from **glycerate 3-phosphate**.

Photosynthesis

The **Calvin Cycle** Needs to Turn **Six Times** to Make **One Hexose Sugar**

1) **Three turns** of the cycle produces **six** molecules of **triose phosphate** (TP), because two molecules of TP are made for every one CO_2 molecule used.
2) **Five** out of **six** of these TP molecules are used to **regenerate ribulose bisphosphate** (RuBP).
3) This means that for **three turns** of the cycle only **one TP** is produced that's used to make a **hexose sugar**.
4) A hexose sugar has **six carbons** though, so **two TP** molecules are needed to form one hexose sugar.
5) This means the cycle must turn **six times** to produce **two molecules** of **TP** that can be used to make **one hexose sugar**.
6) Six turns of the cycle need **18 ATP** and **12 reduced NADP** from the light-dependent reaction.

Practice Questions

Q1 Where in the chloroplasts does the light-independent reaction occur?

Q2 Name one method that can be used to separate photosynthetic pigments in plants.

Q3 What is the equation to work out an R_f value?

Q4 What three substances does non-cyclic photophosphorylation produce?

Q5 What is an electron carrier?

Q6 Describe the role of water in the light-dependent reaction.

Q7 Which photosystem is involved in cyclic photophosphorylation?

Q8 Name the two products from the light-dependent reaction that are used in the light-independent reaction.

Q9 Name two organic substances made from triose phosphate.

Q10 How many CO_2 molecules need to enter the Calvin cycle to make one hexose sugar?

Exam Questions

Q1 The diagram below shows the light-dependent reaction of photosynthesis.

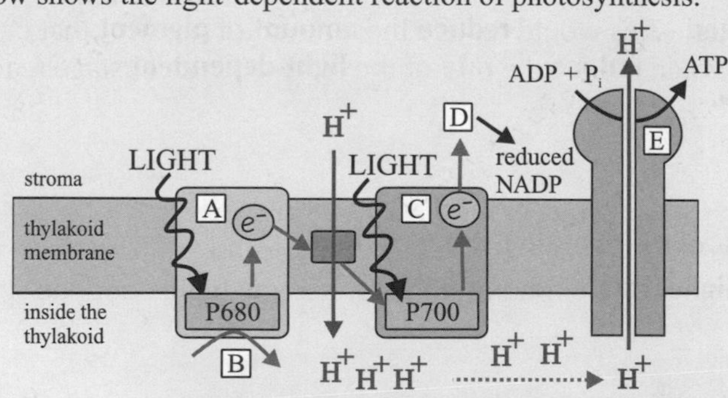

a) Where precisely in a plant does the light-dependent reaction of photosynthesis occur? [1 mark]

b) What is A? [1 mark]

c) Describe process B and explain its purpose. [4 marks]

d) What is reactant D? [1 mark]

Q2 RuBisCO is an enzyme that catalyses the first reaction of the Calvin cycle. CA1P is an inhibitor of RuBisCO.

a)* Describe how triose phosphate is produced in the Calvin cycle. [6 marks]

b) Briefly explain how ribulose bisphosphate (RuBP) is regenerated in the Calvin cycle. [2 marks]

c) Explain the effect that CA1P would have on glucose production. [3 marks]

* You will be assessed on the quality of your written response in this question.

Calvin cycles — bikes made by people that normally make pants...

Next thing we know there'll be people swanning about in their pants riding highly fashionable bikes. Sounds awful I know, but let's face it, anything would look better than cycling shorts. Anyway, it would be a good idea to go over these pages a couple of times — I promise you, there's still room left in your head for more information..

Limiting Factors in Photosynthesis

Now you know what photosynthesis is it's time to find out what conditions make it speedy and what slows it down. I'd start by making sure you have the best conditions for revision — oodles of biscuits and your thinking cap on.

There are Optimum Conditions for Photosynthesis

The **ideal conditions** for photosynthesis vary from one plant species to another.
Most plants in temperate climates, like in the UK, would be happy with the conditions below:

1. High light intensity of a certain wavelength

- Light is needed to provide the **energy** for the **light-dependent reaction** — the **higher** the **intensity** of the light, the **more energy** it provides.
- Only certain **wavelengths** of light are used for photosynthesis. The photosynthetic pigments chlorophyll a, chlorophyll b and carotene only **absorb** the **red** and **blue** light in sunlight. (**Green** light is **reflected**, which is why plants look green.)

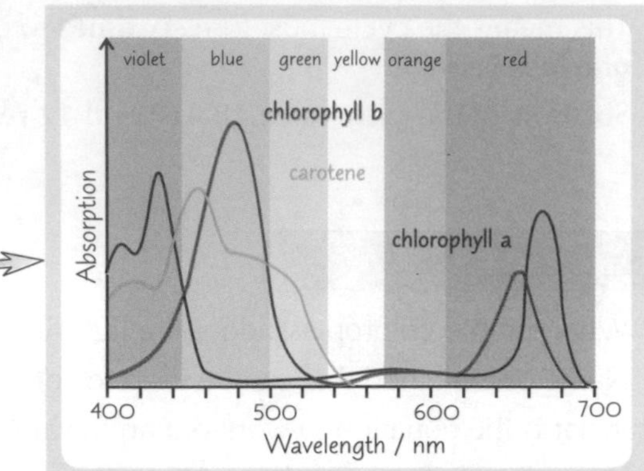

2. Temperature around 25 °C

- Photosynthesis involves **enzymes** (e.g. ATP synthase, RuBisCO). If the temperature falls **below 10 °C**, the enzymes become **inactive**, but if the temperature is **more than 45 °C** they may start to **denature**.
- Also, at **high** temperatures:
  1) **Stomata close** to avoid losing too much water. This causes photosynthesis to slow down because **less CO_2** enters the leaf when the stomata are closed.
  2) **The thylakoid membranes** may be damaged. This could **reduce** the **rate** of the **light-dependent** stage reactions by **reducing** the number of sites **available** for **electron transfer**.
  3) The **membranes around** the **chloroplasts** could be damaged, which could cause **enzymes** important in the **Calvin cycle** to be **released** into the cell. This would **reduce** the **rate** of the **light-independent** stage reactions.
  4) **Chlorophyll** could be **damaged**. This would **reduce** the **amount** of **pigment** that can **absorb light energy**, which would **reduce** the **rate** of the **light-dependent** stage reactions.

The width of the opening of stomata is called the stomatal aperture.

3. Carbon dioxide at 0.4%

- Carbon dioxide makes up **0.04%** of the gases in the atmosphere.
- Increasing this to **0.4%** gives a **higher rate** of photosynthesis, but any higher and the stomata start to **close**.

Light, Temperature and CO_2 can all Limit Photosynthesis

1) **All three** of these things need to be at the **right level** to allow a plant to photosynthesise as quickly as possible.
2) If any **one** of these factors is **too low** or **too high**, it will **limit photosynthesis** (slow it down). Even if the other two factors are at the perfect level, it won't make **any difference** to the speed of photosynthesis as long as that factor is at the wrong level.
3) On a warm, sunny, windless day, it's usually **CO_2** that's the limiting factor, and at night it's the **light intensity**.
4) However, **any** of these factors could become the limiting factor, depending on the **environmental conditions**.

All that Murray and Fraser knew was that limiting photosynthesis was a tasty business...

Limiting Factors in Photosynthesis

*You Might Have to **Interpret Graphs** About **Limiting Factors***

Light intensity

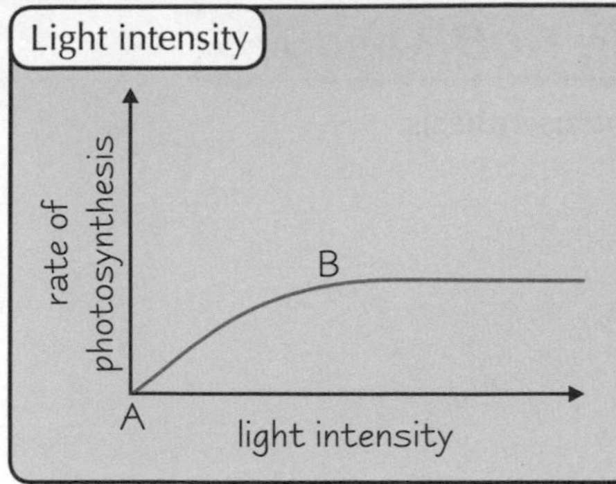

Between points A and B, the rate of photosynthesis is limited by the **light intensity**. So as the light intensity **increases**, so can the rate of photosynthesis. Point B is the **saturation point** — increasing light intensity after this point makes no difference, because **something else** has become the limiting factor. The graph now **levels off**.

The saturation point is where a factor is no longer limiting the reaction — something else has become the limiting factor.

Temperature

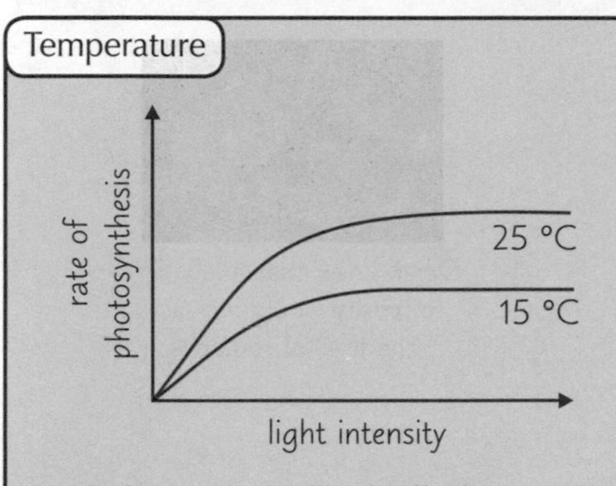

Both these graphs level off when **light intensity** is no longer the limiting factor. The graph at **25 °C** levels off at a **higher point** than the one at **15 °C**, showing that **temperature** must have been a limiting factor at **15 °C**.

CO_2 concentration

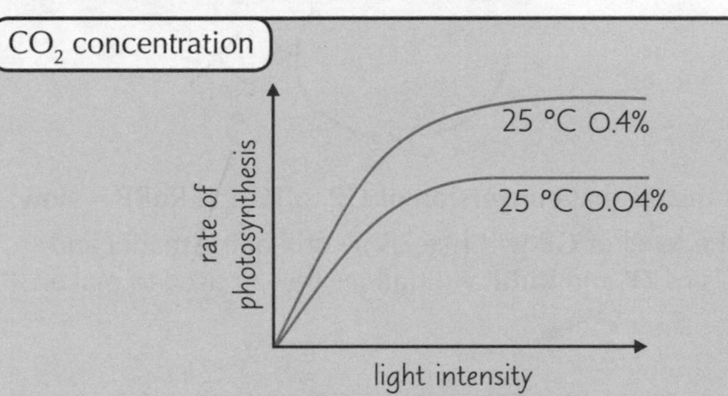

Again, both these graphs level off when **light intensity** is no longer the limiting factor. The graph at **0.4% CO_2** levels off at a **higher point** than the one at **0.04%**, so **CO_2 concentration** must have been a limiting factor at **0.04% CO_2**. The limiting factor here **isn't temperature** because it's the **same** for both graphs (25 °C).

Water Stress** Can Also Affect **Photosynthesis

When plants **don't** have **enough water**, their **stomata** will **close** to preserve what little water they do have, leading to **less CO_2** entering the leaf for the Calvin cycle and **slowing** photosynthesis down.

Practice Questions

Q1 Why is a high light intensity an optimum condition for photosynthesis?

Q2 What is the optimum concentration of carbon dioxide for photosynthesis?

Q3 What are the possible likely limiting factors for photosynthesis on a warm, sunny day?

Q4 Explain how a lack of water slows down photosynthesis in a plant.

Exam Question

Q1 An experiment was carried out to investigate how temperature affects photosynthesis.
The rate of photosynthesis was measured at 10 °C, 25 °C and 45 °C.
At which temperature would the rate of photosynthesis have been greatest? Explain your answer. [4 marks]

I'm a whizz at the factors that limit revision...

... watching Hollyoaks, making tea, watching EastEnders, walking the dog... not to mention staring into space. These pages aren't that bad though. You just need to learn how light, CO_2, temperature and water stress affect the rate of photosynthesis. Try shutting the book and writing down what you know — you'll be amazed at what you remember.

Limiting Factors in Photosynthesis

Well, I hope you didn't think we'd finished covering limiting factors.... ohhhhhh no, I could write a whole book on them. But just for you I've added an experiment to spice things up a bit. It's time to polish your test tubes.

Light, Temperature and CO_2 Affect the Levels of GP, RuBP and TP

Light intensity, **temperature** and **CO_2 concentration** all **affect** the **rate** of **photosynthesis**, which means they affect the **levels** of **GP**, **RuBP** and **TP** in the **Calvin cycle**.

1. Light intensity

- In **low light intensities**, the products of the light-dependent stage (**reduced NADP** and **ATP**) will be in **short supply**.

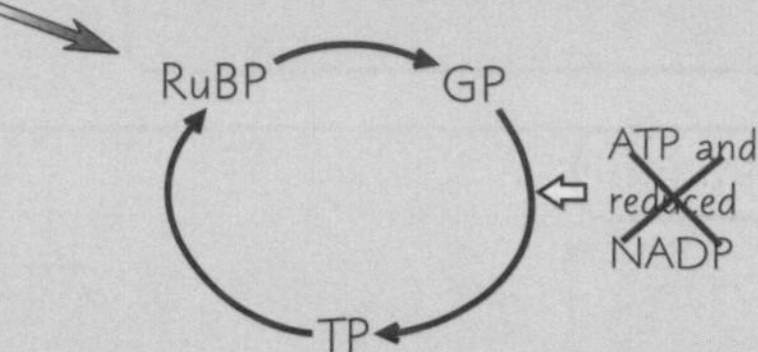

- This means that **conversion of GP** to TP and RuBP is **slow**.
- So the level of **GP** will **rise** (as it's still being made) and levels of **TP** and **RuBP** will **fall** (as they're used to make GP).

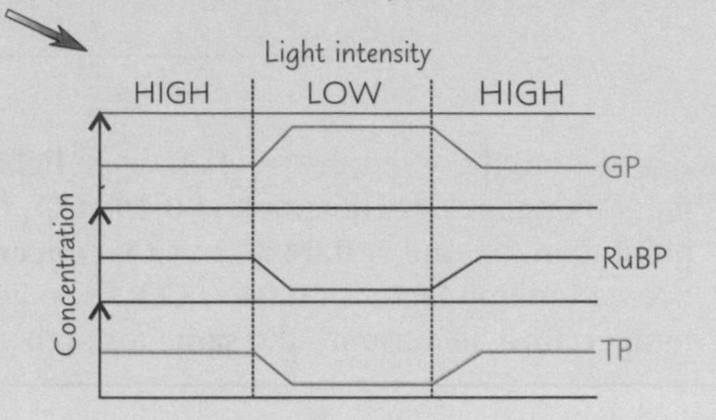

Derek knew that a low light intensity would increase the level of romance.

2. Temperature

- All the reactions in the Calvin cycle are catalysed by **enzymes** (e.g. RuBisCO).
- At **low temperatures**, all of the reactions will be **slower** as the enzymes work more **slowly**.

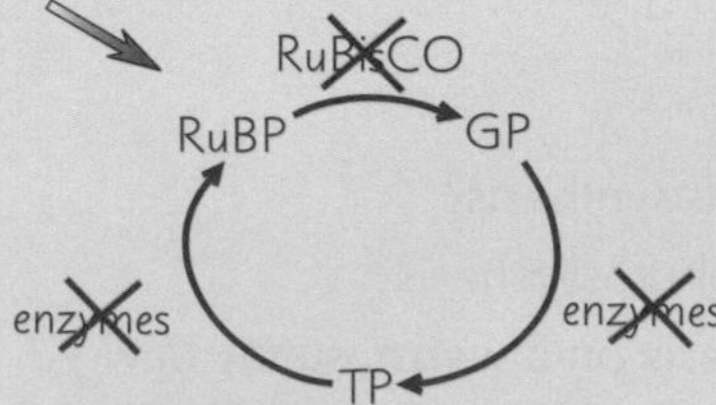

- This means the levels of **RuBP**, **GP** and **TP** will **fall**.
- GP, TP and RuBP are affected in the same way at **very high temperatures**, because the **enzymes** will start to **denature**.

3. Carbon Dioxide concentration

- At **low CO_2 concentrations**, **conversion of RuBP** to GP is also **slow** (as there's less CO_2 to combine with RuBP to make GP).

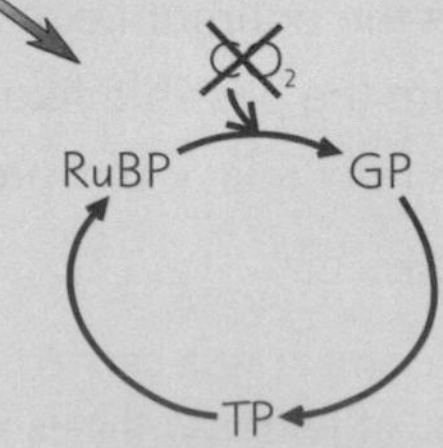

- So the level of **RuBP** will **rise** (as it's still being made) and levels of **GP** and **TP** will **fall** (as they're used up to make RuBP).

Limiting Factors in Photosynthesis

Limiting Factors can be Investigated using Pondweed

1) **Canadian pondweed** (***Elodea***) can be used to measure the effect of light intensity, temperature and CO_2 concentration on the **rate of photosynthesis**.
2) The rate at which **oxygen** is **produced** by the pondweed can be easily **measured** and this **corresponds** to the rate of photosynthesis.
3) For example, the **apparatus** below is used to **measure** the **effect** of **light intensity** on photosynthesis.

Remember photosynthesis produces glucose and oxygen (see page 44).

- A **test tube** containing the **pondweed** and **water** is connected to a **capillary tube** full of water.
- The tube of water is connected to a **syringe**.
- A **source of white light** is placed at a **specific distance** from the pondweed.
- The pondweed is left to photosynthesise for a **set** amount of **time**. As it photosynthesises, the **oxygen released** will **collect** in the **capillary tube**.
- At the end of the experiment, the syringe is used to **draw** the gas **bubble** in the tube **up** alongside a **ruler** and the **length** of the gas bubble is **measured**. This is proportional to the volume of O_2 produced.
- Any **variables** that could affect the results should be **controlled**, e.g. temperature, the time the weed is left to photosynthesise.
- The experiment is **repeated** and the **average** length of gas bubble is calculated, to make the results **more precise**.
- The whole experiment is then **repeated** with the **light source** placed at **different distances** from the pondweed.

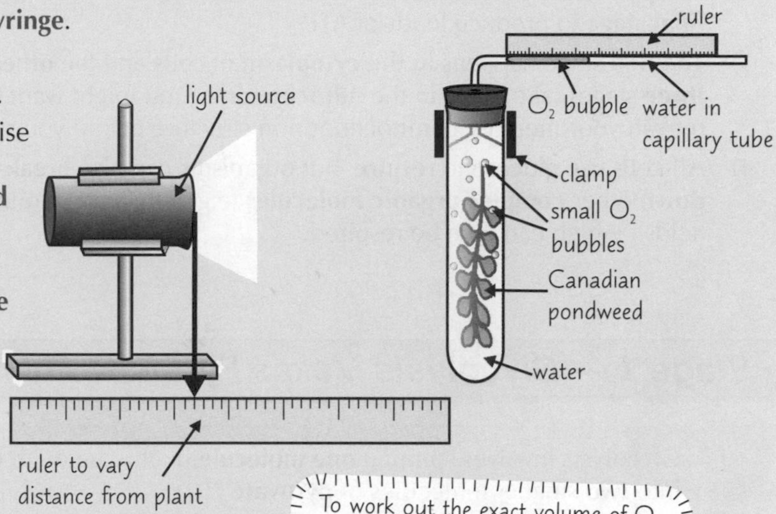

To work out the exact volume of O_2 produced, you also need to know the radius of the capillary tube.

The volume of O_2 can also be measured by counting the number of small O_2 bubbles released by the pondweed, but this is less accurate.

4) The apparatus above can be adapted to **measure** the **effect** of **temperature** on photosynthesis — the test tube of pondweed is put in a **beaker of water** at a **set temperature** (then the experiment's repeated with different temperatures of water).

Practice Questions

Q1 How does a low CO_2 concentration in the air affect the level of TP in a plant?

Q2 In an experiment on the rate of photosynthesis, how can light intensity be varied?

Q3 In the experiment above, give two variables that must be controlled.

Exam Questions

Q1 A scientist was investigating the effect of different conditions on the levels of GP, TP and RuBP in a plant. Predict the results of his experiment under the following conditions. Explain your answers.

a) Low light intensity, optimum temperature and optimum CO_2 concentration. [3 marks]

b) Low temperature, optimum light intensity and optimum CO_2 concentration. [3 marks]

Q2* Briefly describe the apparatus and method you would use to investigate how temperature affects photosynthesis in Canadian pondweed. [6 marks]

* You will be assessed on the quality of your written response in this question.

Aah, Canadian pondweed — a biology student's best friend...

Well... sometimes — usually you end up staring endlessly at it while it produces lots of tiny bubbles. Thrilling. If you have to describe an experiment in the exam make sure you include details about the apparatus, the method and the variables you'd keep constant to make your results accurate, precise, valid, repeatable and reproducible.

Aerobic Respiration

From the last gazillion pages you know that plants make their own glucose. Unfortunately, that means now you need to learn how plant and animal cells release energy from glucose. It's not the easiest thing in the world to understand, but it'll make sense once you've gone through it a couple of times.

There are **Four Stages** in **Aerobic Respiration**

1) The four stages in aerobic respiration are **glycolysis**, the **link reaction**, the **Krebs cycle** and **oxidative phosphorylation**.
2) The **first three** stages are a **series of reactions**. The **products** from these reactions are **used** in the **final stage** to produce loads of ATP.
3) The **first** stage happens in the **cytoplasm** of cells and the **other three** stages take place in the **mitochondria**. You might want to refresh your memory of mitochondrion structure before you start.
4) All cells use **glucose** to **respire**, but organisms can also **break down** other **complex organic molecules** (e.g. fatty acids, amino acids), which can then be respired.

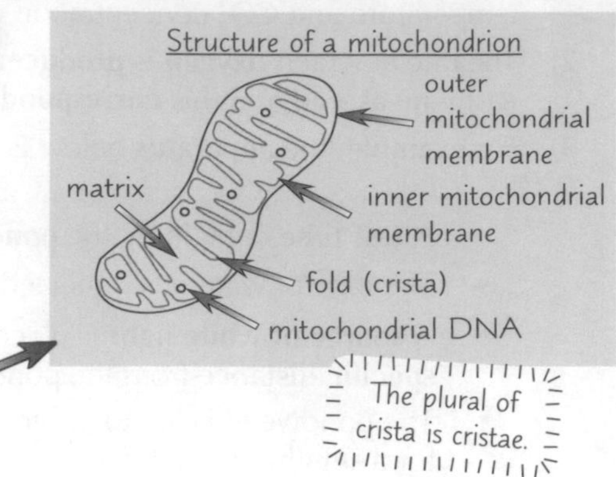

The plural of crista is cristae.

Stage 1 — **Glycolysis** Makes **Pyruvate** from **Glucose**

1) Glycolysis involves splitting **one molecule** of glucose (with 6 carbons — 6C) into **two** smaller molecules of **pyruvate** (3C).
2) The process happens in the **cytoplasm** of cells.
3) Glycolysis is the **first stage** of both aerobic and anaerobic respiration and **doesn't need oxygen** to take place — so it's an **anaerobic** process.

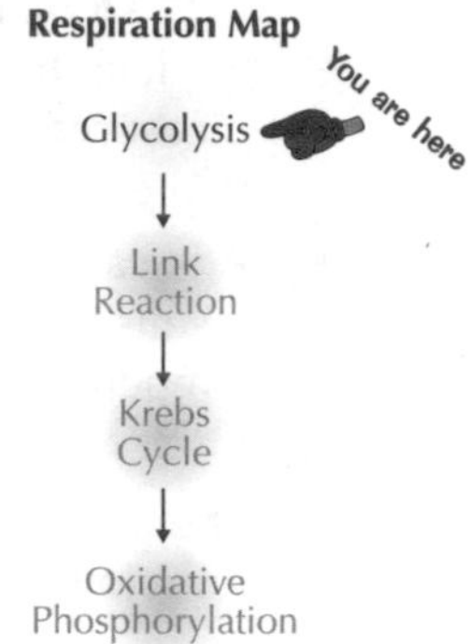

There are **Two Stages** in **Glycolysis** — **Phosphorylation** and **Oxidation**

First, **ATP** is **used** to **phosphorylate glucose** to triose phosphate. Then **triose phosphate** is **oxidised**, **releasing ATP**. Overall there's a **net gain** of **2 ATP**.

1) Stage One — Phosphorylation

1) Glucose is **phosphorylated** by adding **2 phosphates** from **2** molecules of **ATP**.
2) This creates **1** molecule of **hexose bisphosphate** and **2** molecules of **ADP**.
3) Then, **hexose bisphosphate** is **split** up into **2** molecules of **triose phosphate**.

2) Stage Two — Oxidation

1) Triose phosphate is **oxidised** (loses hydrogen), forming **2** molecules of **pyruvate**.
2) **NAD** collects the hydrogen ions, forming **2 reduced NAD**.
3) **4 ATP** are **produced**, but 2 were used up in stage one, so there's a **net gain** of **2 ATP**.

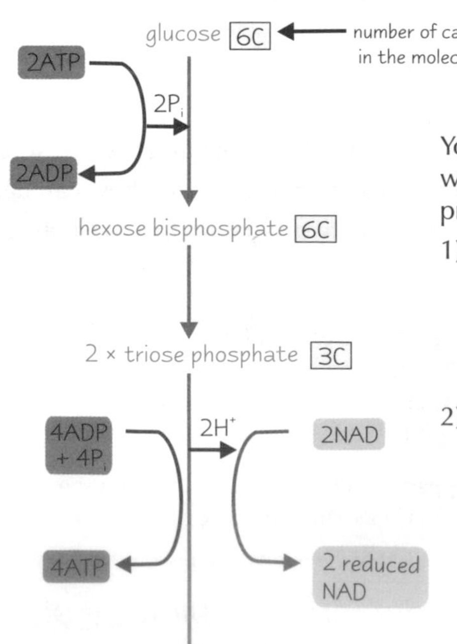

You're probably wondering what now happens to all the products of glycolysis...

1) The **two** molecules of **reduced NAD** go to the **last stage** (oxidative phosphorylation — see page 57).
2) The **two pyruvate** molecules are **actively transported** into the **matrix** of the **mitochondria** for the **link reaction** (see the next page).

Aerobic Respiration

Stage 2 — The Link Reaction Converts Pyruvate to Acetyl Coenzyme A

The **link reaction** takes place in the **mitochondrial matrix**:

1) **Pyruvate** is **decarboxylated** — **one carbon atom** is **removed** from pyruvate in the form of CO_2.
2) **NAD** is **reduced** — it collects **hydrogen** from pyruvate, changing **pyruvate** into **acetate**.
3) **Acetate** is combined with **coenzyme A** (CoA) to form **acetyl coenzyme A** (**acetyl CoA**).
4) **No ATP** is produced in this reaction.

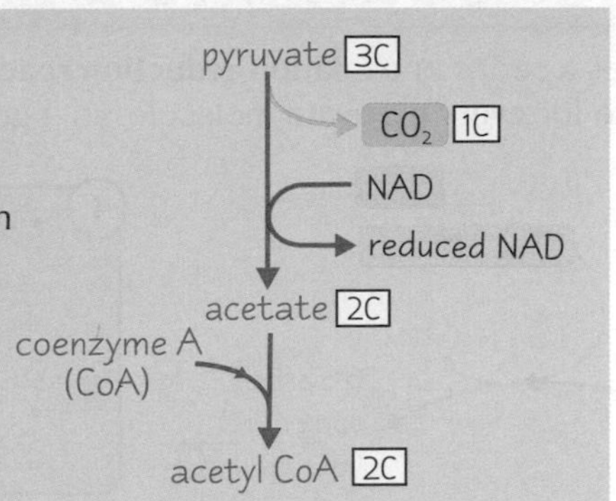

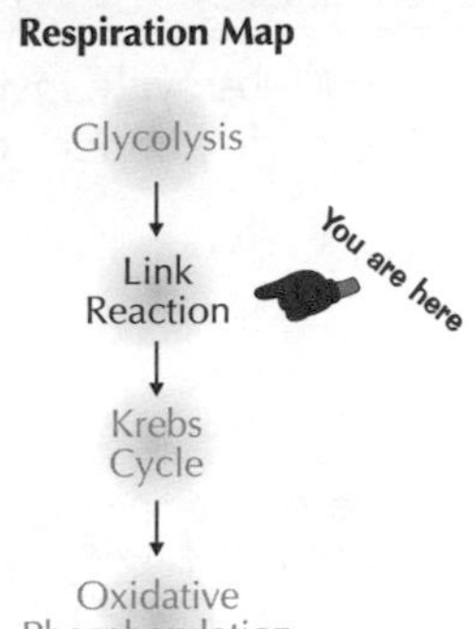

The Link Reaction Occurs Twice for Every Glucose Molecule

Two pyruvate molecules are made for **every glucose molecule** that enters glycolysis. This means the **link reaction** and the third stage (the **Krebs cycle**) happen **twice** for every glucose molecule. So for each glucose molecule:

- **Two** molecules of **acetyl coenzyme A** go into the Krebs cycle (see next page).
- **Two CO_2 molecules** are released as a waste product of respiration.
- **Two** molecules of **reduced NAD** are formed and go to the last stage (oxidative phosphorylation, see page 57).

Practice Questions

Q1 In the mitochondrial structure, what is a crista?

Q2 Where in the cell does glycolysis occur?

Q3 Is glycolysis an anaerobic or aerobic process?

Q4 How many ATP molecules are used up in glycolysis?

Exam Questions

Pyruvate
A
B
C
D
Coenzyme A
(CoA)
E

Q1 The diagram on the right shows a stage of aerobic respiration.
a) Identify compounds A, D and E. [3 marks]
b) What is the role of compound B in this reaction? [1 mark]
c) Where does this reaction happen in the cell? [1 mark]

Q2 Which of the following best describes acetyl coenzyme A?
A A 6-carbon molecule formed during the first stage of glycolysis.
B A 3-carbon molecule that is a product of glycolysis and the first reactant in the link reaction.
C A 2-carbon molecule that is the product of the link reaction and feeds into the Krebs cycle.
D A 3-carbon molecule formed by the splitting of hexose bisphosphate in the first stage of glycolysis. [1 mark]

Q3 Aerobic respiration involves several different steps. Which of the following statement(s) is/are true?
Statement 1: One glucose molecule is broken down into two molecules of pyruvate during glycolysis.
Statement 2: In glycolysis, there is an overall gain of 4 ATP molecules.
Statement 3: In aerobic respiration, the link reaction immediately follows the Krebs cycle.
A 1, 2 and 3 / B Only 1 and 2 / C Only 2 and 3 / D Only 1 [1 mark]

Q4* Describe how a 6-carbon molecule of glucose is converted to pyruvate. [6 marks]

* You will be assessed on the quality of your written response in this question.

No ATP was harmed during this reaction...

Ahhhh... too many reactions. I'm sure your head hurts now, 'cause mine certainly does. Just think of revision as like doing exercise — it can be a pain while you're doing it (and maybe afterwards too), but it's worth it for the well-toned brain you'll have. Just keep going over and over it, until you get the first two stages of respiration straight in your head.

Aerobic Respiration

As you've seen, glycolysis produces a net gain of two ATP. Pah, we can do better than that. The Krebs cycle and oxidative phosphorylation are where it all happens — ATP galore.

Stage 3 — The Krebs Cycle Produces Reduced Coenzymes and ATP

The Krebs cycle involves a series of **oxidation-reduction reactions**, which take place in the **matrix** of the **mitochondria**. The cycle happens **once** for **every pyruvate** molecule, so it goes round **twice** for **every glucose** molecule.

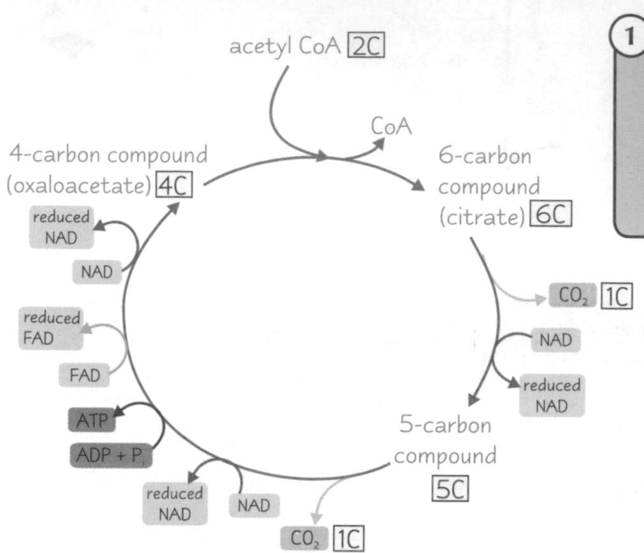

1
- **Acetyl CoA** from the link reaction combines with **oxaloacetate** to form **citrate** (citric acid). This is catalysed by citrate synthase.
- **Coenzyme A** goes back to the **link reaction** to be used again.

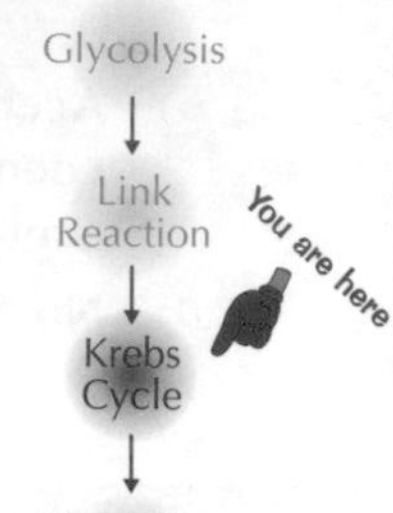

2
- The **6C citrate molecule** is converted to a **5C molecule**.
- **Decarboxylation** occurs, where **CO_2** is **removed**.
- **Dehydrogenation** also occurs, where **hydrogen** is **removed**.
- The hydrogen is used to **produce reduced NAD** from NAD.

3
- The **5C molecule** is then converted to a **4C molecule**. (There are some intermediate compounds formed during this conversion, but you don't need to know about them.)
- **Decarboxylation** and **dehydrogenation** occur, producing **one** molecule of **reduced FAD** and **two** of **reduced NAD**.
- **ATP** is **produced** by the **direct transfer** of a **phosphate** group from an **intermediate** compound **to ADP**. When a phosphate group is directly transferred from one molecule to another it's called **substrate-level phosphorylation**. **Citrate** has now been **converted** into **oxaloacetate**.

Some Products of the Krebs Cycle are Used in Oxidative Phosphorylation

Some products are **reused**, some are **released** and others are used for the **next stage** of respiration:

Product from one Krebs cycle	Where it goes
1 coenzyme A	Reused in the next link reaction
Oxaloacetate	Regenerated for use in the next Krebs cycle
2 CO_2	Released as a waste product
1 ATP	Used for energy
3 reduced NAD	To oxidative phosphorylation
1 reduced FAD	To oxidative phosphorylation

Stage 4 — Oxidative Phosphorylation Produces Lots of ATP

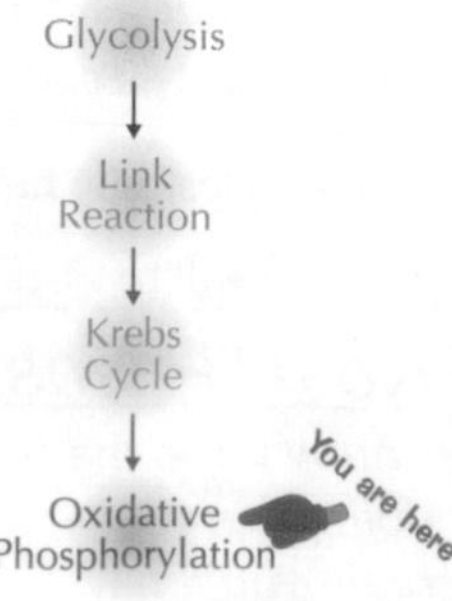

1) Oxidative phosphorylation is the process where the **energy** carried by **electrons**, from **reduced coenzymes** (reduced NAD and reduced FAD), is used to **make ATP**. (The whole point of the previous stages is to make reduced NAD and reduced FAD for the final stage.)
2) Oxidative phosphorylation takes place in the **inner mitochondrial membrane**. A description of the process is on the next page.

Aerobic Respiration

Protons are Pumped Across the Inner Mitochondrial Membrane

So now on to how **oxidative phosphorylation** actually **works**:

1) **Hydrogen atoms** are released from **reduced NAD** and **reduced FAD** as they're oxidised to NAD and FAD. The H atoms **split** into **protons (H^+)** and **electrons (e^-)**.
2) The **electrons** move along the **electron transport chain** (made up of three **electron carriers**), **losing energy** at each carrier. (The electron transport chain is located in the **inner mitochondrial membrane**. This membrane is folded into **cristae**, which **increases** the membrane's **surface area** to maximise respiration.)
3) This energy is used by the electron carriers to **pump protons** from the **mitochondrial matrix into** the **intermembrane space** (the space **between** the inner and outer **mitochondrial membranes**).
4) The **concentration** of **protons** is now **higher** in the **intermembrane space** than in the mitochondrial matrix — this forms an **electrochemical gradient** (a **concentration gradient** of **ions**).
5) Protons **move down** the **electrochemical gradient**, back into the mitochondrial matrix, via **ATP synthase**. This **movement** drives the synthesis of **ATP** from **ADP** and **inorganic phosphate** (P_i).
6) This process of ATP production driven by the movement of H^+ ions across a membrane (due to electrons moving down an electron transport chain) is called **chemiosmosis** (which is described by the **chemiosmotic theory**).
7) In the mitochondrial matrix,at the end of the transport chain, the **protons**, **electrons** and **O_2** (from the blood) combine to form **water**. Oxygen is said to be the final **electron acceptor**.

The regenerated coenzymes are reused in the Krebs cycle.

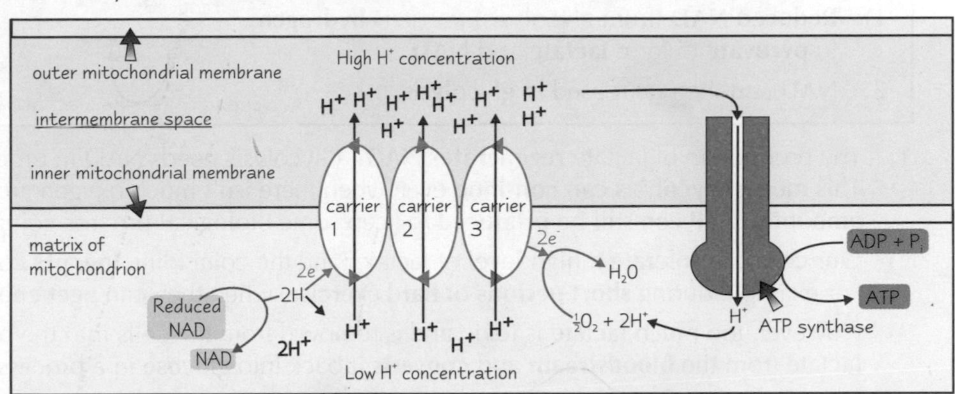

32 ATP Can be Made from One Glucose Molecule

As you know, **oxidative phosphorylation makes ATP** using energy from the reduced coenzymes — **2.5 ATP** are made from each **reduced NAD** and **1.5 ATP** are made from each **reduced FAD**. The table on the right shows **how much** ATP a cell can make from **one molecule** of **glucose** in **aerobic respiration**. (Remember, one molecule of glucose produces 2 pyruvate, so the link reaction and Krebs cycle happen twice.)

Stage of respiration	Molecules produced	Number of ATP molecules
Glycolysis	2 ATP	2
Glycolysis	2 reduced NAD	2 × 2.5 = 5
Link Reaction (×2)	2 reduced NAD	2 × 2.5 = 5
Krebs cycle (×2)	2 ATP	2
Krebs cycle (×2)	6 reduced NAD	6 × 2.5 = 15
Krebs cycle (×2)	2 reduced FAD	2 × 1.5 = 3
		Total ATP = 32

Practice Questions

Q1 Where in the cell does the Krebs cycle occur?

Q2 How many times does decarboxylation happen during one turn of the Krebs cycle?

Q3 What do the electrons lose as they move along the electron transport chain in oxidative phosphorylation?

Exam Question

Q1 Carbon monoxide inhibits the final electron carrier in the electron transport chain.
- a) Explain how this affects ATP production via the electron transport chain. [2 marks]
- b) Explain how this affects ATP production via the Krebs cycle. [2 marks]

The electron transport chain isn't just a FAD with the examiners...

Oh my gosh, I didn't think it could get any worse... You may be wondering how to learn these pages of crazy chemistry. Basically, you have to put in the time and go over and over it. Don't worry though, it WILL pay off and before you know it, you'll be set for the exam. And once you know this section you'll be able to do anything, e.g. world domination.

Anaerobic Respiration and RQs

If you need a little extra ATP, but there's not enough oxygen to increase your aerobic respiration, anaerobic respiration has got your back. Even in low oxygen conditions, your cells can still produce a little bit of ATP.

There are **Two Types** *of* **Anaerobic Respiration**

1) **Anaerobic** respiration **doesn't use oxygen**.
2) It **doesn't** involve the **link reaction**, the **Krebs cycle** or **oxidative phosphorylation**.
3) There are **two types** of anaerobic respiration — **alcoholic fermentation** and **lactate fermentation.**
4) These two processes are **similar**, because they both take place in the **cytoplasm** and they both **start** with **glycolysis** (which produces pyruvate).
5) They **differ** in **which organisms** they occur in and what happens to the **pyruvate** (see below).

Lactate Fermentation *Occurs in* **Mammals** *and Produces* **Lactate**

1) **Reduced NAD** (from glycolysis) transfers **hydrogen** to **pyruvate** to form **lactate** and **NAD**.
2) **NAD** can then be reused in **glycolysis**.

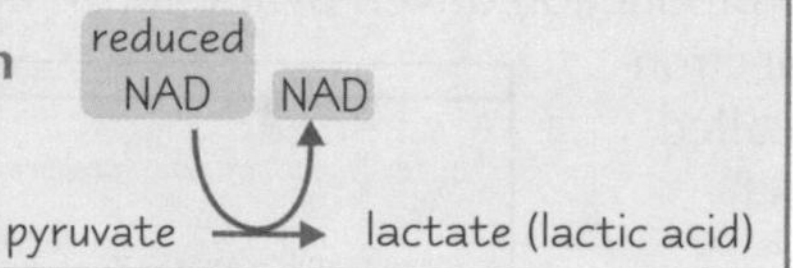

Some bacteria carry out lactate fermentation.

1) The production of lactate **regenerates NAD**. Glycolysis needs NAD in order to take place. This means **glycolysis** can **continue** even when there **isn't** much oxygen around, so a **small amount of ATP** can still be **produced** to keep some biological process going.
2) Our cells can **tolerate** a high level of lactate (and the coinciding **low pH** conditions) for **short periods** of time. For example during **short periods** of **hard exercise**, when they can't get **enough ATP** from aerobic respiration.
3) However, too much lactate is toxic and is removed from the cells into the bloodstream. The **liver** takes up lactate from the **bloodstream** and **converts** it back into **glucose** in a process called **gluconeogenesis** (see p. 14).

Alcoholic Fermentation *Occurs in* **Yeast Cells** *and Produces* **Ethanol**

1) **CO_2** is **removed** from **pyruvate** to form **ethan<u>al</u>**.
2) **Reduced NAD** (from glycolysis) transfers **hydrogen** to **ethan<u>al</u>** to form **ethan<u>ol</u>** and NAD.
3) **NAD** can then be reused in **glycolysis**.

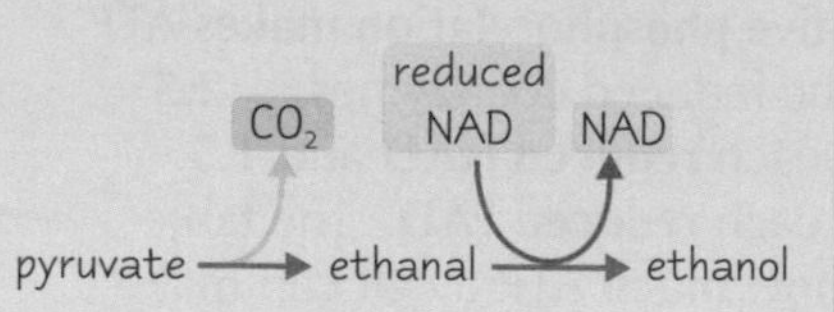

Alcoholic fermentation also occurs in plants.

The production of ethanol also **regenerates NAD** so **glycolysis** can **continue** when there isn't much oxygen around.

Anaerobic Respiration Releases Less Energy *than* **Aerobic Respiration**

1) The **ATP yield** from **anaerobic** respiration is **always lower** than from **aerobic** respiration.
2) This is because **anaerobic** respiration **only** includes **one energy-releasing stage** (**glycolysis**), which only produces **2 ATP** per glucose molecule.
3) The energy-releasing reactions of the **Krebs cycle** and **oxidative phosphorylation** need **oxygen**, so they **can't** occur during anaerobic respiration.

Cells *Can* **Respire Different Substrates**

1) Cells **respire glucose**, but they also respire **other carbohydrates**, **lipids** and **proteins**.
2) Any **biological molecule** that can be **broken down** in **respiration** to **release energy** is called a **respiratory substrate**.

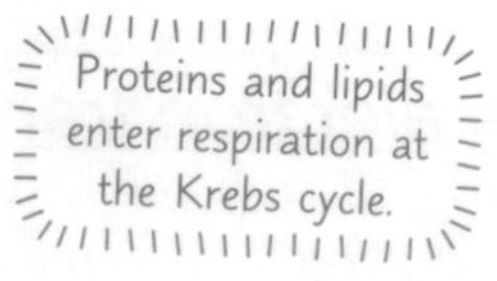

Anaerobic Respiration and RQs

Different Respiratory Substrates Have Different Energy Values

Respiratory Substrate	Average Energy Value (kJ g^{-1})
Carbohydrates	15.8
Lipids	39.4
Proteins	17.0

1) **Different respiratory substrates** release different amounts of **energy** when they're **respired**. **Lipids** have the **highest energy value**, followed by **proteins**, then **carbohydrates**.
2) This is because **most ATP** is made in **oxidative phosphorylation**, which requires **hydrogen atoms** from **reduced NAD** and **reduced FAD**. This means that respiratory substrates that contain **more hydrogen atoms per unit of mass** cause **more ATP** to be produced when respired. **Lipids** contain the **most** hydrogen atoms per unit of mass, followed by proteins and then carbohydrates.

The Respiratory Quotient Can be Calculated Using a Formula

1) When an organism respires a specific **respiratory substrate**, the **respiratory quotient** (RQ) can be **worked out**.
2) The **respiratory quotient** is the volume of **carbon dioxide** produced when that **substrate** is **respired**, **divided** by the volume of **oxygen consumed**, in a set period of **time**.

$$RQ = \frac{\text{Volume of } CO_2 \text{ released}}{\text{Volume of } O_2 \text{ consumed}}$$

3) For example, you can work out the **RQ** for cells that **only respire glucose**:
   - The basic equation for aerobic respiration using glucose is: $C_6H_{12}O_6 + 6O_2 \rightarrow 6CO_2 + 6H_2O$ + energy
   - The RQ of glucose = molecules of **CO_2 released** ÷ molecules of **O_2 consumed = 6 ÷ 6 = 1**.
4) Respiratory quotients have been worked out for the respiration of **other respiratory substrates**. **Lipids** and **proteins** have an RQ value **lower than one** because **more oxygen** is needed to oxidise fats and lipids than to oxidise carbohydrates.

Respiratory Substrate	RQ
Lipids (triglycerides)	0.7
Proteins or amino acids	0.9
Carbohydrates	1

The Respiratory Quotient tells you what Substrate is being Respired

1) The **respiratory quotient** for an organism is **useful** because it tells you **what kind** of **respiratory substrate** an organism is respiring and what **type** of **respiration** it's using (aerobic or anaerobic).
2) For example, under **normal conditions** the **usual RQ** for humans is between **0.7** and **1.0**. An RQ in this range shows that some **fats** (**lipids**) are being used for respiration, as well as **carbohydrates** like glucose. Protein **isn't** normally used by the body for respiration unless there's **nothing else**.
3) **High RQs** (greater than 1) mean that an organism is **short** of **oxygen**, and is having to respire **anaerobically** as well as aerobically.
4) **Plants** sometimes have a **low RQ**. This is because the **CO_2 released** in respiration is **used** for **photosynthesis** (so it's not measured).

Practice Questions

Q1 What molecule is made when CO_2 is removed from pyruvate during alcoholic fermentation?

Q2 Does anaerobic respiration release more or less energy per glucose molecule than aerobic respiration?

Q3 What is a respiratory substrate?

Exam Questions

Q1 A culture of mammalian cells was incubated with glucose, pyruvate and antimycin C.
Antimycin C inhibits an electron carrier in the electron transport chain of aerobic respiration.
Explain why these cells can still produce lactate. [1 mark]

Q2 This equation shows the aerobic respiration of a fat called triolein: $C_{57}H_{104}O_6 + 80O_2 \rightarrow 52H_2O + 57CO_2$
Calculate the respiratory quotient for this reaction. Show your working. [2 marks]

My little sis has an RQ of 157 — she's really clever...

I know, I'm really pushing the boundary between humour and non-humour here. Oh well, make sure that you know the benefits of anaerobic respiration and the two different types. Also, you really need to be able to work out RQs...

Respiration Experiments

These pages give you some examples of experiments you could carry out to measure the rate of respiration...

Aerobic and *Anaerobic Respiration Rates in Yeast* can be *Investigated*

Yeast can respire **aerobically** when **plenty** of **oxygen** is **available** and **anaerobically** when **oxygen isn't available**. Both aerobic and anaerobic respiration in yeast produce **CO_2**. So the **rate of CO_2 production** gives an indication of the yeast's **respiration rate**. One way to measure CO_2 production is by using a **gas syringe** to collect the CO_2 as shown in the methods below:

Aerobic Respiration

1) Put a **known volume** and **concentration** of **substrate solution** (e.g. glucose) in a test tube.
2) Add a **known volume** of buffer solution to keep the **pH constant**. (Choose the optimum pH for the yeast you're testing — usually 4-6).
3) Place the test tube in a **water bath** set to 25 °C. This ensures that the temperature stays **constant** throughout the experiment. Leave it there for **10 minutes** to allow the temperature of the **substrate** to **stabilise**.
4) Add a **known mass** of **dried yeast** (e.g. *Saccharomyces cerevisiae*) to the test tube and **stir** for two minutes.
5) After the yeast has dissolved into the solution, put a **bung** with a **tube attached** to a **gas syringe** in the top of the test tube. The **gas syringe** should be set to **zero**.
6) **Start** a **stop watch** as soon as the bung has been put in the test tube.
7) As the yeast **respire**, the **CO_2 formed** will travel up the tube and into the **gas syringe**, which is used to measure the **volume** of **CO_2 released**.
8) At **regular time intervals** (e.g. every minute), record the **volume** of **CO_2** that is **present** in the **gas syringe**. Do this for a set amount of time (e.g. 10 minutes).
9) A **control** experiment should also be set up, where **no yeast** is present. **No CO_2** should be formed without the yeast.
10) **Repeat** the experiment three times. Use your data to **calculate** the **mean rate of CO_2 production**.

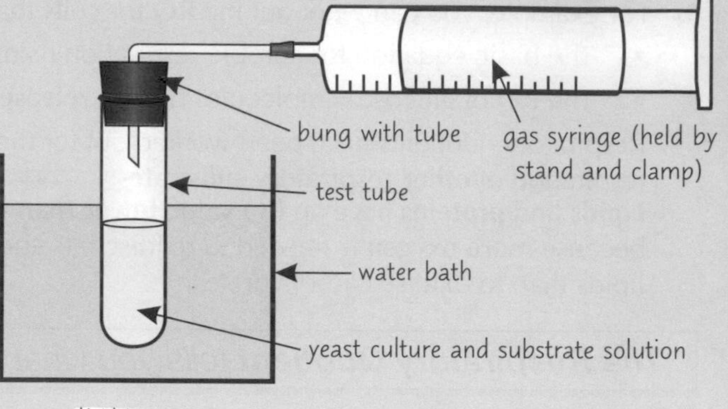

The yeast will only respire aerobically until the oxygen trapped in the tube is all used up. If you wanted to run the experiment for more time or with more yeast or glucose, you could use a conical flask that can trap more oxygen.

Anaerobic Respiration

1) Set up the apparatus according to **steps 1-4** of the experiment above.
2) After the yeast has dissolved into the substrate solution, trickle some **liquid paraffin** down the **inside** of the test tube so that it **settles** on and **completely covers** the **surface** of the solution. This will **stop oxygen** getting in, which will force the yeast to respire **anaerobically**.
3) Put a **bung**, with a **tube attached** to a **gas syringe**, in the top of the test tube. The **gas syringe** should be set to **zero**.
4) Perform **steps 6-10** from the method above.

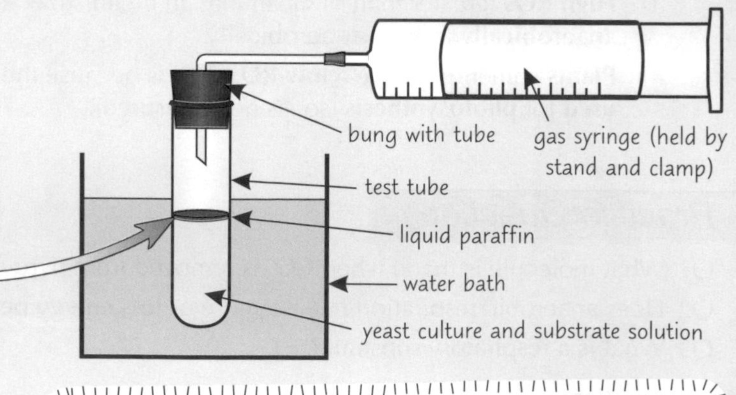

You could look up published results about the rate of respiration in yeast and see how they compare to yours. If there are any differences, you could try and work out what caused them and how you could improve the way you carried out your own experiment.

The **only** difference between these experiments is the **presence** or **absence** of **oxygen**, so you can directly **compare** your **results** for both experiments with **each other** to find out how the **respiration rate** of yeast under **aerobic** and **anaerobic** conditions **differs**.

You can also easily **adapt** these methods to investigate the **effects** of **variables**, such as **temperature**, **substrate concentration** and the use of **different respiratory substrates** (e.g. sucrose), on the **respiration rate**. For example, to investigate the effect of **different temperatures** on the respiration rate, you could perform the experiment with the test tubes in **water baths** set at **different temperatures**.

Respiration Experiments

The Rate of Respiration can be Measured using a Respirometer

Respirometers can be used to indicate the **rate** of **aerobic respiration** by measuring the **amount** of **oxygen consumed** by an organism over a **period** of **time**. The example below shows how a respirometer can be used to measure the respiration rate of **woodlice**. You could also use it to measure the respiration rate of other small organisms or of plant seeds.

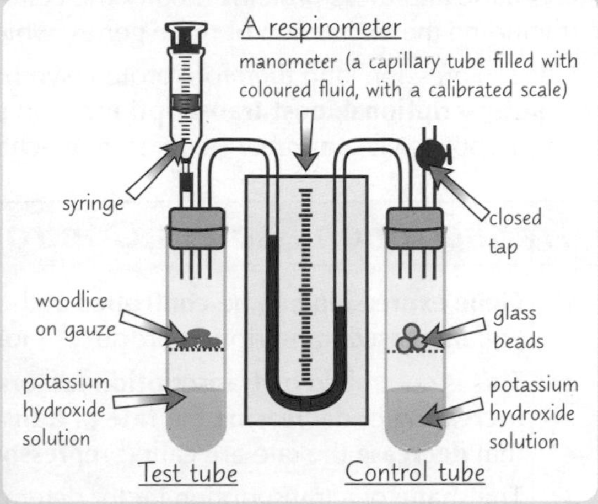

- The apparatus is set up as shown on the right.
- **Each tube** contains **potassium hydroxide** solution (or soda lime), which **absorbs carbon dioxide**.
- The **control tube** is set up in exactly the **same way** as the test tube, but **without** the **woodlice**, to make sure the **results** are **only** due to the woodlice **respiring** (e.g. it contains beads that have the same mass as the woodlice).
- **Coloured fluid** is added to the **manometer** by dipping the **end** of the **capillary tube** into a **beaker** of **fluid**. Capillary action will make the fluid **move into** the tube. The **syringe** is then used to set the **fluid** to a **known level**.
- The apparatus is **left** for a **set** period of **time** (e.g. 20 minutes).
- During that time there'll be a **decrease** in the **volume** of the **air** in the test tube, due to **oxygen consumption** by the **woodlice** (all the CO_2 produced is absorbed by the potassium hydroxide).
- The decrease in the volume of the air will **reduce the pressure** in the tube and cause the **coloured liquid** in the manometer to **move towards** the test tube.
- The **distance moved** by the **liquid** in a **given time** is **measured**. This value can then be used to **calculate** the **volume of oxygen** taken in by the woodlice **per minute**. (You also need to know the **diameter** of the **capillary tube** in the manometer to do this.)
- Any **variables** that could **affect** the results are **controlled**, e.g. temperature, volume of potassium hydroxide solution in each test tube.
- To produce more **precise** results, the experiment is **repeated** and a **mean volume** of O_2 is calculated.

This experiment has some limitations. For example, it can be difficult to accurately read the meniscus of the fluid in the manometer.

You can use a respirometer to investigate the effect of different factors on the rate of respiration by changing the independent variable.

Respirometers can be set up with an electronic **oxygen sensor** to measure the **oxygen concentration** inside the **respirometer chamber** at set intervals and also with **data loggers** to **automatically** record the data measured by the sensor. Using technology like this reduces the chance of human error when it comes to recording data. The data collected by the data logger can be put into **data analysis software**, which can help you to analyse your data and draw **conclusions** from your experiment.

Practice Questions

Q1 Why is CO_2 production a suitable factor to measure when investigating the rate of both aerobic and anaerobic respiration in yeast?

Q2 What does a respirometer measure?

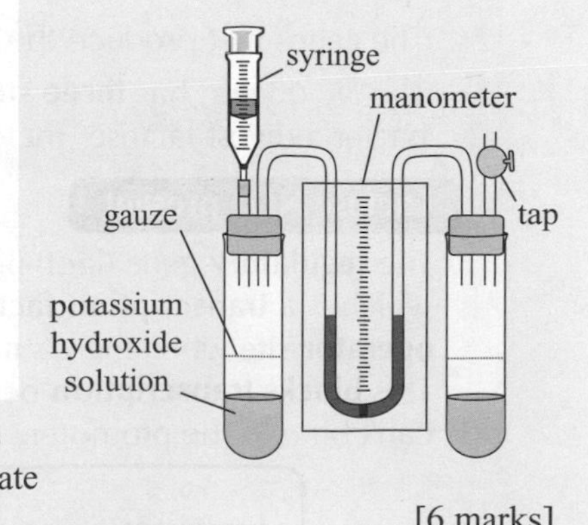

Exam Question

Q1* Suggest a suitable method using the respirometer shown above right, as well as any other apparatus that you think is appropriate, that could be used to investigate the effect of temperature on the respiration rate of germinating mung beans. [6 marks]

* You will be assessed on the quality of your written response in this question.

My results are dodgy — I'm sure the woodlice are holding their breath...

Okay, that wasn't very funny, but these pages don't really give me any inspiration. You probably feel the same way. They're the sort of pages that you just have to plough through. You could try drawing a few pretty diagrams to get the experiments in your head. And after you've got it sorted do something exciting, like trying to stick your toe in your ear...

Regulating Gene Expression

In cells, genes are transcribed and translated into proteins, but it doesn't just happen willy-nilly...

Genes can be Switched On or Off

All the **cells** in an organism carry the **same genes** (DNA) but the **structure** and **function** of different cells **varies**. This is because **not all** the **genes** in a cell are **expressed** (transcribed and used to make a functional protein) — they are selectively switched on or off. Because **cells** show **different gene expression**, **different proteins** are made and these proteins modify the cell — they determine the **cell structure** and control **cell processes** (including the expression of more genes, which produce more proteins).

Gene expression (and therefore protein synthesis) can be controlled at the **transcriptional**, **post-transcriptional** and **post-translational** level. This happens via a number of different mechanisms.

You'll have covered transcription and translation in Module 2.

Transcription Factors Control Gene Expression at the Transcriptional Level

1) **Gene expression** can be **controlled** at the **transcriptional level** by **altering** the rate of **transcription** of genes. E.g. **increased** transcription produces **more mRNA**, which can be used to make **more protein**.
2) This is controlled by **transcription factors** — proteins that **bind** to **DNA** and **switch** genes **on** or **off** by **increasing** or **decreasing** the **rate** of **transcription**. Factors that **increase** the rate are called **activators** and those that **decrease** the rate are called **repressors**.
3) The **shape** of a transcription factor determines whether it **can bind to DNA** or **not**, and can sometimes be **altered** by the binding of some molecules, e.g. certain hormones and sugars.
4) This means the **amount** of certain **molecules** in an environment or a cell can **control** the **synthesis** of some **proteins** by affecting **transcription factor binding**.
5) In **eukaryotes**, transcription factors bind to **specific DNA sites** near the **start** of their **target genes** — the genes they **control** the **expression** of.
6) In **prokaryotes** control of gene expression often involves transcription factors binding to **operons** (see below).
7) An **operon** is a **section** of **DNA** that contains a cluster of **structural genes,** that are **transcribed together**, as well as **control elements** and sometimes a **regulatory gene**:
   - The **structural genes** code for **useful proteins**, such as **enzymes**.
   - The **control elements** include a **promoter** (a DNA sequence located **before** the structural genes that **RNA polymerase** binds to) and an **operator** (a DNA sequence that **transcription factors** bind to).
   - The **regulatory gene** codes for an **activator** or **repressor**.
8) Here's an example of an operon that you need to learn about:

EXAMPLE: The *lac* operon in *E. coli*

1) ***E. coli*** is a bacterium that **respires glucose**, but it can use **lactose** if glucose isn't available.
2) The genes that produce the **enzymes** needed to **respire lactose** are found on an operon called the ***lac* operon**.
3) The *lac* operon has **three structural genes** — **lacZ, lacY** and **lacA**, which produce proteins that help the bacteria digest lactose (including **β-galactosidase** and **lactose permease**).

Lactose NOT present

The **regulatory** gene (lacI) produces the **lac repressor**, which is a **transcription factor** that **binds** to the **operator** site when there's **no lactose** present. This **blocks transcription** because RNA polymerase can't bind to the promoter.

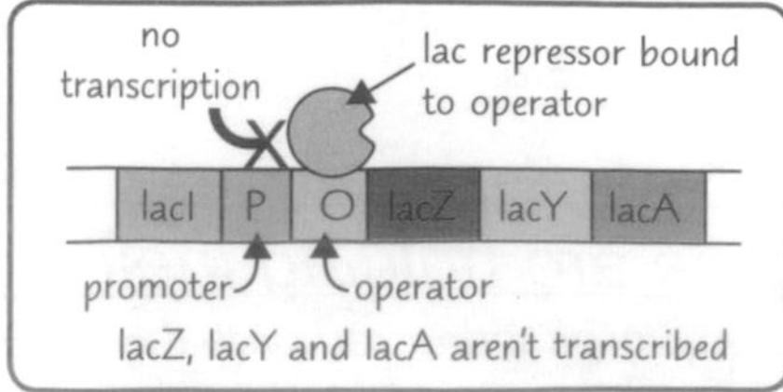

Lactose present

When **lactose is present**, it **binds** to the **repressor**, **changing** the repressor's **shape** so that it can **no longer bind** to the operator site.

RNA polymerase can now **begin transcription** of the structural genes.

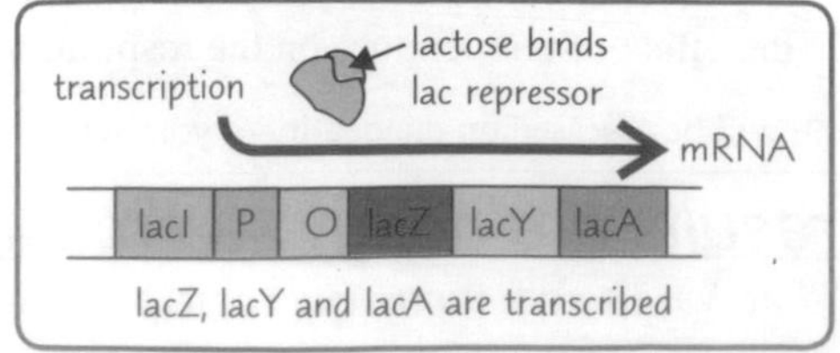

Regulating Gene Expression

mRNA is Edited at a Post-Transcriptional Level

1) Genes in **eukaryotic DNA** contain sections that **don't code** for amino acids.
2) These sections of DNA are called **introns**. All the bits that **do** code for amino acids are called **exons**.
3) During transcription the introns and exons are both **copied** into mRNA. mRNA strands containing introns and exons are called **primary mRNA transcripts** (or pre-mRNA).
4) Introns are **removed** from primary mRNA strands by a process called **splicing** — introns are removed and exons joined, forming mature **mRNA** strands. This takes place in the **nucleus**.
5) The mature mRNA then **leaves** the nucleus for the next stage of protein synthesis (**translation**).

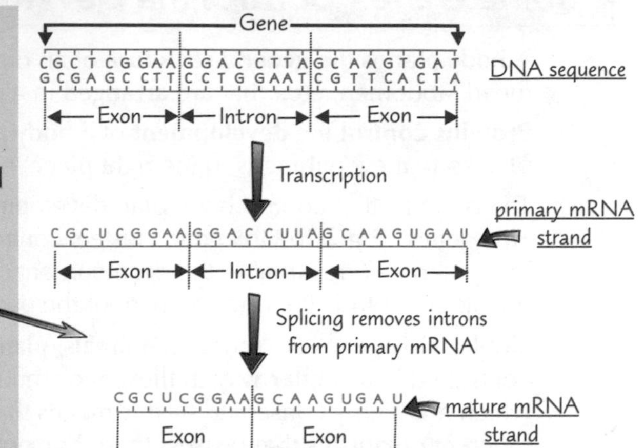

cAMP Activates Some Proteins at the Post-Translational Level

1) Some **proteins** aren't **functional** straight after they have been synthesised — they need to be **activated** to work (become a functional protein).
2) **Protein activation** is controlled by **molecules**, e.g. **hormones** and **sugars**.
3) Some of these molecules work by **binding** to **cell membranes** and **triggering** the production of **cyclic AMP** (**cAMP**) **inside** the **cell**.
4) cAMP then **activates proteins** inside the cell by **altering** their **three-dimensional** (3D) **structure**.
5) For example, altering the 3D structure can **change** the **active site** of an enzyme, making it become **more** or **less active**.
6) Here is how **cAMP** activates **protein kinase A** (**PKA**):

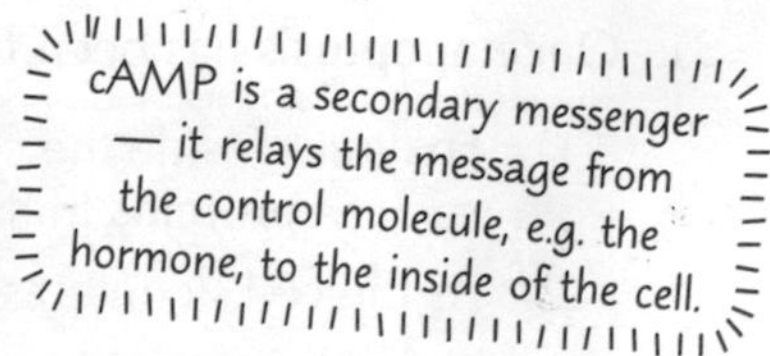

1) **PKA** is an **enzyme** made of four subunits.
2) When cAMP **isn't bound**, the four units are bound together and are **inactive**.
3) When cAMP **binds**, it causes a **change** in the enzyme's **3D structure**, releasing the active subunits — PKA is now **active**.

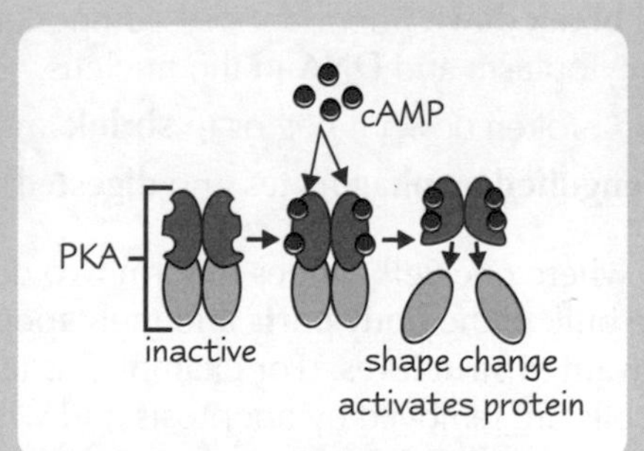

Practice Questions

Q1 What does a transcription factor do?

Q2 What is an operon?

Q3 How does cAMP activate a protein?

Exam Questions

Q1 Describe how mRNA is edited at a post-transcriptional level [2 marks]

Q2 Explain how the presence of lactose causes *E. coli* to produce ß-galactosidase and lactose permease. [4 marks]

Genes are a bit like my concentration — they can be switched on or off...

The lac operon is a great example of how gene expression can be controlled at the transcriptional level and it's well worth learning because you might get asked about it in your exam. Don't forget that gene expression can also be controlled post-transcriptionally, by splicing out the introns, and proteins can even be controlled post-translationally.

Regulating Gene Expression

I know these pages look pretty packed, but it's all good stuff. It's about the control of development and mutations.

Some Genes Control the Development of Body Plans

1) A **body plan** is the **general structure** of an organism, e.g. the *Drosophila* fruit fly has various **body parts** (head, abdomen, etc.) that are **arranged** in a **particular way** — this is its body plan.
2) **Proteins control** the **development** of a **body plan** — they help set up the basic body plan so that everything is in the right place, e.g. legs grow where legs should grow.
3) The proteins that control body plan development are **coded for** by genes called **Hox genes**. E.g. two Hox gene clusters control the development of the *Drosophila* body plan — one controls the development of the head and anterior thorax and the other controls the development of the posterior thorax and abdomen.

4) **Similar Hox genes** are found in **animals**, **plants** and **fungi**, which means that **body plan development** is controlled in a **similar way** in flies, mice, humans, etc. Hox genes have **regions** called **homeobox sequences**, which are highly conserved — this means that these sequences have **changed** very little during the **evolution** of different organisms that possess these homeobox sequences.
5) Here's how Hox genes control development:
   - **Homeobox sequences** code for a **part** of the **protein** called the **homeodomain**.
   - The homeodomain **binds** to specific **sites** on **DNA**, enabling the protein to work as a **transcription factor** (see p. 62).
   - The proteins bind to DNA at the **start** of **developmental genes**, **activating** or **repressing transcription** and so altering the production of proteins involved in the development of the body plan.

Apoptosis and Mitosis are Involved in the Development of Body Plans

1) Some cells **die** and **break down** as a **normal** part of **development**.
2) This is a **highly controlled process** called **apoptosis**, or **programmed cell death**.
3) Once **apoptosis** has been **triggered** the **cell** is **broken down** in a series of steps:
   1) **Enzymes** inside the cell **break down** important cell components such as **proteins** in the cytoplasm and **DNA** in the nucleus.
   2) As the cell's contents are broken down it begins to **shrink** and **breaks up** into **fragments**.
   3) The **cell fragments** are **engulfed** by **phagocytes** and **digested**.
4) **Mitosis** (part of the cell cycle where one cell divides to form two daughter cells) and **differentiation create** the bulk of the **body parts** and then apoptosis **refines** the parts by **removing** the **unwanted structures**. For example, as tadpoles develop into frogs, their tail cells are removed by apoptosis and when **hands** and **feet** first develop in humans, the **digits** (fingers and toes) are **connected** — they're only **separated** when cells in the **connecting tissue** undergo **apoptosis**.
5) During development, genes that **control** apoptosis and genes that control mitosis are **switched on** and **off** in **appropriate** cells. This means that **some cells die**, whilst **some new cells** are **produced** and the **correct body plan develops**.

Although it sounded daunting, Graham was thankful for apoptosis because he no longer looked like a giant sperm.

Genes that Regulate Apoptosis and the Cell Cycle can Respond to Stimuli

The genes that **regulate apoptosis** and progression through the **cell cycle** (e.g. cells undergoing mitosis) can **respond** to both **internal** and **external stimuli**.

- An **internal** stimulus could be **DNA damage**. If DNA damage is **detected** during the cell cycle, this can result in the expression of genes which cause the cycle to be **paused** and can even trigger **apoptosis**.
- An **external** stimulus, such as **stress** caused by a **lack** of **nutrient availability**, could result in gene expression that prevents cells from undergoing mitosis. Gene expression which leads to **apoptosis** being triggered can also be caused by an external stimulus such as **attack** by a **pathogen**.

Regulating Gene Expression

Mutations are Changes to the Base Sequence of DNA

1) Any change to the **base** (**nucleotide**) **sequence** of DNA is called a **mutation**. Types of mutations include:
   - **Substitution** — one or more bases are swapped for another, e.g. AT**G**CCT becomes AT**T**CCT
   - **Deletion** — one or more bases are removed, e.g. AT**GC**CT becomes ATCT
   - **Insertion** — one or more bases are added, e.g. ATGCCT becomes ATG**A**CCT
2) The **order** of **DNA bases** in a gene determines the **order of amino acids** in a particular **protein**. If a mutation occurs in a gene, the **primary structure** (amino acid chain) of the protein it codes for could be altered.
3) This may **change** the final **3D shape** of the protein so it **doesn't work properly**, e.g. **active sites** in enzymes may not form properly, meaning that **substrates can't bind** to them.

Mutations can be Neutral, Beneficial or Harmful

1) Some mutations can have a **neutral effect** on a protein's **function**. They may have a neutral effect because:
   - The mutation changes a base in a triplet, but the **amino acid** that the triplet codes for **doesn't change**. This happens because **some amino acids** are coded for by **more than one triplet**. E.g. both **TAT** and **TAC** code for **tyrosine**, so if TAT is changed to TAC the **amino acid won't change**.
   - The mutation produces a triplet that codes for a **different amino acid**, but the amino acid is **chemically similar** to the original so it functions like the original amino acid. E.g. **arginine** (AGG) and **lysine** (AAG) are coded for by similar triplets — a **substitution** mutation can **swap** the amino acids. But this mutation could have a **neutral effect** on a **protein** as the amino acids are **chemically similar**.
   - The mutated triplet codes for an amino acid **not involved** with the protein's **function**, e.g. one that's located **far away** from an enzyme's **active site**, so the protein **works** as it **normally** does.
2) A **neutral effect** on protein function **won't** affect an **organism** overall.
3) However, some mutations **do** affect a protein's **function** — they can make a protein **more** or **less active**, e.g. by **changing** the **shape** of an enzyme's **active site**.
4) If protein function **is affected** it can have a **beneficial** or **harmful effect** on the **whole organism**:

Mutations with beneficial effects

These have an **advantageous effect** on an organism, i.e. they **increase** its chance of **survival**.

E.g. some bacterial **enzymes break down** certain **antibiotics**. **Mutations** in the genes that code for these enzymes could make them work on a **wider range** of antibiotics. This is **beneficial** to the **bacteria** because antibiotic resistance can help them to survive.

Mutations with harmful effects

These have a **disadvantageous effect** on an organism, i.e. they **decrease** its chance of **survival**.

E.g. **cystic fibrosis** (CF) can be caused by a **deletion** of three bases in the gene that codes for the **CFTR** (cystic fibrosis transmembrane conductance regulator) **protein**. The mutated CFTR protein **folds incorrectly**, so it's **broken down**. This leads to **excess mucus production**, which affects the **lungs** of CF sufferers.

5) Mutations can also affect **whether or not** a protein is **produced**. E.g. if a mutation occurs at the start of a gene, so that **RNA polymerase** can't bind to it and begin transcription, the protein coded for by the gene won't be made. The **loss of production** of a protein can have **harmful effects** — some **genetic disorders** are caused by this.

Practice Question

Q1 Describe the process of apoptosis.

Exam Questions

Q1 Huntington's disease is caused by a mutation in the HTT gene, which results in the nucleotide triplet 'CAG' being repeated an abnormally high number of times, increasing the length of the gene. What name is given to this type of mutation? [1 mark]

Q2 Explain why the genetic control of body plan development is similar in plants, animals and fungi. [2 marks]

Too much revision stimulates apoptosis in your brain...

OK, that's not true. There's lots to learn here and some of it can be quite hard to get your head around. Just take your time and keep going over it until it all makes sense — it will click eventually and you'll be all set for your exam.

Types and Causes of Variation

You might remember learning about variation in Module 4... Well, you need to learn it again for Module 6, but in a bit more detail. Not very varied, I know — but that's revision for you.

Variation Within a Species can be Continuous...

1) **Continuous variation** is when the **individuals** in a population vary **within a range** — there are **no distinct categories**, e.g. **humans** can be **any height** within a range (139 cm, 175 cm, 185.9 cm, etc.), not just tall or short.
2) Some more examples of continuous variation include:

- **Waist circumference** — e.g. humans can have any waist size within a range.
- **Fur length** — e.g. dogs can have any length of fur within a range.

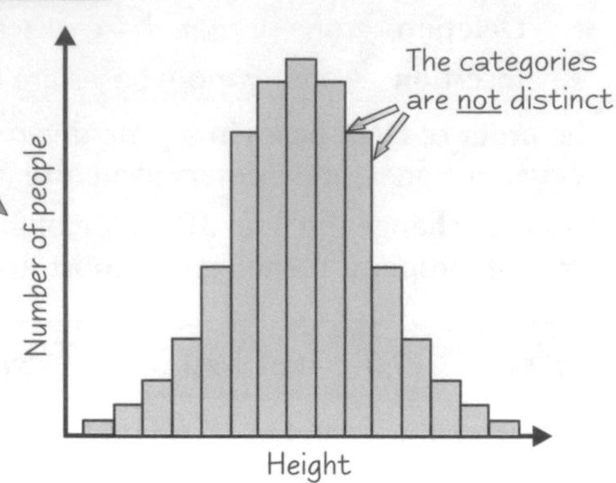

...or Discontinuous

1) **Discontinuous variation** is when there are two or more **distinct categories** — each individual falls into **only one** of these categories, there are **no intermediates**.
2) Here are some examples of discontinuous variation:

- **Blood group** — e.g. humans can be group A, B, AB or O.
- **Violet flower colour** — e.g. violets can either be coloured or white.

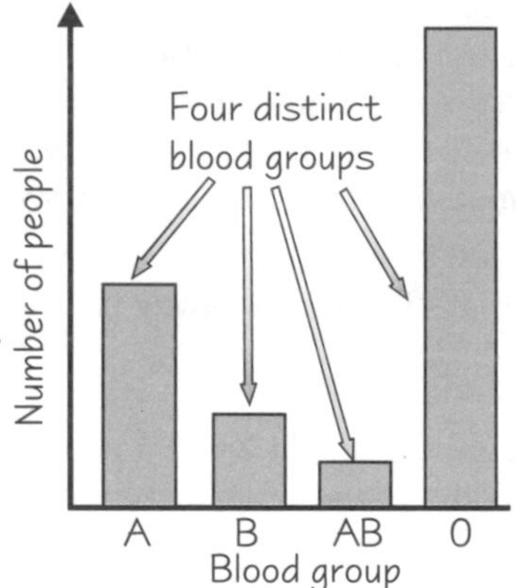

Variation — a concept lost on the army.

Variation can be Influenced by Your Genes...

1) **Different species** have **different genes**.
2) Individuals of the **same species** have the **same genes**, but **different versions** of them (called **alleles**).
3) The genes and alleles an organism has make up its **genotype**.
4) **Sexual reproduction** leads to **variation** in genotypes within a species. **Meiosis** makes gametes with a **unique** assortment of **alleles** through **crossing-over** and the **independent assortment** of **chromosomes**. The **random fusion** of gametes during **fertilisation** also increases genetic variation in the offspring.
5) The **differences** in **genotype** result in **variation** in **phenotype** — the **characteristics** displayed by an organism. Variation in phenotype is also referred to as **phenotypic variation**.

EXAMPLE — **Human blood group** — there are **three** different **blood group alleles**, which result in **four different blood groups**.

Meiosis is covered in Module 2.

6) **Inherited** characteristics that show **continuous** variation are usually **influenced** by **many genes** — these characteristics are said to be **polygenic**.

EXAMPLE — **Human skin colour** is **polygenic**— it comes in **loads of different shades** of colour.

7) **Inherited** characteristics that show **discontinuous** variation are usually influenced by only **one gene** (or a **small number** of genes). Characteristics controlled by **only one gene** are said to be **monogenic**.

EXAMPLE — **Violet flower colour** is **monogenic**— can either be **coloured** or **white**.

Types and Causes of Variation

...the Environment...

Variation can also be caused by **differences in the environment**, e.g. climate, food, lifestyle. Characteristics controlled by environmental factors can **change** over an organism's life.

EXAMPLES

1) **Etiolation** — this is when plants grow **abnormally long** and **spindly** because they're **not getting** enough **light**.
2) **Chlorosis** — this is when plants **don't produce** enough **chlorophyll** and turn **yellow**. It's caused by several environmental factors, e.g. a **lack of magnesium** in soil.

abiotic factor

...or Both

Genetic factors determine genotype and the characteristics an organism's **born with**, but **environmental factors** can **influence** how some characteristics **develop**. Most phenotypic variation is caused by the **combination** of **genotype** and **environmental factors**. Phenotypic variation influenced by both usually shows **continuous variation.**

EXAMPLES

1) **Height of pea plants** — pea plants come in **tall** and **dwarf** forms (**discontinuous** variation), which is determined by **genotype**. However, the **exact height** of the tall and dwarf plants **varies** (**continuous** variation) because of **environmental factors** (e.g. **light intensity** and **water availability** affect how tall a plant grows).

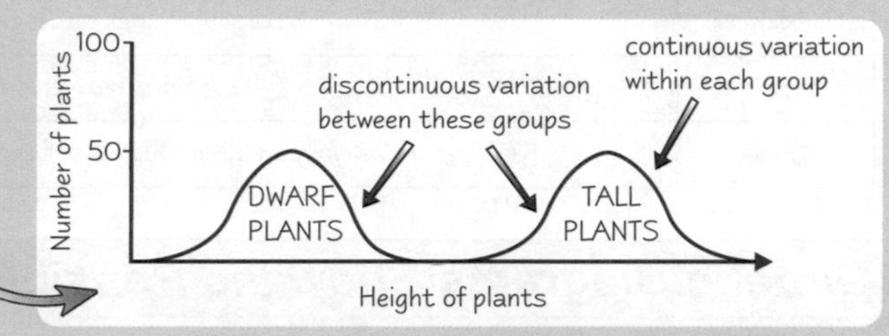

2) **Body mass in animals** — this is **partly genetic**, but it's also **strongly influenced** by **environmental factors**, like **diet**. For example, if your diet doesn't contain enough of the right nutrients, your body mass is likely to be lower than that determined by your genes. Body mass **varies** within a **range**, so it's **continuous** variation.

Practice Questions

Q1 What is a monogenic characteristic?

Q2 Give an example of phenotypic variation in plants that's caused only by the environment.

Exam Question

Q1 The mass and coat colour of 15 Labrador puppies is shown in the table.

Puppy	Mass / kg	Colour
1	10.04	yellow
2	10.23	chocolate
3	15.65	black
4	18.99	black
5	9.45	black

Puppy	Mass / kg	Colour
6	10.39	yellow
7	10.55	chocolate
8	15.87	chocolate
9	16.99	black
10	10.47	yellow

Puppy	Mass / kg	Colour
11	9.25	black
12	11.06	black
13	12.45	yellow
14	14.99	yellow
15	10.93	chocolate

a) Which of the characteristics shown in the table, mass or coat colour, is most likely to be influenced by only a small number of genes? Explain your answer. [1 mark]

b) Which of the characteristics described in the table is most likely to be influenced by both genotype and the environment? Explain your answer. [1 mark]

c) Calculate the range of puppy mass. [1 mark]

Revision boredom shows discontinuous variation — always bored with it...

Remember, continuous variation is usually influenced by many genes. Discontinuous variation is usually influenced by only one or a few genes. Make sure you've learnt some examples of genetic and environmental factors that affect phenotypic variation too — particularly etiolation and chlorosis in plants, and diet in animals.

Inheritance

Nope, this isn't about who gets Mum's best china — we're talking genetic inheritance here...

You Need to Know These Genetic Terms

'Codes for' means 'contains the instructions for'.

TERM	DESCRIPTION
Gene	A sequence of bases on a DNA molecule that codes for a protein (polypeptide), which results in a characteristic, e.g. a gene for eye colour.
Allele	A different version of a gene. Most plants and animals, including humans, have two alleles of each gene, one from each parent. The order of bases in each allele is slightly different — they code for different versions of the same characteristic. They're represented using letters, e.g. the allele for brown eyes (B) and the allele for blue eyes (b).
Genotype	The alleles an organism has, e.g. BB, Bb or bb for eye colour.
Phenotype	The characteristics the alleles produce, e.g. brown eyes.
Dominant	An allele whose characteristic appears in the phenotype even when there's only one copy. Dominant alleles are shown by a capital letter. E.g. the allele for brown eyes (B) is dominant — if a person's genotype is Bb or BB, they'll have brown eyes.
Recessive	An allele whose characteristic only appears in the phenotype if two copies are present. Recessive alleles are shown by a lower case letter. E.g. the allele for blue eyes (b) is recessive — if a person's genotype is bb, they'll have blue eyes.
Codominant	Alleles that are both expressed in the phenotype — neither one is recessive, e.g. the alleles for haemoglobin.
Locus	The fixed position of a gene on a chromosome. Alleles of a gene are found at the same locus on each chromosome in a pair.
Homozygote	An organism that carries two copies of the same allele, e.g. BB or bb.
Heterozygote	An organism that carries two different alleles, e.g. Bb.
Carrier	A person carrying an allele which is not expressed in the phenotype but that can be passed on to offspring.

Genetic Diagrams Show the Possible Genotypes of Offspring

The body cells of individuals have **two alleles** for **each gene**. **Gametes** (sex cells) contain only **one allele** for each gene. When gametes from two parents fuse together, the alleles they contain form the **genotype** of the **offspring** produced. **Genetic diagrams** can be used to **predict** the **genotypes** and **phenotypes** of the offspring produced if two parents are **crossed** (bred).

You need to know how to use genetic diagrams to predict the results of various crosses, including **monogenic crosses**. **Monogenic inheritance** is the inheritance of a **characteristic** controlled by a **single gene**. **Monogenic crosses** show the **likelihood** of the **different alleles** of that gene (and so different versions of the characteristic) being **inherited** by offspring of particular parents. This genetic diagram shows how **wing length** is inherited in fruit flies:

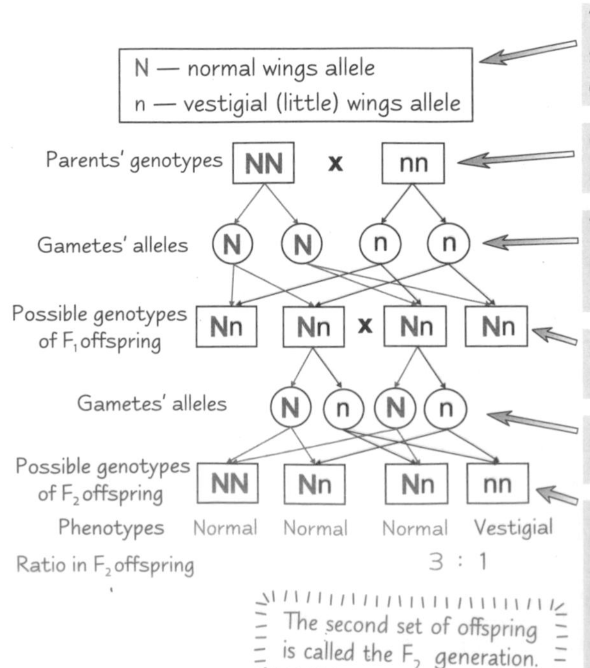

The second set of offspring is called the F_2 generation.

The allele for **normal wings** is **dominant**, so it's shown by a **capital** letter N. Any flies that have even one N allele will have normal wings.

One parent is **homozygous** with **normal wings** (NN) and one is **homozygous** with **vestigial wings** (nn).

The normal winged parent **only** produces gametes with the allele for **normal wings** (N). The vestigial winged parent **only** produces gametes with the allele for **vestigial wings** (n).

All F_1 offspring are **heterozygous** (Nn), as one allele is inherited from **each** parent.

The first set of offspring is called the F_1 generation.

The gametes produced by the F_1 offspring may contain the allele for **either normal** (N) or **vestigial wings** (n).

The F_2 offspring could have **either** normal or vestigial wings. But there's a **75%** chance they'll have the **normal wings phenotype** (genotype of **NN** or **Nn**) and a **25%** chance they'll have the **vestigial wings phenotype** (genotype **nn**). So you'd expect a **3:1** ratio of normal : vestigial wings in the offspring. **Whenever** you do a monogenic cross with **two heterozygous** parents you get a **3:1** ratio of **dominant : recessive** characteristic.

Inheritance

A **Punnett square** is just another way of showing a **genetic diagram** — they're also used to predict the **genotypes** and **phenotypes** of offspring. The Punnett squares below show the same crosses from the previous page:

1) First work out the alleles the **gametes** would have.

Parents' genotypes: NN, nn

Gametes' alleles: N, N, n, n

2) Next **cross** the **parents' gametes** to show the possible genotypes of the F_1 **generation** — **all heterozygous**, Nn.

F_1	n	n
N	Nn	Nn
N	Nn	Nn

3) Then **cross** the **gametes' alleles** of the F_1 **generation** to show the possible **genotypes** of the F_2 **generation**. The Punnett square shows a **75%** chance that offspring will have **normal wings** and a **25%** chance that they'll have **vestigial wings**, i.e. a **3:1 ratio**.

F_2	N	n
N	NN	Nn
n	Nn	nn

1 in 4 chance of offspring having the genotype NN (normal wings)
2 in 4 chance of offspring having the genotype Nn (normal wings)
1 in 4 chance of offspring having the genotype nn (vestigial wings)
So phenotype ratio = normal : vestigial = 3 : 1

Some **Genes** Have **Codominant Alleles**

Occasionally, alleles show **codominance** — **both alleles** are expressed in the **phenotype**, **neither one** is recessive. One example in humans is the allele for **sickle-cell anaemia**:

1) People who are **homozygous** for **normal haemoglobin** (**H^NH^N**) don't have the disease.
2) People who are **homozygous** for **sickle haemoglobin** (**H^SH^S**) have **sickle-cell anaemia** — all their **blood cells** are **sickle-shaped** (crescent-shaped).
3) People who are **heterozygous** (**H^NH^S**) have an **in-between** phenotype, called the **sickle-cell trait** — they have **some** normal haemoglobin and some sickle haemoglobin. The two alleles are **codominant** because they're **both expressed** in the **phenotype**.
4) The **genetic diagram** on the right shows the possible offspring from **crossing** two parents with **sickle-cell trait** (**heterozygous**).

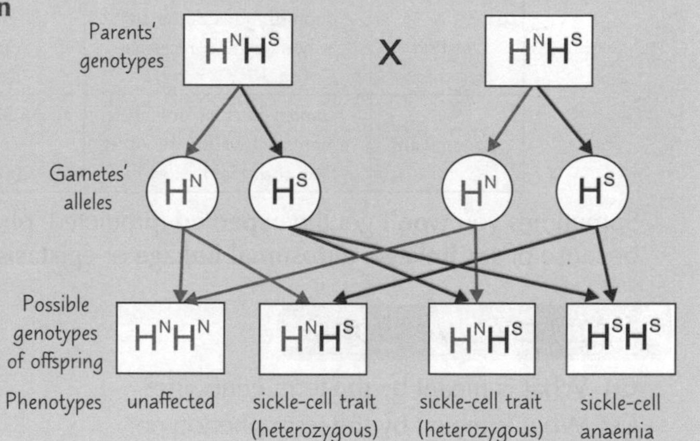

Some **Genes** Have **Multiple Alleles**

Inheritance is **more complicated** when there are **more than two** alleles of the same gene (**multiple alleles**).

Example In the **ABO blood group system** in humans there are **three alleles** for blood type:

I^O is the allele for blood group **O**. **I^A** is the allele for blood group **A**. **I^B** is the allele for blood group **B**.

Allele **I^O** is **recessive**. Alleles **I^A** and **I^B** are **codominant** — people with genotype **I^AI^B** will have blood group **AB**.

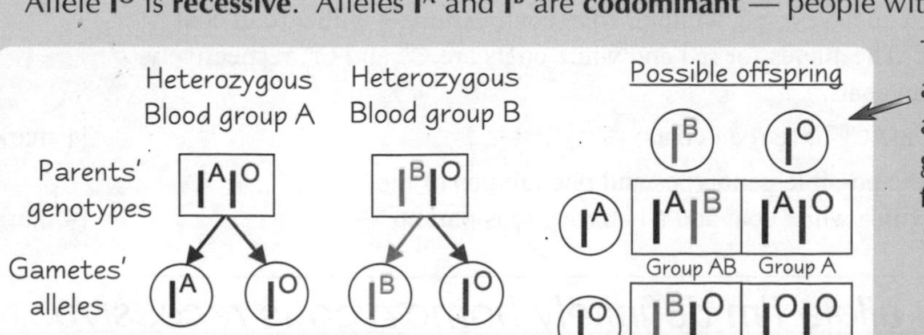

The genetic diagram shows a cross between a **heterozygous** person with blood group **A** and a **heterozygous** person with blood group **B**. Any offspring could have one of **four** different blood groups — **A, B, O** or **AB**.

Recessive blood groups are normally really rare, but it just so happens that loads of people in Britain are descended from people who were $I^O I^O$, so O's really common.

Inheritance

Genetic Diagrams can Show how More Than One Characteristic is Inherited

You can use genetic diagrams to work out the chances of offspring inheriting certain **combinations** of characteristics. **Dihybrid inheritance** is the inheritance of **two characteristics** which are controlled by different genes. You can use a **dihybrid cross** to look at how the **two different genes** are inherited at the **same time**. The diagram below is a **dihybrid cross** showing how seed texture **and** colour are inherited in **pea plants**.

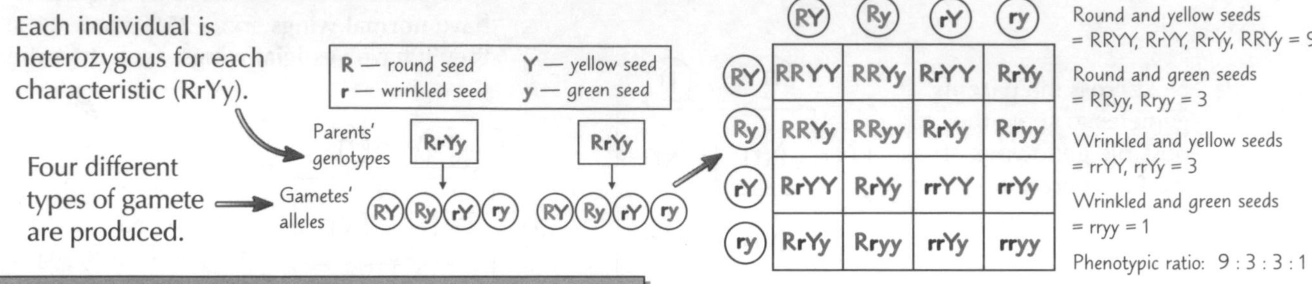

Phenotypic Ratios can be Predicted

The **phenotypic ratio** is the **ratio** of **different phenotypes** in offspring. Genetic diagrams allow you to **predict** the phenotypic ratios in **F_1 and F_2 offspring**. Here's a handy summary table of ratios for the following crosses:

Type of cross	Parents	Phenotypic ratio in F_1	Phenotypic ratio in F_2
Monogenic	Homozygous dominant × homozygous recessive (e.g. RR × rr)	All heterozygous offspring (e.g. Rr)	3 : 1 dominant : recessive
Dihybrid	Homozygous dominant × homozygous recessive (e.g. RRYY × rryy)	All heterozygous offspring (e.g. RrYy)	9 : 3 : 3 : 1 dominant both : dominant 1st recessive 2nd : recessive 1st dominant 2nd : recessive both
Codominant	Homozygous for one allele × homozygous for the other allele (e.g. H^NH^N x H^SH^S)	All heterozygous offspring (e.g. H^NH^S)	1 : 2 : 1 homozygous for one allele : heterozygous : homozygous for the other allele

Sometimes you **won't** get the **expected** (predicted) phenotypic ratio — it'll be quite different. This can be because of **sex linkage**, **autosomal linkage** or **epistasis** — all of which are covered on pages 71-73.

Practice Questions

Q1 What is meant by the term genotype?

Q2 What is meant by the term phenotype?

Q3 What's dihybrid inheritance?

Q4 In the cross aabb × AABB, what would be the expected phenotypic ratios in the F_1 generation and the F_2 generation?

Exam Questions

Q1 In pea plants, seed texture (round or wrinkled) is passed from parent to offspring by monogenic inheritance. The allele for round seeds is represented by R and the allele for wrinkled seeds is represented by r.

Draw a genetic diagram to show the possible genotypes of F_1 offspring produced by crossing a homozygous round seed pea plant with a homozygous wrinkled-seed pea plant. [3 marks]

Q2 Individuals of a particular breed of cow can have a red, white or roan coat. Animals with a roan coat have patches of both red and white hair. The alleles for red and white coats are C^R and C^W respectively. Heterozygotes for these alleles have roan coats.

a) Explain why heterozygotes for C^W and C^R have roan coats. [1 mark]

b) Draw a genetic diagram to predict the possible genotypes and phenotypes of the F_1 offspring produced by a parent with a white coat and a heterozygous parent. [4 marks]

If there's a dominant revision allele I'm definitely homozygous recessive...

OK, so there are a lot of fancy words on these pages and yes, you do need to know them all. Sorry. But don't despair — once you've learnt what the words mean and know how genetic diagrams work it'll all just fall into place.

Linkages and Epistasis

Right, this stuff is fairly hard, so if you don't get it first time don't panic. Make sure you're happy with the genetic diagrams and phenotypic ratios on the previous three pages before you get stuck into this lot.

Some **Characteristics** are **Sex-linked**

1) The genetic information for **gender** is carried on two **sex chromosomes**.
2) In mammals, **females** have **two X** chromosomes (XX) and **males** have **one X** and **one Y** chromosome (XY).
3) A **characteristic** is said to be **sex-linked** when the allele that codes for it is located on a **sex chromosome**.
4) The **Y chromosome** is **smaller** than the X chromosome and carries **fewer genes**.
So most genes on the sex chromosomes are **only carried** on the X chromosome (called **X-linked** genes).
5) As **males** only have **one X chromosome**, they often only have **one allele** for sex-linked genes.
So because they **only** have one copy, they **express** the **characteristic** of this allele even if it's **recessive**.
This makes males **more likely** than females to show **recessive phenotypes** for genes that are sex-linked.
6) Genetic disorders caused by **faulty alleles** on sex chromosomes include **colour blindness** and **haemophilia**.
The faulty alleles for both of these disorders are carried on the X chromosome — they're called **X-linked disorders**.

Example

1) **Colour blindness** is a **sex-linked disorder** caused by a faulty allele carried on the **X** chromosome.
2) As it's sex-linked **both** the chromosome and the allele are **represented** in the **genetic diagram**, e.g. $\mathbf{X^n}$, where **X** represents the **X chromosome** and **n** the **faulty allele** for **colour vision**.
3) The **Y chromosome** doesn't have an allele for colour vision so is **just** represented by **Y**.
4) **Females** would need **two copies** of the **recessive allele** to be colour blind, while **males** only need **one copy**. This means colour blindness is **much rarer** in **women** than **men**.

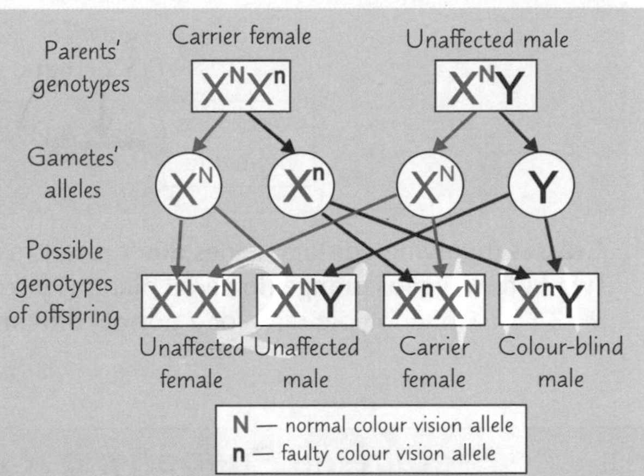

7) In the example above there's a **3 : 1 ratio** of offspring **without** colour blindness : offspring **with** colour-blindness.
8) But when a **female carrier** and a **male without colour-blindness** have children (as in this example), only their **male offspring** are at risk of being colour-blind. So you can also say that there's a predicted **2 : 1 : 1 ratio** — of **female** offspring **without** colour-blindness : **male** offspring **without** colour-blindness : **male** offspring **with** colour-blindness.
9) This ratio will **change** if a female carrier (X^NX^n) and a male **with** colour-blindness (X^nY) have children.
The predicted ratio will then be **1 : 1** — of offspring **with** colour-blindness : offspring **without** colour-blindness. The ratio will be the **same** for offspring of **each gender**. You only end up with this predicted ratio for a monogenic F_2 cross with a **sex-linked characteristic**.

Some **Autosomal** Genes are **Linked**

Crossing over is when two homologous (paired) chromosomes 'swap bits'. It happens in meiosis I before independent assortment. You'll have learnt about this in Year 1 of your course.

1) **Autosome** is the fancy name for any chromosome that **isn't** a sex chromosome.
Autosomal genes are the genes located on the autosomes.
2) Genes on the **same autosome** are said to be **linked** — because they're on the same autosome they'll stay together during the **independent assortment of chromosomes** in meiosis I, and their alleles will be **passed on to the offspring together**. The only reason this won't happen is if **crossing over** splits them up first.
3) The **closer together** two genes are on the autosome, the **more closely** they are said to be **linked**. This is because **crossing over** is **less likely** to split them up.
4) If two genes are autosomally linked, you **won't get** the phenotypic ratio you expect in the offspring of a cross.

Genes A, B and C are all linked.
An autosome
Genes A and B are more closely linked than genes A and C.

5) For example, in the $\mathbf{F_2}$ **generation** of a **dihybrid cross** (see previous page) you'd expect a **9 : 3 : 3 : 1 ratio**. Instead, the phenotypic ratio is more likely to be that expected for the F_2 generation of a **monohybrid cross** (3 : 1) because the two autosomally-linked alleles are **inherited together**. This means that a **higher proportion** of the **offspring** will have their **parents'** (heterozygous) **genotype** and **phenotype**.
6) This allows you to use the **predicted phenotypic ratio** to **identify** autosomal linkage.

Linkages and Epistasis

*An **Epistatic Gene Masks** the **Expression** of **Another Gene***

1) **Many different genes** can control the **same** characteristic — they **interact** to form the phenotype.
2) This can be because the **allele** of one gene **masks** (blocks) **the expression** of the alleles of other genes — this is called **epistasis**.

Example 1 In humans a **widow's peak** (see picture) is controlled by one gene and **baldness** by others. If you have the **alleles** that code for baldness, it **doesn't matter** whether you have the allele for a widow's peak or not, as you have **no hair**. The baldness genes are **epistatic** to the widow's peak gene, as the baldness genes **mask** the expression of the widow's peak gene.

Example 2 **Flower pigment** in a plant is controlled by two genes. **Gene 1** codes for a **yellow pigment** (Y is the dominant yellow allele) and **gene 2** codes for an enzyme that **turns** the yellow pigment **orange** (R is the dominant orange allele). If you **don't have** the **Y** allele it **won't matter** if you have the R allele or not as the flower **will be colourless**. Gene 1 is **epistatic** to gene 2 as it can **mask** the expression of gene 2.

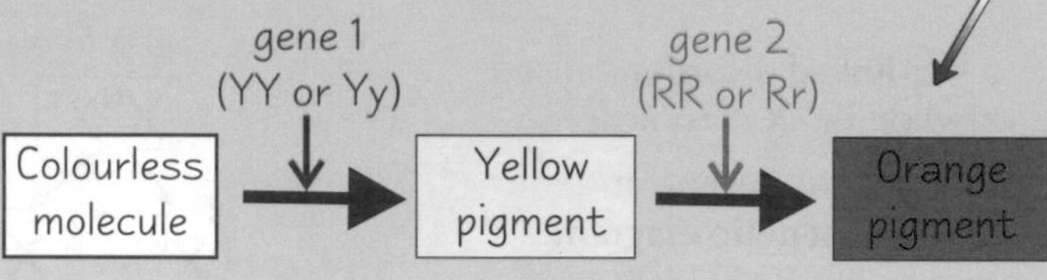

3) **Crosses** involving epistatic genes **don't result** in the **expected phenotypic ratios** given above, e.g. if you cross **two heterozygous orange** flowered plants (YyRr) from the above example you wouldn't get the expected **9 : 3 : 3 : 1** phenotypic ratio for a **normal dihybrid cross**.

*You can **Predict** the **Phenotypic Ratios** for Some **Epistatic Genes***

Just as you can **predict** the phenotypic ratios for **normal dihybrid crosses** (see page 70), you can predict the phenotypic ratios for dihybrid crosses involving some **epistatic genes** too:

A dihybrid cross involving a recessive epistatic allele — 9 : 3 : 4

Having **two copies** of the **recessive** epistatic allele **masks** (**blocks**) the expression of the **other gene**. If you cross a **homozygous recessive** parent with a **homozygous dominant** parent you will get a **9 : 3 : 4** phenotypic ratio of **dominant both : dominant epistatic recessive other : recessive epistatic** in the **F_2 generation**.

E.g. the **flower example above** is an example of a **recessive epistatic allele**. If a plant is **homozygous recessive** for the **epistatic gene** (**yy**) then it will be **colourless**, **masking** the expression of the orange gene. So if you cross homozygous parents, you should get a **9 : 3 : 4** ratio of **orange : yellow : white** in the **F_2 generation**. You can check the **phenotypic ratio** is right **using a genetic diagram**:

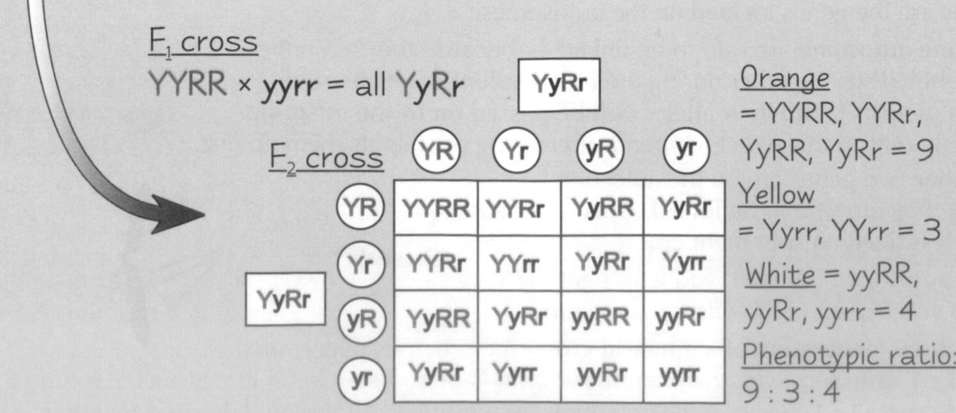

	YR	Yr	yR	yr
YR	YYRR	YYRr	YyRR	YyRr
Yr	YYRr	YYrr	YyRr	Yyrr
yR	YyRR	YyRr	yyRR	yyRr
yr	YyRr	Yyrr	yyRr	yyrr

Linkages and Epistasis

A dihybrid cross involving a dominant epistatic allele — 12 : 3 : 1

Dominant 12:3:1

Having **at least one** copy of the **dominant epistatic** allele **masks** (**blocks**) the expression of the other gene. Crossing a **homozygous recessive** parent with a **homozygous dominant** parent will produce a **12 : 3 : 1** phenotypic ratio of **dominant epistatic : recessive epistatic dominant other : recessive both** in the F_2 generation.

E.g. **squash colour** is controlled by two genes — the **colour epistatic gene** (**W/w**) and the **yellow gene** (**Y/y**). The **no-colour**, **white** allele (**W**) is **dominant** over the **coloured** allele (**w**), so **WW** or **Ww** will be **white** and **ww** will be **coloured**. The yellow gene has the **dominant yellow** allele (**Y**) and the **recessive green** allele (**y**). So if the plant has **at least one W**, then the squash **will be white**, **masking** the expression of the yellow gene. So if you cross **wwyy** with **WWYY**, you'll get a **12 : 3 : 1** ratio of **white : yellow : green** in the F_2 generation. Here's a **genetic diagram** to prove it:

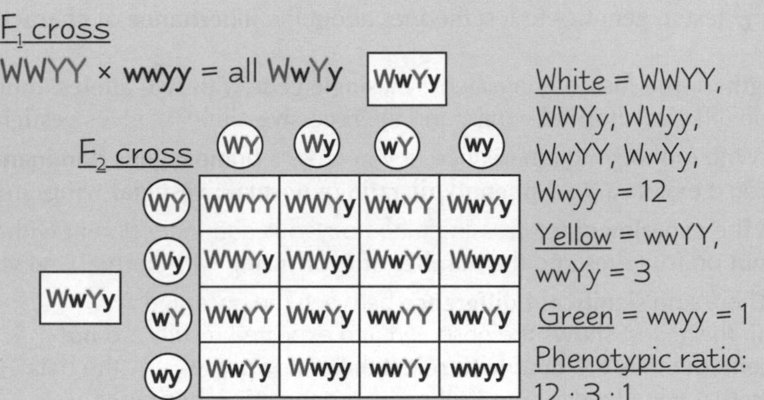

Practice Questions

Q1 What is a sex-linked characteristic?

Q2 Two genes are autosomally-linked. What does this mean?

Q3 The cross AaBb x AaBb produces a 3 : 1 ratio of phenotypes in the offspring, instead of the expected 9 : 3 : 3 : 1 ratio. What does this tell you about the two genes involved?

Q4 What is an epistatic gene?

Q5 A dihybrid cross produces the phenotypic ratio 9 : 3 : 4 in the F_2 generation. What does this indicate about the genes involved?

Exam Questions

Q1 Haemophilia A is a sex-linked genetic disorder caused by a recessive allele carried on the X chromosome (X^h).

a) Draw a genetic diagram for a female carrier and a male with haemophilia A to predict the possible genotypes of their offspring. [3 marks]

b) Explain why haemophilia is more common in males than females. [3 marks]

Q2 Coat colour in mice is controlled by two genes. Gene 1 controls whether fur is coloured (C) or albino (c). Gene 2 controls whether the colour is grey (G) or black (g). Gene 1 is epistatic over gene 2.

Describe and explain the phenotypic ratio produced in the F_2 generation from a CCGG × ccgg cross. [4 marks]

Q3 Hair type in organism A is controlled by two genes: hair (H bald, h hair) and type (S straight, s curly). The F_2 offspring of a cross are shown in the table on the right. State and explain the phenotypic ratio shown by the cross. [3 marks]

Homozygous curly hair (hhss) crossed with a homozygous bald (HHSS)

Phenotypes of the F_2 offspring produced		
Bald	Straight hair	Curly hair
36	9	3

Biology students — 9 : 1 phenotypic ratio normal : geek...

I don't know about you but I think I need a lie-down after these pages. Epistasis is a bit of a tricky topic, but you just need to understand what it is and learn the phenotypic ratios for the two types of epistasis — dominant and recessive.

The Chi-Squared Test

Just when you thought it was safe to turn the page... I stick in some maths. Surprise!

The Chi-Squared Test Can Be Used to Check the Results of Genetic Crosses

1) The **chi-squared** (χ^2) **test** is a **statistical test** that's used to see if the **results** of an experiment **support** a **theory**.
2) First, the theory is used to **predict** a **result** — this is called the **expected result**. Then, the experiment is carried out and the **actual result** is recorded — this is called the **observed result**.
3) To see if the results support the theory you have to make a **hypothesis** called the **null hypothesis**.
4) The null hypothesis is always that there's **no significant difference** between the observed and expected results (your experimental result will usually be a bit different from what you expect, but you need to know if the difference is just **due to chance**, or because your **theory is wrong**).
5) The χ^2 **test** is then carried out and the **outcome** either **supports** or **rejects** the **null hypothesis**.
6) You can use the χ^2 test in **genetics** to test theories about the **inheritance** of **characteristics**. For example:

<u>Theory</u>: **Wing length** in fruit flies is controlled by a **single gene** with **two alleles** (**monogenic inheritance**). The **dominant** allele (N) gives **normal** wings, and the **recessive** allele (n) gives **vestigial** wings.

<u>Expected results</u>: With monogenic inheritance, if you cross a **homozygous dominant** parent with a **homozygous recessive** parent, you'd expect a **3 : 1 phenotypic ratio** of **normal : vestigial** wings in the F_2 generation (see p. 68).

<u>Observed results</u>: The **experiment** (of crossing a homozygous dominant parent with a homozygous recessive parent) is **carried out** on fruit flies and the **number of F_2 offspring** with normal and vestigial wings is **counted**.

<u>Null hypothesis</u>: There's **no significant difference** between the observed and expected results. (If the χ^2 test shows the observed and expected results are **not significantly different**, then we are **unable to reject** the null hypothesis — the data **supports** the **theory** that wing length is controlled by **monogenic inheritance**.)

In this kind of statistical test, you can never prove that the null hypothesis is true — you can only 'fail to reject it'. This just means that the evidence doesn't give you a reason to think the null hypothesis is wrong.

First, Work Out the Chi-Squared Value...

Chi-squared (χ^2) is calculated using this formula: where **O** = **observed** result and **E** = **expected** result.

$$\chi^2 = \sum \frac{(O-E)^2}{E}$$

The best way to understand the χ^2 test is to work through an example — here's one for testing the **wing length** of **fruit flies** as explained above:

You don't need to learn the formula for chi-squared — it'll be given to you in the exam.

Homozygous dominant (NN) flies are crossed with homozygous recessive (nn) flies. **160 offspring** are produced in the F_2 generation.

1) First, the **number of offspring** (out of a total of 160) **expected** for each phenotype is worked out. E for normal wings: 160 (total) ÷ 4 (ratio total) × 3 (predicted ratio for normal wings) = 120. E for vestigial wings: 160 ÷ 4 × 1 = 40.

Phenotype	Ratio	Expected Result (E)	Observed Result (O)
Normal wings	3	120	
Vestigial wings	1	40	

2) Then the **actual number** of offspring **observed** with each phenotype (out of the 160 offspring) is **recorded**, e.g. 111 with normal wings.

Phenotype	Ratio	Expected Result (E)	Observed Result (O)
Normal wings	3	120	111
Vestigial wings	1	40	49

3) The results are used to work out χ^2, taking it **one step at a time**:

a) First calculate **O – E** (**subtract** the **expected result** from the **observed result**) for each phenotype. E.g. for normal wings: 111 – 120 = –9.

b) Then the resulting numbers are **squared**, e.g. $9^2 = 81$

c) These figures are divided by the **expected results**, e.g. 81 ÷ 120 = 0.675.

d) Finally, the numbers are **added** together to get χ^2, e.g. 0.675 + 2.025 = **2.7**.

Phenotype	Ratio	Expected Result (E)	Observed Result (O)	O – E	$(O-E)^2$	$\frac{(O-E)^2}{E}$
Normal wings	3	120	111	–9	81	0.675
Vestigial wings	1	40	49	9	81	2.025
					$\sum\frac{(O-E)^2}{E}$ =	2.7

Remember, you need to work it out for each phenotype first, then add all the numbers together.

The Chi-Squared Test

...Then Compare it to the Critical Value

1) To find out if there is a **significant difference** between your observed and expected results you need to **compare** your **χ^2 value** to a **critical value.**
2) The critical value is the value of χ^2 that corresponds to a 0.05 (**5%**) level of **probability** that the **difference** between the observed and expected results is **due to chance.**
3) If your χ^2 value is **larger** than or equal to the critical value then there **is a significant difference** between the observed and expected results (something **other than chance** is causing the difference) — and the **null hypothesis** can be **rejected.**
4) If your χ^2 value is **smaller** than the critical value then there **is no significant difference** between the observed and expected results — the null hypothesis **can't be rejected**. E.g. for the example on the previous page the χ^2 value is **2.7**, which is **smaller** than the critical value of **3.84** (see table below) — there's **no significant difference** between the observed and expected results. We've failed to reject the null hypothesis, so the **theory** that wing length in fruit flies is controlled by **monogenic inheritance** is **supported.**
5) In the exam you might be **given** the **critical value** or asked to **work it out** from a **table**:

Using a χ^2 table:

If you're not given the critical value, you may have to find it yourself from a **χ^2 table** — this shows a range of **probabilities** that correspond to different **critical values** for different **degrees of freedom** (explained below). Biologists normally use a **probability** level of **0.05** (5%), so you only need to look in that column.

- First, the **degrees of freedom** for the experiment are worked out — this is the **number of classes** (number of phenotypes) **minus one.** E.g. 2 – 1 = 1.
- Next, the **critical value** corresponding to a **probability** of **0.05** at **one degree of freedom** is found in the table — here it's **3.84.**
- Then just **compare** your χ^2 value of **2.7** to this critical value, as explained above.

degrees of freedom	no. of classes	Critical values					
1	2	0.46	1.64	2.71	3.84	6.64	10.83
2	3	1.39	3.22	4.61	5.99	9.21	13.82
3	4	2.37	4.64	6.25	7.82	11.34	16.27
4	5	3.36	5.99	7.78	9.49	13.28	18.47
probability that result is due to chance only		0.50 (50%)	0.20 (20%)	0.10 (10%)	0.05 (5%)	0.01 (1%)	0.001 (0.1%)

Abridged from Statistical Tables for Biological Agricultural and Medical Research (6th ed.)

Practice Questions

Q1 What is a χ^2 test used for?

Q2 What can the results of the χ^2 test tell you?

Q3 How do you tell if the difference between your observed and expected results is due to chance?

Exam Question

Q1 A scientist is investigating petal colour in a flower. It's thought to be controlled by two separate genes (dihybrid inheritance), the colour gene — B = blue, b = purple, and the spots gene — W = white, w = yellow. A cross involving a homozygous dominant parent and a homozygous recessive parent should give a 9 : 3 : 3 : 1 ratio in the F_2 generation. The scientist observes the number of offspring showing each of four phenotypes in 240 F_2 offspring. Her results are shown in the table.

Her null hypothesis is that there is no significant difference between the observed and expected ratios.

a) Complete the table to calculate χ^2 for this experiment. [3 marks]

b) The critical value for this experiment is 7.82. Explain whether the χ^2 value supports or rejects the null hypothesis. [2 marks]

Phenotype	Ratio	Expected Result (E)	Observed Result (O)	O – E	$O - E^2$	$\frac{(O-E^2)}{E}$
Blue with white spots	9	135	131			
Purple with white spots	3	45	52			
Blue with yellow spots	3	45	48			
Purple with yellow spots	1	15	9			

$\sum\frac{(O-E)^2}{E} =$

The expected result of revising these pages — boredom...

...the observed result — boredom (except for the maths geeks among you). Don't worry if you're not brilliant at maths though, you don't have to be to do the chi-squared test — just make sure you know the steps above off by heart.

Evolution by Natural Selection and Genetic Drift

You already know that evolution occurs by natural selection. The twist is that it can also happen by genetic drift.

Evolution** is a **Change** in **Allele Frequency

A population is a group of organisms of the same species living in a particular area.

1) The complete range of **alleles** present in a **population** is called the **gene pool.**
2) **New alleles** are usually generated by **mutations** in **genes.**
3) How **often** an **allele occurs** in a population is called the **allele frequency**.
   It's usually given as a **percentage** of the total population, e.g. 35%, or a **number**, e.g. 0.35.
4) The **frequency** of an **allele** in a population **changes** over time — this is **evolution.**

Evolution** Occurs by **Natural Selection

You might remember **natural selection** from Module 4. Here's a reminder of how it works:

Variation is generated by meiosis and mutations.

1) **Individuals** within a population **vary** because they have **different alleles.**
2) **Predation, disease** and **competition (selection pressures)** create a **struggle for survival.**
3) Because individuals vary, some are **better adapted** to the selection pressures than others.
4) Individuals that have an allele that **increases** their **chance of survival** (an **advantageous** allele) are **more likely** to **survive, reproduce** and **pass on** the advantageous allele, than individuals with different alleles.
5) This means that a **greater proportion** of the next generation **inherit** the **advantageous allele.**
6) They, in turn, are **more likely** to **survive, reproduce** and **pass on** their genes.
7) So the **frequency** of the advantageous allele **increases** from generation to generation.
8) This process is called **natural selection.**

A selection pressure is anything that affects an organism's chance of survival and reproduction.

An allele is only advantageous with the right **selection pressure.**
Without a selection pressure, natural selection **won't take place.**

*The **Environment** Affects **Which Characteristics Become More Common***

Whether the **environment** is **changing** or **stable** affects **which characteristics are selected for** by natural selection:

When the **environment isn't changing** much, individuals with alleles for characteristics towards the **middle** of the range are more likely to **survive** and **reproduce.** This is called **STABILISING SELECTION** and it **reduces the range** of possible **phenotypes.**

EXAMPLE In any **mammal population** there's a **range** of **fur length.** In a **stable climate,** having fur at the **extremes** of this range **reduces** the **chances** of **surviving** as it's harder to maintain the **right body temperature.** Animals with alleles for **average fur length** are the **most** likely to **survive, reproduce** and **pass on** their alleles. So these alleles **increase** in **frequency.** The **proportion** of the **population** with **average fur length increases** and the **range** of fur lengths **decreases.**

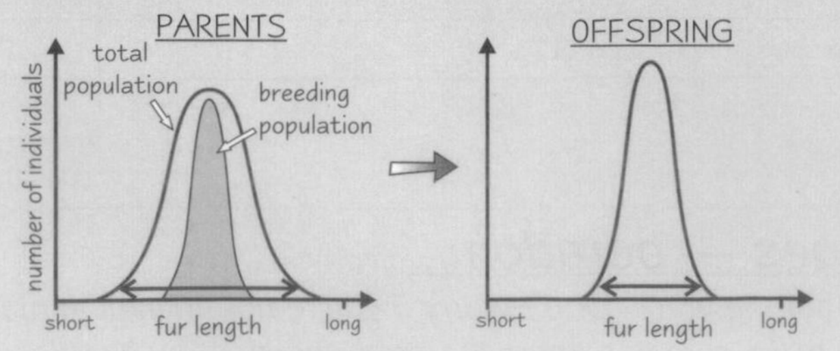

When there's a **change** in the environment, individuals with alleles for characteristics of an **extreme type** are more likely to **survive** and **reproduce.** This is called **DIRECTIONAL SELECTION.**

EXAMPLE If the environment becomes **very cold,** individual mammals with **alleles** for **long fur length** will find it **easier** to **maintain** the **right body temperature** than animals with short fur length. So they're **more likely** to **survive, reproduce** and **pass on** their alleles. Over time the **frequency** of alleles for **long fur length increases.**

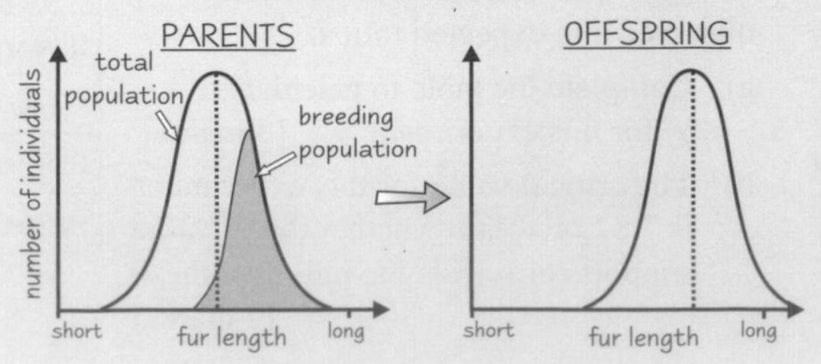

Evolution by Natural Selection and Genetic Drift

Evolution Also Occurs via Genetic Drift

1) **Natural selection** is just **one** process by which **evolution** occurs.
2) Evolution **also** occurs due to **genetic drift** — instead of **environmental factors** affecting which individuals **survive**, **breed** and pass on their alleles, **chance** dictates **which alleles** are **passed on**. Here's how it works:

- Individuals within a population show **variation** in their **genotypes** (e.g. A and B).
- By **chance**, the **allele** for **one genotype** (B) is **passed on** to the offspring **more often** than others.
- So the number of individuals with the allele **increases**.
- If by chance the same allele is passed on more often again and again, it can lead to **evolution** as the allele becomes **more common** in the population.

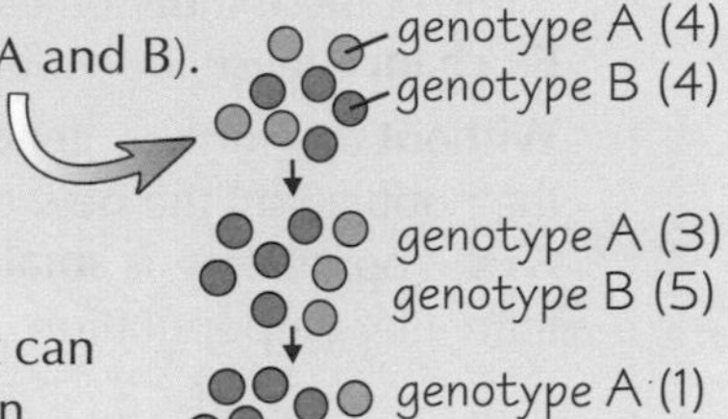

3) Natural selection and genetic drift work **alongside each other** to drive evolution, but one process can drive evolution **more** than the other depending on the **population size**.
4) **Evolution by genetic drift** usually has a **greater effect** in **smaller populations** where **chance** has a **greater influence**. In larger populations any **chance variations** in allele frequency tend to **even out** across the whole population.
5) The evolution of **human blood groups** is a good example of **genetic drift**:

- Different **Native American tribes** show different **blood group frequencies**. For example, **Blackfoot Indians** are mainly **group A**, but **Navajos** are mainly **group O**.
- Blood group doesn't affect **survival** or **reproduction**, so the differences **aren't** due to evolution by natural selection.
- In the past, human populations were much **smaller** and were often found in **isolated groups**. The blood group differences were due to evolution by **genetic drift** — by **chance** the allele for **blood group O** was **passed on more often** in the **Navajo tribe**, so over time this **allele** and blood group became **more common**.

Genetic Drift Has a Greater Effect if There's a Genetic Bottleneck

A **genetic bottleneck** is an **event** (such as a natural disaster) that causes a **big reduction** in a **population's size**, leading to a **reduction** in the **gene pool**. For example:

The gene pool is the complete range of alleles in a population.

1) The **mice** in a **large population** are either **black or grey**. The coat colour **doesn't** affect their **survival** or **reproduction**.
2) A **large flood** hits the population and the **only survivors** are **grey** mice and **one black** mouse.
3) **Grey** becomes the **most common colour** due to **genetic drift**.

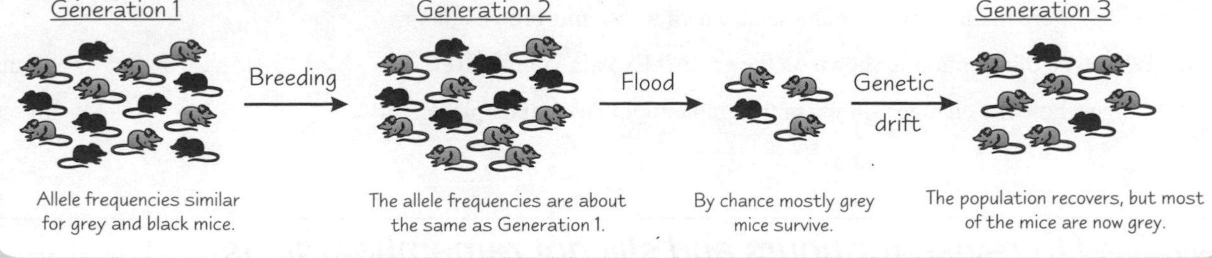

Evolution by Natural Selection and Genetic Drift

Genetic Drift Also Has a Greater Effect if There's a Founder Effect

The **founder effect** describes what happens when just a **few organisms** from a population **start a new population** and there are only a **small number of different alleles** in the **initial gene pool**:

1) Individuals within a population show **variation** in their **genotypes** (e.g. A and B).
2) Some of these individuals start a **new population**. By **chance** these individuals are mostly **one particular genotype** (A).
3) **Without** any further **'gene flow'** (i.e. the introduction of new alleles from outside the population) the new population will **grow** with **reduced genetic variation**. As the population is **small**, it's **more heavily influenced** by **genetic drift** than a larger population.

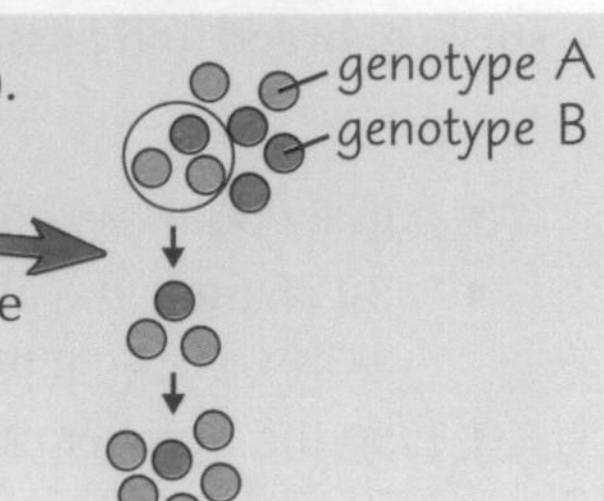

The founder effect can occur as a result of **migration** leading to geographical **separation** or if a new colony is separated from the original population for **another reason**, such as **religion**.

Example — The Amish

The **Amish population** of North America are all descended from a **small** number of Swiss who **migrated** there. The population shows **little genetic diversity**. They have remained **isolated** from the surrounding population due to their **religious beliefs**, so **few new alleles** have been introduced. The population has an unusually high incidence of certain **genetic disorders**.

Practice Questions

Q1 What is evolution?

Q2 What is allele frequency?

Q3 What is genetic drift?

Q4 Does genetic drift have a greater effect in smaller or larger populations? Why?

Q5 What situation does the founder effect describe?

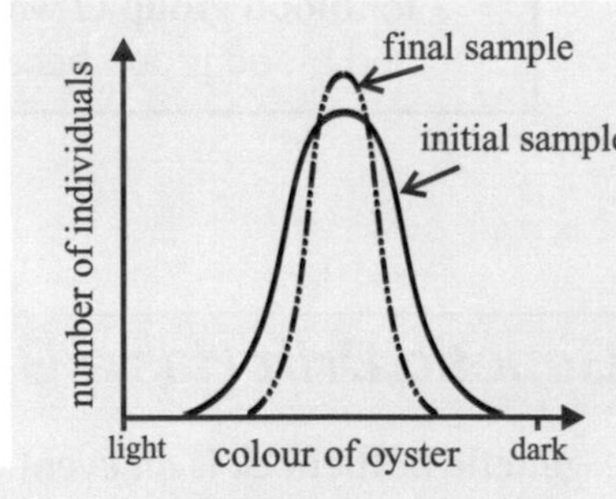

Exam Questions

Q1 Northern elephant seals were hunted by humans in the late 1800s. Their original population was reduced to about 20 seals at their lowest point, which have since reproduced to a population of over 100 000. Southern elephant seals were not hunted to the same extent.

Northern elephant seals now show much less genetic variation than southern elephant seals. Explain why this is the case. [3 marks]

Q2 A group of scientists monitored how the colour of oyster shells on a beach changed over time. The graph above right shows the colour of the oyster shells in the scientists' initial sample and in their final sample. The oysters were mainly found on the sand, which was a mid-brown colour.

a) What type of selection is shown on the graph? Explain your answer. [3 marks]

b) Suggest how the changes shown in the graph might have taken place. [4 marks]

I've evolved to revise for hours and still not remember things...

The trickiest thing here is tying all the information together in your head. Basically, natural selection and genetic drift drive evolution. And the characteristics selected for in natural selection are determined by what the environment's like. The characteristics that become more common by genetic drift do so purely by chance.

Hardy-Weinberg Principle and Artificial Selection

Now you know what allele frequency is you need to be able to calculate it. So switch your maths brain on now. Then you can take a breather and learn all about artificial selection.

The **Hardy-Weinberg Principle** Predicts **Allele Frequencies Won't Change**

1) The **Hardy-Weinberg principle** predicts that the **frequencies** of **alleles** in a population **won't change** from **one generation** to the **next**.
2) But this prediction is **only true** under **certain conditions** — it has to be a **large population** where there's **no immigration, emigration, mutations** or **natural selection**. There also needs to be **random mating** — all possible genotypes can breed with all others.
3) The **Hardy-Weinberg equations** (see below) are based on this principle. They can be used to **estimate the frequency** of particular **alleles** and **genotypes** within populations.
4) If the allele frequencies **do change** between generations in a large population then immigration, emigration, natural selection or mutations have happened.

The **Hardy-Weinberg Equations** Can be Used to **Predict Allele Frequency**...

You can **figure out** the frequency of one allele if you **know the frequency of the other**, using this equation:

$$p + q = 1$$

Where: **p** = the **frequency** of the **dominant** allele
q = the **frequency** of the **recessive** allele

The total frequency of all possible alleles for a characteristic in a certain population is 1.0. So the frequencies of the individual alleles (the dominant one and the recessive one) must add up to 1.0.

E.g. a species of plant has either **red** or **white** flowers. Allele **R** (red) is **dominant** and allele **r** (white) is **recessive**. If the frequency of **R** is **0.4**, then the frequency of **r** is:

1 – 0.4 = **0.6**.

...and **Genotype Frequency**

You can **figure out** the frequency of one genotype if you **know the frequencies of the others**, using this equation:

$$p^2 + 2pq + q^2 = 1$$

Where: p^2 = the **frequency** of the **homozygous dominant genotype**
$2pq$ = the **frequency** of the **heterozygous genotype**
q^2 = the **frequency** of the **homozygous recessive genotype**

The total frequency of all possible genotypes for one characteristic in a certain population is 1.0. So the frequencies of the individual genotypes must add up to 1.0.

E.g. if there are **two alleles** for **flower colour** (R and r), there are **three possible genotypes** — **RR**, **Rr** and **rr**. If the frequency of genotype **RR** (**p^2**) is **0.34** and the frequency of genotype **Rr** (**2pq**) is **0.27**, the frequency of genotype **rr** (**q^2**) must be:

1 – 0.34 – 0.27 = **0.39**.

Hardy-Weinberg Principle and Artificial Selection

Sometimes You Need to Use **Both Hardy-Weinberg Equations**

EXAMPLE

The **frequency** of **cystic fibrosis** (genotype ff) in the UK is currently approximately **1 birth in every 2500**. From this information you can estimate the **percentage** of people in the UK that are cystic fibrosis **carriers** (Ff). To do this you need to find the **frequency** of **heterozygous genotype** Ff, i.e. **2pq**, using **both** equations:

$$p + q = 1$$

$$p^2 + 2pq + q^2 = 1$$

First calculate q:
Frequency of cystic fibrosis (homozygous recessive, ff) is 1 in 2500
$ff = q^2 = 1 \div 2500 = 0.0004$
So, $q = \sqrt{0.0004} = 0.02$

Next calculate p:
Using $p + q = 1$, $p = 1 - q$
$p = 1 - 0.02 = 0.98$

Then calculate 2pq:
$2pq = 2 \times 0.98 \times 0.02 = 0.039$

The **frequency** of **genotype Ff** is **0.039**, so the **percentage** of the UK population that are **carriers** is **3.9%**.

Artificial Selection *Involves* ***Breeding*** *Individuals with* ***Desirable Traits***

Artificial selection is when **humans select individuals** in a population to **breed together** to get **desirable traits**. In can be done in both **animals** and **plants**. Here are **two examples**:

Artificial selection is also called selective breeding.

Modern Dairy Cattle

Modern **dairy cows** produce **many litres of milk** a day as a result of **artificial selection**:

1) Farmers **select** a **female** with a **very high milk yield** and a **male** whose **mother** had a very high milk yield and **breed** these two **together**.
2) Then they **select** the **offspring** with the **highest milk yields** and **breed** them **together**.
3) This is continued over **several generations** until a **very high milk-yielding cow** is produced.

Bread Wheat

Bread wheat (*Triticum aestivum*) is the plant from which **flour** is produced for **bread-making**. It produces a **high yield** of wheat because of **artificial selection** by **humans**:

1) Wheat plants with a **high wheat yield** (e.g. large ears) are **bred together**.
2) The **offspring** with the **highest yields** are then **bred together**.
3) This is continued over **several generations** to produce a plant that has a **very high yield**.

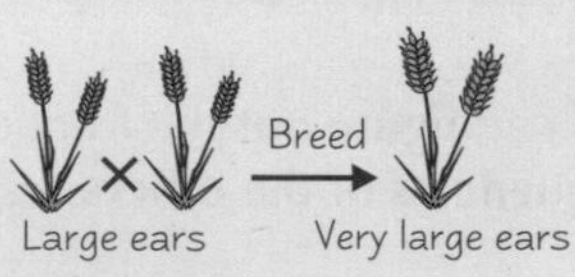

Artificial Selection ***Reduces*** *the* ***Gene Pool***

1) Artificial selection means that only organisms with **similar traits** and therefore **similar alleles** are bred together. This leads to a **reduction** in the **number of alleles** in the **gene pool**.
2) A reduced gene pool could cause us **problems** in the **future** — for example, if a **new disease** appears, there's **less chance** of the **alleles** that could offer **resistance** to that disease being present in the population.
3) Artificial selection could also mean that **potentially useful alleles** are **accidentally lost** from the population when other alleles are being selected for.
4) That's why it's important to **maintain resources** of **genetic material** for use in the future, e.g. by **preserving** the original '**wild type**' organisms that haven't undergone any artificial selection.

Hardy-Weinberg Principle and Artificial Selection

Artificial Selection Can Cause *Problems* for the *Organisms Involved*

1) Artificial selection can **exaggerate** certain traits, leading to **health problems** for the organisms involved.

Example: Pedigree Dogs...

Modern pedigree dog breeds are all descended from a single wolf-like ancestor. Each breed has gone through **many generations** of **artificial selection** to produce the dogs we know today. Pedigree dogs such as **Pugs** and **French Bulldogs** have been bred to have **flat, squashed up faces**. This trait has become so exaggerated that many of these dogs now suffer **breathing problems** as a result.

2) A reduced gene pool also tends to result in an **increased incidence** of **genetic disease**.

Example continued...

There's a high incidence of **hereditary deafness** in certain dog breeds, e.g. **Dalmatians** and **English Bull Terriers**.

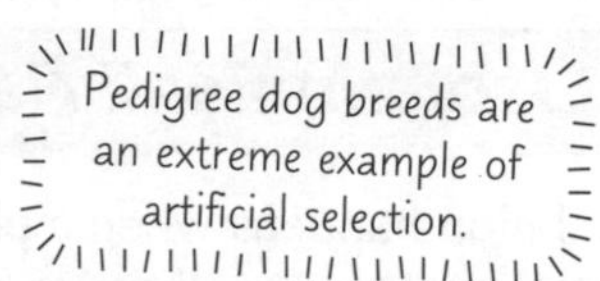

3) Problems like these mean that there are **ethical issues** surrounding the use of artificial selection. For example, many people don't think it's fair to keep artificially selecting traits in dogs that cause them health problems.

Practice Questions

Q1 Which term represents the frequency of the dominant allele in the Hardy-Weinberg equations?

Q2 Which term represents the frequency of the recessive allele in the Hardy-Weinberg equations?

Q3 What is artificial selection?

Q4 Give one ethical issue surrounding artificial selection.

Exam Questions

Q1 Modern beef cattle (raised for meat production) produce a very high meat yield.
Explain how artificial selection by farmers could have led to this. [3 marks]

Q2 A breed of dog has either a black or brown coat. Allele B (black) is dominant and allele b (brown) is recessive. The frequency of the recessive allele is 0.23. The Hardy-Weinberg equations are:

$$p^2 + 2pq + q^2 = 1 \quad \text{and} \quad p + q = 1.$$

Find the frequency of the heterozygous (Bb) genotype. [2 marks]

Q3 Cleft chins are controlled by a single gene with two alleles. The allele coding for cleft chin (C) is dominant over the allele coding for a non-cleft chin (c). In a particular population, the frequency of the homozygous dominant genotype for cleft chin is 0.14. The Hardy-Weinberg equations are:

$$p^2 + 2pq + q^2 = 1 \quad \text{and} \quad p + q = 1.$$

a) What is the frequency of the recessive allele in the population? [2 marks]

b) What is the frequency of the homozygous recessive genotype in the population? [1 mark]

This stuff's surely not that bad — Hardly worth Weining about...

Not many of you will be thrilled with the maths content on the first two pages of this topic, but don't worry. Make sure you know what to use each Hardy-Weinberg equation for and what the different terms mean, so you can plug the numbers you're given into the right places. Don't forget to take a calculator into the exam with you, either.

Speciation

Evolution leads to the development of lots of different species. I bet you can't guess the name for this process...

Speciation *is the Development of a* ***New Species***

1) A **species** is defined as a group of **similar organisms** that can **reproduce** to give **fertile offspring**.
2) **Speciation** is the development of a **new species**.
3) It occurs when **populations** of the **same species** become **reproductively isolated** — changes in allele frequencies cause changes in phenotype that mean they can **no longer breed** together to produce **fertile offspring**.

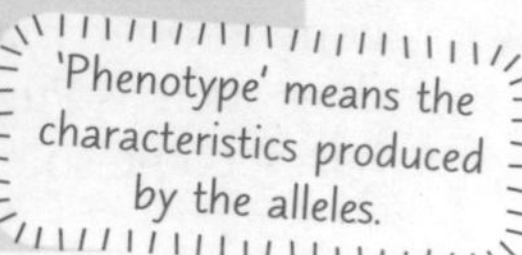

Geographical Isolation *and* ***Natural Selection*** *Lead to* ***Allopatric Speciation***

1) Geographical isolation happens when a **physical barrier divides** a population of a species — **floods**, **volcanic eruptions** and **earthquakes** can all cause barriers that isolate some individuals from the main population.
2) **Conditions** on either side of the barrier will be slightly **different**. For example, there might be a **different climate** on each side.
3) Because the environment is different on each side, **different characteristics** will become **more common** due to **natural selection** (because there are **different selection pressures**):

- Because different **characteristics** will be **advantageous** on each side, the **allele frequencies** will change in each population, e.g. if one allele is more advantageous on one side of the barrier, the frequency of that allele on that side will **increase**.
- **Mutations** will take place **independently** in each population, also changing the **allele frequencies**.
- The changes in allele frequencies will lead to changes in **phenotype frequencies**, e.g. the advantageous characteristics (**phenotypes**) will become more common on that side.

4) Eventually, individuals from different populations will have changed so much that they won't be able to breed with one another to produce **fertile** offspring — they'll have become **reproductively isolated**.
5) The two groups will have become separate **species**.

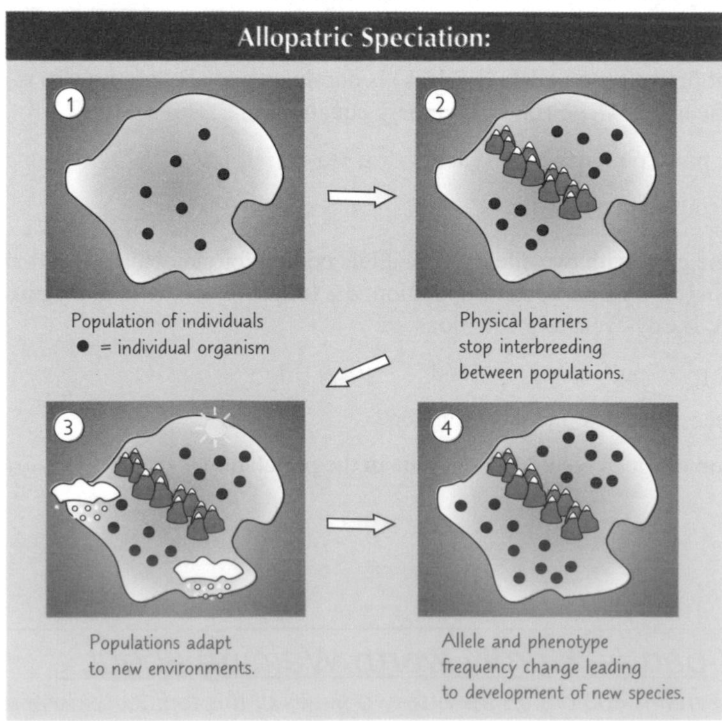

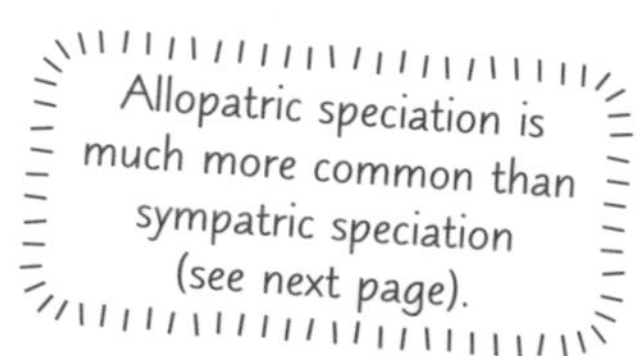

Bill wasn't going to let a mountain get in the way of his reproductive success.

Speciation

Reproductive Isolation Occurs in Many Ways

Reproductive isolation occurs because the **changes** in the alleles and phenotypes of the two populations **prevent** them from **successfully breeding together**. These changes include:

1) **Seasonal changes** — individuals from the same population develop different **flowering** or **mating** seasons, or become **sexually active** at **different times** of the year.
2) **Mechanical changes** — changes in **genitalia** prevent successful mating.
3) **Behavioural changes** — a group of individuals develop **courtship rituals** that **aren't attractive** to the main population.

Janice's courtship ritual was still successful in attracting mates.

Sympatric Speciation Doesn't Require Geographical Isolation

A population **doesn't** have to become **geographically isolated** to become **reproductively isolated**. Random mutations could occur **within a population**, resulting in the changes mentioned above, **preventing** members of that population breeding with other members of the species. Speciation without geographical isolation is called **sympatric speciation**.

Example:

1) Most eukaryotic organisms are **diploid** — they have **two sets** of **homologous** (matched) **chromosomes** in their cells. Sometimes, **mutations** can occur that **increase** the number of **chromosomes**. This is known as **polyploidy**.
2) Individuals with different numbers of chromosomes **can't reproduce** sexually to give **fertile offspring** — so if a polyploid organism emerges in a diploid population, the polyploid organism will be **reproductively isolated** from the diploid organisms.
3) If the polyploid organism then reproduces **asexually**, a **new species** could develop.
4) Polyploidy can only lead to speciation if it **doesn't prove fatal** to the organism and more polyploid organisms can be produced. It's **more common** in **plants** than animals.

Practice Questions

Q1 What is speciation?

Q2 What is the difference between allopatric and sympatric speciation?

Exam Question

Group fed starch-based food

Many generations pass

Single species of fruit fly

Group fed maltose-based food

Q1 The diagram shows an experiment conducted with fruit flies. One population was split in two and each population was fed a different food. After many generations the two populations were placed together and it was observed that they were unable to breed together.

a) What evidence shows that speciation occurred? [1 mark]

b) Explain why the experiment resulted in speciation. [3 marks]

c) Suggest two possible reasons why members of the two populations were not able to breed together. [2 marks]

d) During the experiment, populations of fruit flies were artificially isolated. Suggest one way that populations of organisms could become isolated naturally. [1 mark]

If they were ever separated, Al and Patrick would be heartbroken...

These gags get better and better... Anyway, it's a bit of a toughie getting your head round the different mechanisms that can produce a new species. The key thing to remember is that both allopatric and sympatric speciation involve reproductive isolation. But only allopatric speciation involves geographical isolation.

Common Techniques

This section is all about techniques used to investigate and fiddle about with genes. So get your deerstalker hat on and your magnifying glass out...

Techniques Used to Study Genes

There are lots of **techniques** used to **study genes** and their **function** — you need to learn some of these techniques for the exam. They include:

- The **polymerase chain reaction (PCR)** (see below).
- **Gel electrophoresis** (see next page).
- Cutting out DNA fragments using **restriction enzymes** (see page 86).

"Jeans have an important function in politics — they make me look cool..."

These techniques are also used in **DNA profiling** (see page 87), **DNA sequencing** (see page 93), **genetic engineering** (see page 88) and **gene therapy** (see page 92).

Multiple Copies of a DNA Fragment can be Made Using PCR

The **polymerase chain reaction** (PCR) can be used to **select** a fragment of DNA (containing the gene or bit of DNA you're interested in) and **amplify** it to produce **millions of copies** in just a few hours. PCR has **several stages** and is **repeated** over and over to make lots of copies:

1) A reaction mixture is set up that contains the **DNA sample, free nucleotides, primers** and **DNA polymerase.**
   - **Primers** are short pieces of DNA that are **complementary** to the bases at the **start** of the fragment you want.
   - **DNA polymerase** is an **enzyme** that creates new DNA strands.
2) The DNA mixture is **heated** to **95 °C** to break the **hydrogen bonds** between the two strands of DNA. DNA polymerase **doesn't denature** even at this high temperature — this is important as it means **many cycles** of PCR can be carried out without having to use **new enzymes** each time.

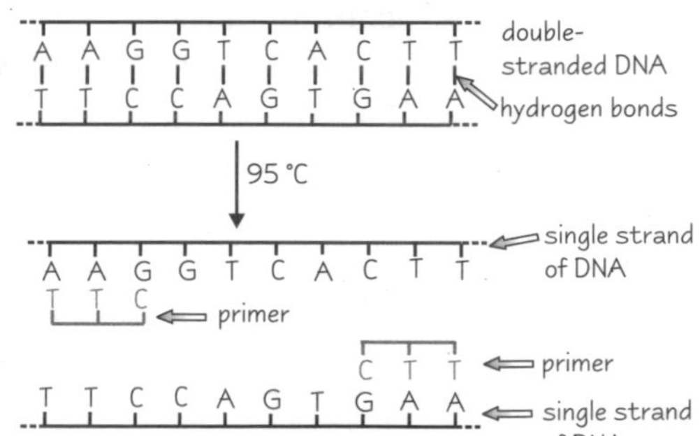

3) The mixture is then **cooled** to between **50** and **65 °C** so that the primers can **bind** (**anneal**) to the strands.
4) The reaction mixture is heated to **72 °C**, so **DNA polymerase** can **work.**
5) The DNA polymerase **lines up** free DNA nucleotides **alongside** each **template strand.** Complementary **base pairing** means **new complementary strands** are formed.

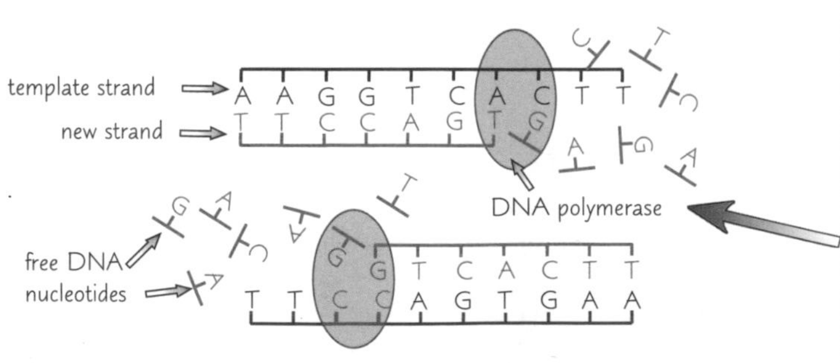

6) **Two new copies** of the fragment of DNA are formed and **one cycle** of PCR is **complete.**
7) The cycle starts again, with the mixture being heated to 95 °C and this time **all four strands** (two original and two new) are used as **templates.**
8) Each PCR cycle **doubles** the amount of DNA, e.g. **1st cycle = 2 × 2 = 4 DNA fragments, 2nd cycle = 4 × 2 = 8 DNA fragments, 3rd cycle = 8 × 2 = 16 DNA fragments**, and so on.

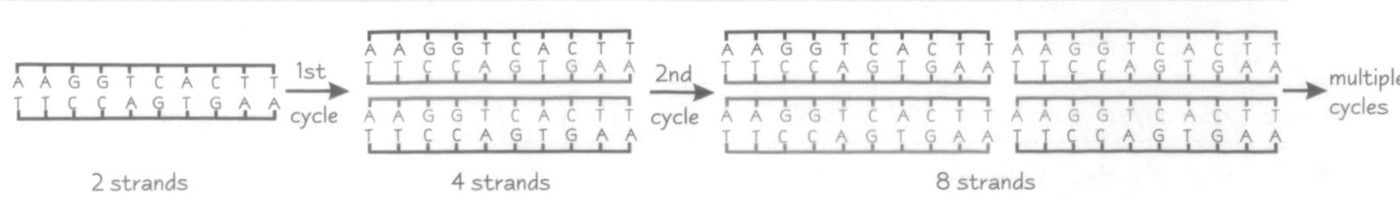

Common Techniques

Electrophoresis Separates DNA Fragments by Size

Electrophoresis is a procedure that uses an **electrical current** to **separate out DNA fragments**, **RNA fragments**, or **proteins** depending on their **size**. Here's how you can carry out electrophoresis in the **lab** using samples of **fragmented DNA** — there are several stages involved...

*Firstly you add a **Gel Tray** to a **Gel Box** (or **Tank**)*

1) Electrophoresis is commonly performed using **agarose gel** that has been poured into a **gel tray** and left to **solidify**. A **row of wells** is created at **one end** of the gel.
2) To perform electrophoresis, firstly you need to put the **gel tray** into a **gel box** (or tank). You need to make sure the end of the gel tray with the wells is closest to the **negative electrode** on the gel box.
3) Then add **buffer solution** to the **reservoirs** at the **sides** of the **gel box** so that the **surface of the gel** becomes **covered** in the buffer solution.

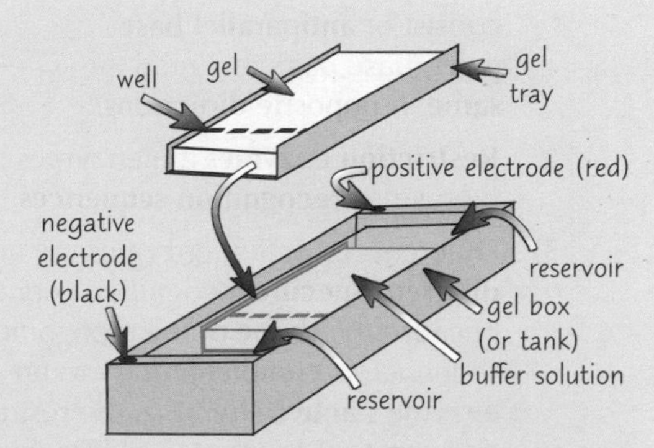

*Next **DNA Samples** are Loaded Into the **Wells***

1) Take your fragmented DNA samples and, using a micropipette, add the same volume of **loading dye** to each — loading dye helps the samples to **sink to the bottom** of the wells and makes them **easier to see**.
2) Next add a set volume (e.g. **10 µl**) of a DNA sample to the first well. You have to be **really careful** when adding the samples to the wells — make sure the **tip** of your micropipette is **in** the **buffer solution** and **just above** the **opening of the well**. **Don't** stick the tip of the micropipette too far into the well or you could **pierce the bottom** of it.
3) Then repeat this process and add the same volume of each of your **other DNA samples** to **other wells** in the gel. Use a **clean micropipette tip** each time.
4) Make sure you **record** which DNA sample you have added to each well.

*Then **Electrophoresis** is Carried Out*

1) Put the **lid** on the **gel box** and **connect the leads** from the gel box to the **power supply**.
2) **Turn on** the power supply and **set it to the required voltage**, e.g. 100 V. This causes an **electrical current** to be **passed through the gel**.
3) DNA fragments are **negatively charged**, so they'll move through the gel **towards the positive electrode** at the far end of the gel (called the **anode**). **Small** DNA fragments move **faster** and **travel further** through the gel, so the DNA fragments will **separate** according to **size**.
4) Let the gel run for about **30 minutes** (or until the dye is **about 2 cm** from the end of the gel) then **turn off** the power supply.
5) **Remove** the gel tray from the gel box and **tip off** any **excess buffer solution**.
6) Wearing **gloves**, **stain** the DNA fragments by covering the surface of the gel with a staining solution then **rinsing** the gel with water. The **bands** of the different **DNA fragments** will now be **visible**. The size of a DNA fragment is **measured** in **bases**, e.g. ATCC = 4 bases or base pairs, 1000 bases is one **kilobase** (**1 kb**).

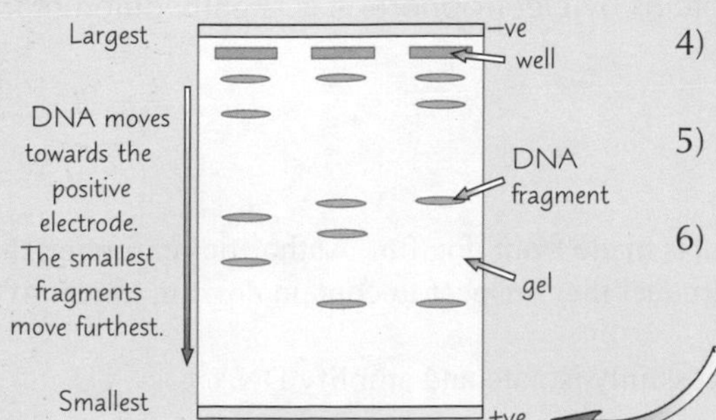

Electrophoresis can be carried out on **RNA fragments** following the **same basic method** as for **DNA fragments**. However, proteins can be positively charged or negatively charged so, before they undergo electrophoresis, they're mixed with a chemical that **denatures** the proteins so they all have the **same charge**. Electrophoresis of proteins has **many uses**, e.g. to identify the proteins present in **urine** or **blood** samples, which may help to **diagnose disease**.

Common Techniques

Restriction Enzymes can be *Used* to *Cut Out DNA Fragments*

As well as PCR, another way to get a DNA fragment from an organism's DNA is by using **restriction enzymes**:

1) Some sections of DNA have **palindromic** sequences of **nucleotides**. These sequences consist of **antiparallel base pairs** (base pairs that read the **same in opposite directions**).

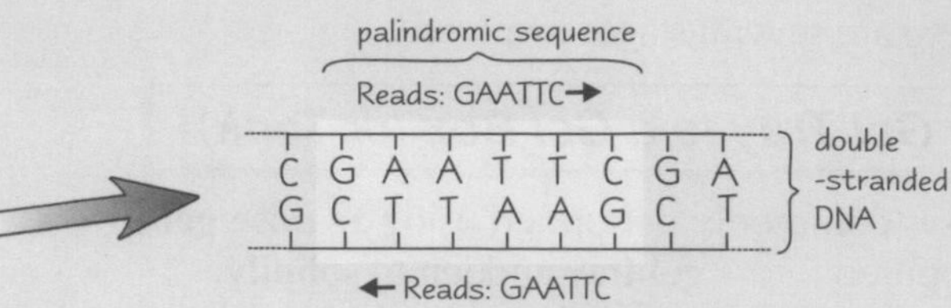

2) **Restriction enzymes** are enzymes that **recognise specific** palindromic sequences (known as **recognition sequences**) and **cut (digest)** the DNA at these places.
3) Different restriction enzymes cut at **different specific** recognition sequences, because the **shape** of the recognition sequence is **complementary** to an enzyme's **active site**. E.g. the restriction enzyme *Eco*RI cuts at GAATTC, but *Hind*III cuts at AAGCTT.
4) If recognition sequences are present at **either side** of the DNA fragment you want, you can use restriction enzymes to **separate** it from the rest of the DNA.
5) The DNA sample is **incubated** with the specific restriction enzyme, which **cuts** the DNA fragment out via a **hydrolysis reaction**.
6) Sometimes the cut leaves **sticky ends** — **small tails** of **unpaired bases** at **each end** of the fragment. Sticky ends can be used to **bind (anneal)** the DNA fragment to another piece of DNA that has sticky ends with **complementary sequences**.

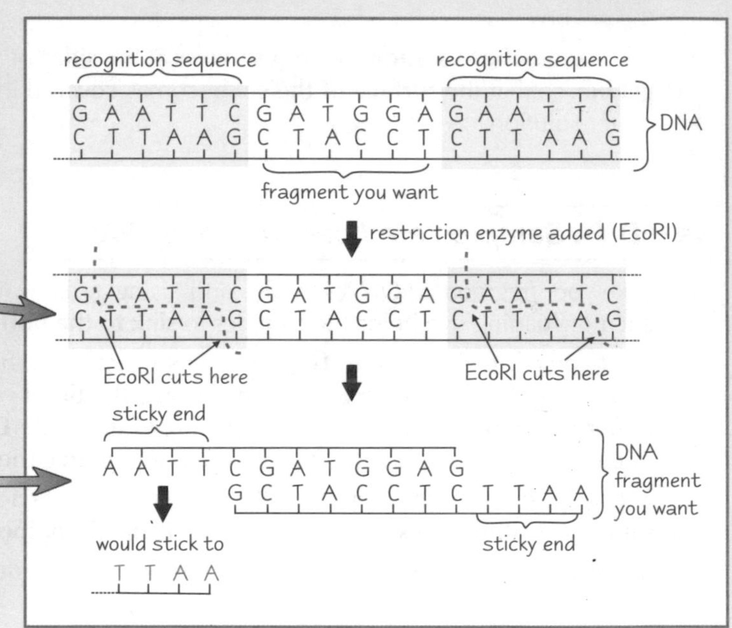

Practice Questions

Q1 What does 'PCR' stand for?

Q2 By what feature does electrophoresis separate DNA fragments?

Q3 During electrophoresis, which electrode do DNA fragments move towards? Explain why.

Q4 Describe how and why the procedure used to separate proteins by electrophoresis is slightly different from the procedure used to separate nucleic acids by electrophoresis.

Q5 What are restriction enzymes?

Exam Question

Q1* In the EU there is a ban on the import and export of any products made from dog fur. Authorities enforcing the ban only need to analyse DNA from a single hair found within a product they suspect to contain dog fur, to identify if the product is illegal.
Describe and explain a procedure that allows scientists to successfully isolate and amplify DNA from such a small original sample. [6 marks]

* You will be assessed on the quality of your written response in this question.

Sticky ends — for once a name that actually makes sense...

Okay, your eyes might have gone funny from seeing so many nucleotides on these pages. But once you've recovered, it's really important to go over these pages as many times as you need to 'cause examiners love throwing in a few questions about PCR or restriction enzymes. Bless 'em — examiners get excited about the strangest things.

DNA Profiling

It's time to see how some of the techniques used to study genes are used in DNA profiling...

Electrophoresis is Used to Produce *DNA Profiles*

1) Some of an organism's **genome** (all the genetic material in an organism) consists of **repetitive**, **non-coding base sequences** — sequences that **don't code** for proteins and **repeat** over and over (sometimes thousands of times).
2) The **number of times** these non-coding sequences are **repeated differs** from person to person, so the **length** of these sequences in nucleotides differs too.
3) The **number** of times a **sequence is repeated** at **different, specific places** (**loci**) in a person's genome (and so the number of nucleotides there) can be analysed using **electrophoresis**. This creates a **DNA profile**.
4) The **probability** of **two individuals** having the **same** DNA profile is **very low** because the **chance** of **two individuals** having the **same number** of sequence repeats at **each locus** in DNA is **very low**.

DNA Profiling can be Used in *Forensic Science...*

Forensic scientists use DNA profiling to **compare** samples of **DNA** collected from **crime scenes** (e.g. DNA from **blood**, **semen**, **skin cells**, **saliva**, **hair** etc.) to samples of DNA from **possible suspects**, to **link them** to crime scenes.

1) The **DNA** is **isolated** from all the collected samples (from the crime scene and from the suspects).
2) **PCR** (see p. 84) is used to amplify multiple areas containing different sequence repeats — primers are used to bind to either side of these repeats and so the whole repeat is amplified.
3) The **PCR products** are run on an **electrophoresis gel** and the DNA profiles produced are **compared** to see if any **match** (i.e. if they have the **same pattern** of bands on the gel).
4) If the samples match, it **links** a **person** to the **crime scene**. E.g. this gel shows that the DNA profile from **suspect C matches** that from the crime scene, **linking** them to the crime scene. All five bands match, so suspect C has the **same number** of repeats (nucleotides) at **five** different places.

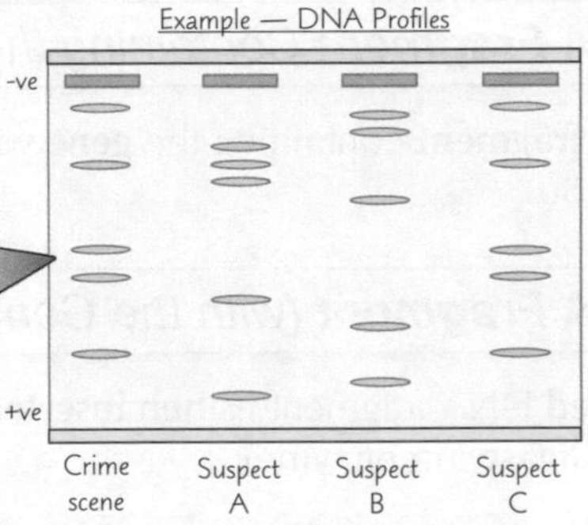

Example — DNA Profiles

-ve

+ve

Crime scene | Suspect A | Suspect B | Suspect C

Electrophoresis could also be used in this way to see if two DNA samples have come from the **same species** (i.e. the more similar the pattern of bands, the more likely the samples are from the same species).

...and Medical Diagnosis

1) In medical diagnosis, a DNA profile can refer to a **unique pattern** of **several alleles**.
2) It can be used to **analyse the risk of genetic disorders**. It's useful when the **specific** mutation **isn't** known or where **several mutations** could have caused the disorder, because it identifies a **broader**, **altered** genetic pattern.

EXAMPLE

Preimplantation genetic haplotyping (**PGH**) **screens embryos** created by **IVF** for genetic disorders **before** they're **implanted** into the uterus. The **faulty regions** of the **parents' DNA** are used to produce **DNA profiles**, which are **compared** to the DNA profile of the **embryo**. If the profiles **match**, the embryo has **inherited** the **disorder**. It can be used to screen for **cystic fibrosis**, **Huntington's disease** etc.

Practice Questions

Q1 Briefly describe what a DNA profile is.

Q2 Outline how DNA profiling can be used to identify the risk of an IVF baby being born with a genetic disorder.

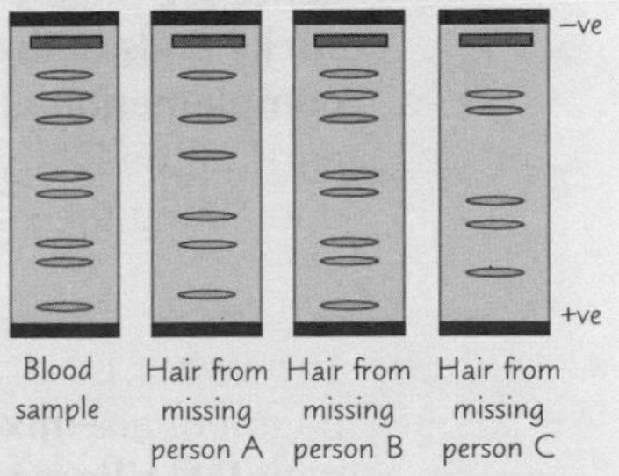

-ve

+ve

Blood sample | Hair from missing person A | Hair from missing person B | Hair from missing person C

Exam Question

Q1 Forensic detectives have discovered blood at a crime scene. They suspect the blood may belong to one of three local missing people. Using the blood, and hair samples gained from the missing people's personal belongings, they produce the DNA profiles above.

a) Describe how a DNA profile is made. [3 marks]

b) Explain which missing person the blood is most likely to belong to. [1 mark]

The Carpenters and The Doors — that's two bands that match...

DNA profiling is pretty fascinating. It's amazing that scientists have learnt how to chop up DNA, make squillions of copies of it, subject it to an electrical current and use the results to fight crime or identify disease risk. Science is fab.*

**Criminals may disagree.*

Genetic Engineering

Genetic engineering — you need to know what it is and how it's done... (unlucky)...

Genetic Engineering is the Manipulation of an Organism's DNA

1) Organisms that have had their **DNA altered** by genetic engineering are called **transformed organisms.**
2) These organisms have **recombinant DNA — DNA** formed by **joining together** DNA from **different sources.**
3) Genetic engineering usually involves **extracting** a **gene** from **one organism** and then **inserting** it **into another organism** (often one that's a **different species**).
4) Genes can also be **manufactured** instead of extracted from an organism.
5) The organism with the inserted gene will then **produce the protein** coded for by that gene.
6) An organism that has been genetically engineered to include a **gene** from a **different species** is sometimes called a **transgenic organism.**

Transformed organisms are also known as genetically engineered or genetically modified organisms.

You Need to Know How Genetic Engineering is Carried Out

1 The DNA Fragment Containing the Desired Gene is Obtained

The **DNA fragment** containing the **gene you want** is isolated using **restriction enzymes** (see page 86).

2 The DNA Fragment (with the Gene in) is Inserted into a Vector

The **isolated** DNA fragment is then **inserted into** a **vector** using **restriction enzymes** and **DNA ligase** (an enzyme):

1) The DNA fragment is inserted into vector DNA — a **vector** is something that's used to **transfer DNA** into a **cell**. They can be **plasmids** (**small**, **circular molecules** of DNA in **bacteria**) or **bacteriophages** (**viruses** that **infect** bacteria).

2) The vector DNA is **cut open** using the **same** restriction enzyme that was used to **isolate** the DNA fragment containing the desired gene (see page 86). So the **sticky ends** of the vector are **complementary** to the sticky ends of the DNA fragment containing the gene.

3) The vector DNA and DNA fragment are **mixed together** with **DNA ligase**. DNA ligase **joins** up the **sugar-phosphate backbones** of the two bits. This process is called **ligation**.

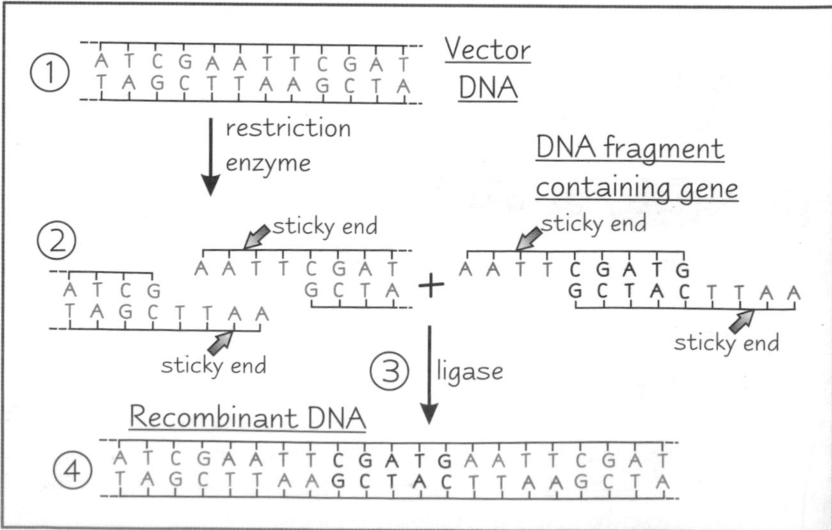

4) The new combination of bases in the DNA (vector DNA + DNA fragment) is called **recombinant DNA.**

Genetic Engineering

3 The Vector Transfers the Gene into the Bacteria

1) The **vector** with the **recombinant DNA** is used to **transfer** the gene into the **bacterial cells**.
2) If a **plasmid vector** is used, the bacterial cells have to be **persuaded** to **take in** the plasmid vector and its DNA:

For example...

- A suspension of the **bacterial cells** is **mixed** with the **plasmid vector** and placed in a machine called an **electroporator**.
- The machine is switched on and an **electrical field** is created in the mixture, which increases the **permeability** of the **bacterial cell membranes** and allows them to **take in** the plasmids.
- This technique is called **electroporation**.

3) With a **bacteriophage** vector, the bacteriophage will **infect** the bacterium by **injecting** its **DNA** into it. The phage DNA (with the desired gene in it) then **integrates** into the bacterial DNA.
4) **Cells** that **take up** the vectors containing the desired gene are genetically engineered, so are called **transformed**.

Practice Questions

Q1 What is the name for an organism that has had its DNA altered?

Q2 What is a vector?

Q3 Other than a plasmid, give an example of a vector.

Q4 Name the type of enzyme that can be used to cut DNA.

Q5 What is the name of the type of DNA formed from vector DNA and an inserted DNA fragment?

Exam Questions

Q1 Genetic engineering involves different enzymes and methods. Which of the following statement(s) is/are true?

Statement 1: DNA ligase is the enzyme used to isolate a DNA fragment from a sample of DNA.
Statement 2: A vector is something that's used to transfer DNA into a cell, e.g. a plasmid.
Statement 3: Electroporation is the technique used to increase the permeability of bacterial cell membranes so they will take up vectors.

A 1, 2 and 3 / B Only 1 and 2 / C Only 2 and 3 / D Only 1 [1 mark]

Q2 A scientist has genetically engineered some bacterial cells to contain the yellow fluorescent protein (YFP) gene, using a plasmid vector. YFP can be visualised under UV light. The cells were grown on an agar plate, which was then studied under a UV light. The results are shown below.

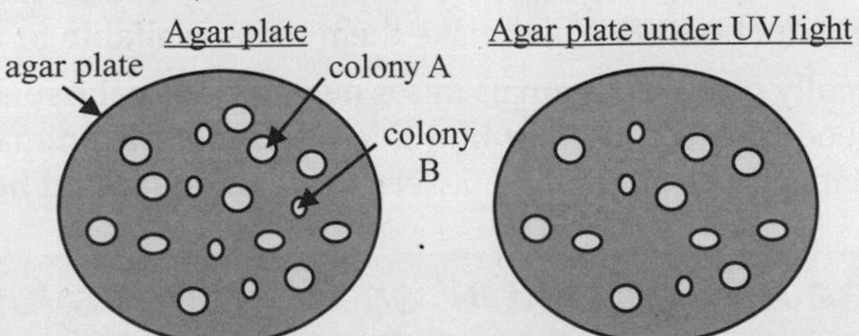

a) Explain why the scientist thinks colony A contains transformed bacterial cells, but colony B doesn't. [2 marks]
b) Explain how the scientist might have inserted the YFP gene into the plasmid. [3 marks]
c) Explain how and why the scientist would have used electroporation during the process. [3 marks]

Transformed parents — made to stop nagging at you to revise...

This stuff might seem tricky the first time you read it, but it's not too bad once you've gone over it a few times. Basically you get the gene you want and bung it in a vector, and the vector gets the gene into the cell (it's kind of like a delivery boy). Easy peasy. Unfortunately you need to know each stage in detail, so get learnin'.

Genetically Modified Organisms

Genetic engineering can be used to benefit humans in loads of different ways. But when scientists are fiddling about with organisms and genes, there are bound to be ethical issues involved...

Genetic Engineering Can be Used to Create **Insect-Resistance** in **Plants**

One way in which plants can be **genetically manipulated** is by having a **gene** inserted into their cells which makes them **resistant** to **insect pests**. For example:

1) **Soybeans** are an important food source across the world, but yields of soybeans can be **greatly reduced** by **insect pests** that feed on the soybean plants.
2) Scientists have successfully **genetically modified** soybean plants to include a **gene** originally found in the bacteria ***Bacillus thuringiensis*** (***Bt***). The gene codes for a **protein** that is **toxic** to some of the **insects** that **feed** on soybean plants.
3) To genetically modify a soybean plant, the **desired gene** can be isolated from *Bt* using **restriction enzymes** and inserted into a **plasmid** taken from the bacterium ***Agrobacterium tumefaciens***. The plasmid is put back into *A. tumefaciens* and then soybean plant cells are deliberately **infected** with the transformed bacteria. The desired gene gets inserted into the soybean plant cells' **DNA**, creating a **genetically modified** (GM) plant.
4) There are **positive ethical issues** concerning GM plants — for example, they will reduce the amount of **chemical pesticides** that farmers use on their crops, which can **harm** the **environment**.
5) But there are also **negative ethical issues** to consider. For example, farming GM soybean plants may encourage **monoculture** (where only one type of crop is planted). Monoculture **decreases biodiversity** and could leave the **whole crop vulnerable** to **disease**, because all the plants are **genetically identical**.

Genetic Engineering Can be Used to Produce **Drugs** from **Animals**

1) Many **pharmaceuticals** (**medicinal drugs**) are produced using **genetically modified organisms**, such as animals. This is called '**pharming**'. For example:
   - **Hereditary antithrombin deficiency** is a disorder that makes **blood clots** more likely to form in the body. The risk of developing blood clots in people with this disorder can be reduced with **infusions** of the protein **antithrombin**.
   - Scientists have developed a way to produce **high yields** of this protein using **goats**.
   - Initially, **DNA fragments** that code for production of human antithrombin in the mammary glands are **injected** into a **goat embryo**.
   - The embryo is **implanted** into a **female goat**, and when the **offspring** is born it is **tested** to see if it produces the antithrombin protein. If it does, **selective breeding** is used to produce a **herd** of goats that produce antithrombin in their **milk**.
   - The protein is **extracted** from the milk and used to produce a **drug** (ATryn®) that can be given to people with hereditary antithrombin deficiency.
2) There are **positive ethical issues** with 'pharming' — drugs made this way can be made in **large quantities** compared to other methods of production. This can make them more **available** to more people.
3) However, the creation of genetically modified animals raises **negative ethical issues**. For example, there is **concern** that manipulating an animal's genes could cause **harmful side-effects** for the animal, and that using an animal in this way is enforcing the idea that animals are merely 'assets' that can be **treated however we choose**.

Genetic Engineering Can be Carried Out on **Pathogens** for **Research**

Scientists are carrying out **research** into **genetically engineered pathogens** (microorganisms that cause disease, such as viruses) in order to find **treatments** for **disease**. For example:

1) Scientists found that some **tumour cells** have **receptors** on their membranes for the **poliovirus** — so the poliovirus will **recognise** and **attack** them.
2) By **genetically engineering** the poliovirus to **inactivate** the **genes** that cause **poliomyelitis**, scientists can use it to **attack and kill** cancer cells **without** causing disease. This may lead to a **treatment** for cancer.

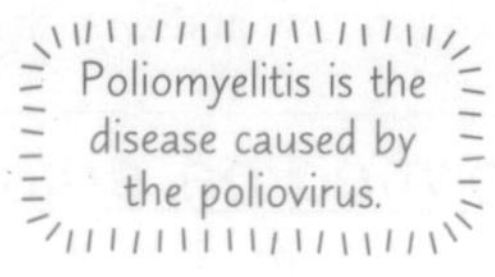

Genetically Modified Organisms

Genetic Engineering of **Pathogens** Raises **Ethical Issues**

1) The genetic modification of pathogens to help cure disease has obvious **positive ethical issues** — e.g. it could mean that **previously untreatable** diseases can now be **treated**, reducing the suffering they would cause.
2) However, there are many possible **negative ethical issues** as well. For example, people worry that:
   - the scientists researching the pathogens could become **infected** with the live pathogen and potentially cause a **mass outbreak of disease**.
   - the genetically modified version of a pathogen could **revert back** to its **original form** and cause an **outbreak of disease**.
   - in the wrong hands, knowledge of how to genetically engineer **dangerous pathogens** could be used **maliciously** to create agents for **biowarfare**.

   Researchers using live pathogens have to follow **strict protocols**, which makes the chance of any of these things happening **very, very low**.

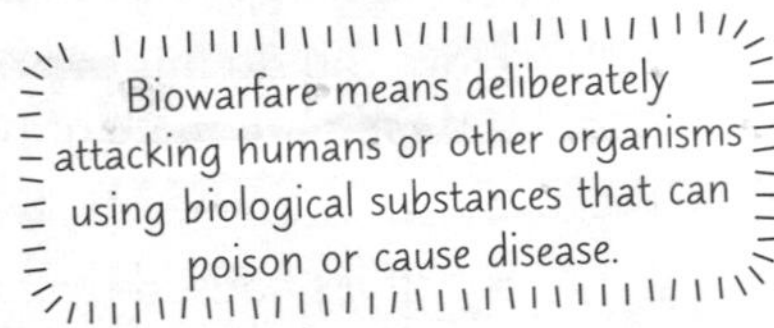

Genetically Engineered Organisms can be **'Owned'** by Big Companies

1) Many scientists around the world are working on techniques to **improve** and **advance** genetic engineering.
2) Scientists working for **different institutions** often **share** their **knowledge** and **skills** in this field so that, globally, beneficial genetically modified products can be created at a **faster rate**. The sharing of knowledge, skills and technology like this is called **technology transfer**.
3) Although they share information, a group of scientists or the company they work for may want to obtain **legal protection** for their genetically modified products, e.g. by getting a patent. This means, **by law**, they can control **who** uses the product and **how** for a **set period of time**.
4) This raises some **positive ethical issues** — it means that the owner of the patent will get **money** generated from selling the product. This encourages scientists to **compete** to be the **first** to come up with a new, beneficial genetic engineering idea, so we get genetically engineered products **faster**.
5) But the process raises many **negative ethical issues** too. For example, **farmers in poorer countries** may not be able to **afford** patented genetically modified seeds. Even if they can afford seeds for one year, some patents mean that they are **not legally allowed** to plant and grow any of the seeds from that crop without **paying again**. Many people think this is **unfair** and that the big companies that own the patents should relax the rules to **help farmers in poorer countries**.

Practice Questions

Q1 What word is used to describe the process where animals are genetically modified to produce pharmaceuticals?

Q2 Give three negative ethical issues surrounding the genetic engineering of pathogens for research.

Q3 What is meant by the term 'technology transfer'?

Exam Question

Q1* Bromoxynil is a herbicide that many farmers spray on their crops to kill weeds. As well as weeds, bromoxynil also damages cotton plants. Some microorganisms, such as the bacterium *Klebsiella ozaenae*, naturally produce an enzyme that can convert bromoxynil to a harmless substance. A large company patented the gene responsible for this enzyme and, with the help of genetic engineering, bromoxynil-resistant cotton plants are now in existence.

Describe how genetic engineering may have been used in the creation of bromoxynil-resistant cotton plants and evaluate the ethical issues surrounding this crop. [6 marks]

* You will be assessed on the quality of your written response in this question.

Pig 'pharming' could produce some very useful oinkments...

Wow, scientists are really busy genetically engineering things aren't they? Plants, animals, microorganisms — they'll have a go at anything. And of course the reason they're doing it is to create products that can benefit our lives somehow, but there are also many negative ethical issues to consider. I reckon it's time to grab a cuppa and a biscuit while you ponder it all...

Gene Therapy

Genetic engineering doesn't have to stop at animals, plants and microorganisms — it could be done to humans too.

Gene Therapy Could be Used to Cure Genetic Disorders

Genetic disorders are **inherited disorders** caused by **abnormal genes** or **chromosomes**. **Gene therapy** could be used to **cure** these disorders — it **isn't** being used widely yet but there is a form of somatic gene therapy available, and other treatments are undergoing **clinical trials**.

See page 68 for more on dominant and recessive alleles.

1) Gene therapy involves altering alleles inside cells to cure genetic disorders.
2) How you do this depends on whether the genetic disorder is caused by a dominant allele or two recessive alleles:
   - If it's caused by two **recessive** alleles you can **add** a working **dominant allele** to make up for them.
   - If it's caused by a **dominant** allele you can '**silence**' the **dominant allele** (e.g. by sticking a bit of DNA in the middle of the allele so it doesn't work any more).
3) To get the 'new' allele (DNA) inside the cell, the allele is **inserted into cells using vectors**.
4) Different **vectors** can be used, e.g. altered **viruses**, **plasmids** or **liposomes** (spheres made of lipid).
5) There are **two types** of gene therapy:
   - **Somatic therapy** — this involves **altering** the **alleles** in **body cells**, particularly the cells that are **most affected** by the disorder. For example, **cystic fibrosis** (CF) is a genetic disorder that's very **damaging** to the **respiratory system**, so somatic therapy for CF **targets** the epithelial cells lining the lungs. Somatic therapy doesn't affect the individual's **sex cells** (sperm or eggs) though, so any **offspring** could **inherit** the disease.
   - **Germ line therapy** — this involves **altering** the **alleles** in the **sex cells**. This means that **every cell** of **any offspring** produced from these cells will be **affected by** the gene therapy and they **won't inherit the disease**. Germ line therapy in humans is currently **illegal** though.

There are Positive and Negative Ethical Issues Surrounding Gene Therapy

Positive Ethical Issues

- It could prolong the lives of people with genetic disorders.
- It could give people with genetic disorders a better quality of life.
- Carriers of genetic disorders might be able to conceive a baby without that disorder or risk of cancer (only in germ line therapy).
- It could decrease the number of people that suffer from genetic disorders (only in germ line therapy).

Negative Ethical Issues

- The technology could potentially be used in ways **other** than for **medical treatment**, such as for treating the **cosmetic effects** of **ageing**.
- There's the potential to do **more harm** than good by using the technology (e.g. risk of overexpression of genes — see below).
- There's concern that gene therapy is **expensive** — some people believe that **health service resources** could be **better spent** on other treatments that have passed clinical trials.

There are other potential **disadvantages** of gene therapy too:

- The effects of the treatment may be **short–lived** (only in somatic therapy).
- The patient might have to undergo **multiple treatments** (only in somatic therapy).
- It might be **difficult** to get the allele into **specific** body cells.
- The body could identify vectors as **foreign bodies** and start an **immune response** against them.
- An allele could be inserted into the **wrong place** in the DNA, possibly causing **more problems**, e.g. cancer.
- An inserted allele could get **overexpressed**, producing too much of the missing protein.

Practice Question

Q1 Give three negative ethical issues surrounding gene therapy.

Exam Question

Q1 A patient with cystic fibrosis was offered gene therapy targeted at his lung epithelial cells to help treat the disease.
   a) What does gene therapy involve? [1 mark]
   b) What type of gene therapy was the patient offered? [1 mark]

Germ line therapy — talking to a counsellor while in a queue at the doctors'...

Make sure you know about the two different types of gene therapy as well as all the positive and negative ethical issues.

Sequencing Genes and Genomes

Scientists have been able to sequence genes since the 1970s, but over time advancements in technology have made the process ever slicker. Some of the basic principles are still the same though, so it's helpful to take a look at how things used to be done before thinking about how things are done nowadays...

DNA can be Sequenced by the Chain-Termination Method

The **chain-termination method** was one of the first methods used to determine the **order** of **bases** in a section of **DNA**:

1) The following mixture is added to **four separate** tubes:
   - A **single-stranded DNA template** — the DNA to sequence.
   - Lots of **DNA primer** — short pieces of DNA (see p. 84).
   - **DNA polymerase** — the enzyme that joins DNA nucleotides together.
   - **Free nucleotides** — lots of free A, T, C and G nucleotides.
   - **Fluorescently-labelled modified nucleotide** — like a normal nucleotide, but once it's added to a DNA strand, **no more** bases can be added after it. A **different** modified nucleotide is added to **each** tube (**A***, **T***, **C***, **G***).
2) The tubes undergo **PCR**, which produces many **strands of DNA**. The strands are **different lengths** because each one **terminates** at a **different point** depending on where the modified nucleotide was added.
3) For example, in tube A (with the **modified adenine** nucleotide A*) sometimes A* is **added** to the DNA at point 4 **instead** of A, **stopping** the **addition** of any more bases (the strand is **terminated**). Sometimes A is added at point 4, then **A*** is added at **point 5**. Sometimes A is added at **point 4**, A again at point 5, G at point 6 and **A*** is added at **point 7**. So strands of **three different lengths** (4 bases, 5 bases and 7 bases) all ending in **A*** are produced.
4) The DNA fragments in each tube are separated by **electrophoresis** and **visualised** under **UV light** (because of the **fluorescent label**).
5) The **complementary base sequence** can be **read** from the gel. The **smallest** nucleotide (e.g. one base) is at the **bottom** of the gel. Each band after this represents **one more base** added. So by reading the bands **from the bottom** of the gel **to the top**, you can build up the **DNA sequence** one base at a time.

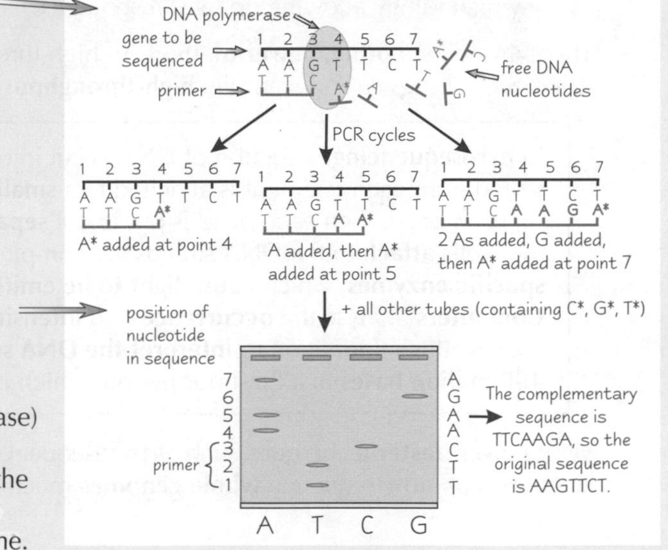

Gene Sequencing Techniques can be Used to Sequence Whole Genomes

The **chain-termination method** only works on fragments up to about **750 bp** long. So if you want to sequence the **entire genome** (all the DNA) of an organism using this method, you need to chop it up into **smaller pieces** first. The smaller pieces are **sequenced** and then **put back in order** to give the sequence of the whole genome. Here's how it's done:

1) A genome is **cut** into **smaller fragments** (about 100 000 bp) using **restriction enzymes**.
2) The fragments are inserted into **bacterial artificial chromosomes** (**BACs**) — these are **man-made plasmids**. **Each** fragment is inserted into a **different BAC**.
3) The BACs are then **inserted** into **bacteria** — **each bacterium** contains a **BAC** with a **different DNA fragment**.
4) The bacteria **divide**, creating **colonies** of **cloned** (**identical**) cells that all contain a **specific DNA fragment**. Together the different colonies make a complete **genomic DNA library**.
5) **DNA** is **extracted** from **each colony** and **cut** up using restriction enzymes, producing **overlapping** pieces of DNA.
6) Each piece of DNA is **sequenced**, using the **chain-termination method**, and the pieces are **put back in order** to give the full sequence **from that BAC** (using **powerful computer systems**).
7) Finally the DNA fragments from **all the BACs** are **put back in order**, by computers, to **complete** the **entire genome**.

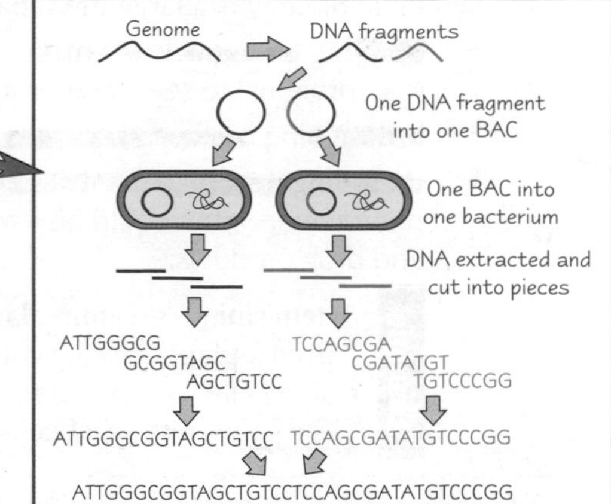

Sequencing Genes and Genomes

Faster, Whole Genome Sequencing Techniques Have Been Developed

1) Continued **research** and **improvements** in **modern technology** have led to **rapid advancements** in the field of gene sequencing.
2) The chain-termination technique described on the previous page is still commonly used but it has become **automated** and is **faster** — nowadays the tube contains **all** the modified nucleotides, each with a different coloured **fluorescent label**, and a **machine** reads the sequence for you. So instead of running a gel and determining the sequence from that, you get a **computer read-out**.

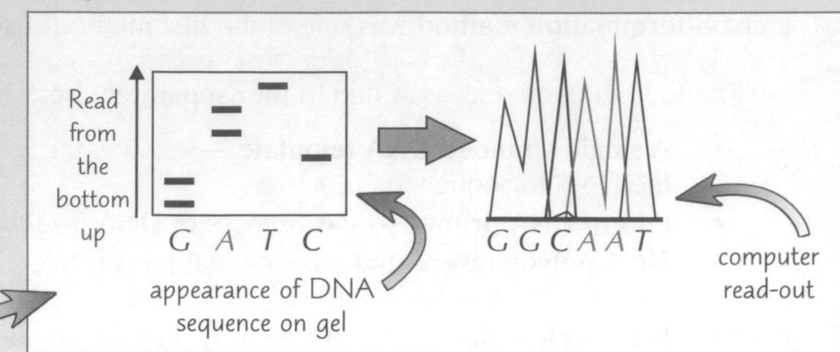

3) Further advances in the field have also led to **high-throughput sequencing** — techniques that can sequence a lot **faster** than original methods (e.g. up to 1000 times more bases in a given time), at a **fraction of the cost**. For example, the chain-termination technique has been made high-throughput by new technology allowing up to 384 sequences to be run **in parallel**.
4) There are several **other, newer methods** of high-throughput sequencing being used too, some of which don't use electrophoresis. For example, **high-throughput pyrosequencing** is a **recently developed** technique:

In **pyrosequencing**, a section of DNA is cut into **fragments**, split into **single strands** and then a strand from each fragment is attached to a **small bead**. **PCR** is used to **amplify** the DNA fragments on each bead, then each bead is put into a **separate well**. Next, **free nucleotides** added to the wells **attach** to the DNA strands via complementary base pairing. The wells also contain **specific enzymes**, which cause **light to be emitted** when bases are added to the DNA strand. **Computers** analyse the **occurrence** and **intensities** of the light emitted in the different wells, and process this information to **interpret the DNA sequence**. This technique can sequence around **400 million bases** in a ten-hour period (which is **super fast** compared to older techniques).

5) With **newer**, **faster** techniques such as pyrosequencing available, scientists can now sequence **whole genomes** much more **quickly**.

Sequencing Genes Shows Polypeptide Structure and Aids Synthetic Biology

1) You might remember from Module 2 that **amino acids** are coded for by **triplets of bases** in a gene.
2) This means that by sequencing a gene, the **sequence** of **amino acids** that a gene **codes for** and so the **primary structure** of a **polypeptide** can be predicted.
3) This has allowed us to create **biological molecules** from scratch and so has led to the development of an area of biology called '**synthetic biology**'.
4) Synthetic biology is a **large field** that includes:
   - **building** biological systems from **artificially made molecules** (e.g. proteins) to see whether they work in the way we think they do.
   - **redesigning** biological systems to **perform better** and include **new molecules**.
   - **designing new** biological systems and molecules that **don't exist** in the natural world, but could be **useful** to humans, e.g. energy products (fuels) and drug products.

Synthetic biology is different from genetic engineering — genetic engineering involves the direct transfer of DNA from one organism to another, whereas in synthetic biology DNA is created from scratch.

Example

Artemisinin is an **antimalarial drug** — until recently we got artemisinin by extracting it from a **plant**. Using **synthetic biology**, scientists have created all the **genes** responsible for producing a **precursor** to artemisinin. They've successfully inserted these genes into **yeast cells**, so we can now use yeast to help produce artemisinin.

Sequencing Genes and Genomes

Sequenced Genes and Genomes can be Compared

Gene sequences and **whole genome** sequences can be compared **between** organisms of **different species** and between organisms of the **same species**. This is a complicated process which is made easier with the use of computers — it involves **computational biology** (using computers to study biology, e.g. to create computer simulations and mathematical models) and **bioinformatics** (developing and using computer software that can analyse, organise and store biological data). There are many reasons why **biological research** can involve comparison of gene sequences and genomes, e.g.:

To study genotype-phenotype relationships

1) Sometimes it's useful to be able to predict an organism's **phenotype** by analysing its **genotype**.
2) For example, **Marfan syndrome** is a **genetic disorder** caused by a **mutation** of the ***FBN1* gene**. The position and nature of the mutation on the gene affects what **symptoms** a person with Marfan syndrome will experience (e.g. they could get a number of problems associated with their vision, cardiovascular system or muscles). Scientists have **sequenced** the *FBN1* gene of **many people** with Marfan syndrome and documented this along with details of their **phenotype**. **Bioinformatics** has allowed the scientists to **compare** all the data and identify **genotype-phenotype correlations** — this could help in the **treatment** of Marfan syndrome by using **gene sequencing** to predict what health problems the person is likely to face.

In epidemiological studies

Epidemiology is the study of **health and disease** within a population — it considers the **distribution** of a disease, its **causes** and its **effects**. Some gene mutations have been linked to a greater risk of **disease** (e.g. mutations in the *BRCA1* gene are linked to breast cancer). **Computerised comparisons** between the genomes of people that have a disease and those that don't can be used to detect **particular mutations** that could be responsible for the increased risk of disease.

To help understand evolutionary relationships

1) **All** organisms **evolved** from **shared common ancestors** (relatives). **Closely related** species **evolved** away from each other **more recently** and so **share more DNA**. Whole genomes of different species can be sequenced and then analysed using **computer software** to tell us **how closely related** different species are. E.g. the genomes of **humans** and **chimpanzees** are about **94%** similar.
2) **Comparing** the **genomes** of members of the **same species** can also **tell us about evolutionary relationships**. For example, when different groups of early **humans separated** and **moved** to different parts of the world, their genomes **changed** in **slightly different ways**. By **using computers to compare** the genomes of people from different parts of the world, it's possible to build up a picture of early human migration.

Look, when we stick our tongues out like this you can just TELL we're related, we don't need a genome comparison.

Practice Questions

Q1 What is a bacterial artificial chromosome?

Q2 How can gene sequencing be used to predict a protein's primary structure?

Q3 Give three uses of synthetic biology.

Q4 What is meant by the terms 'bioinformatics' and 'computational biology'?

Exam Questions

Q1 To sequence a small DNA fragment using the chain-termination technique, a single-stranded DNA template is needed.

a) Name the other four reactants needed for a sequencing reaction using this method. [4 marks]

b) The chain-termination technique has been adapted to be high-throughput. Give two advantages of the high-throughput technique over the original technique. [2 marks]

Q2 Researchers are trying to establish how closely related two different bacterial species are. Suggest how they could do this. [2 marks]

Sequincing — so 80s...

Don't worry the buzzing in your head is normal — information overload. Have a break, then go over some of the difficult bits in this section again. Believe me, the more times you go over it the more things will click into place.

Plant Cloning

Plant cloning is probably more common than you think. These pages tell you all you need to know for your exam.

Some Plants can Produce Natural Clones by Vegetative Propagation

Cloning is the process of producing **genetically identical cells** or **organisms** from the cells of an **existing organism**. Cloning can occur **naturally** in some **plants** and **animals**, but it can also be carried out **artificially**.

Vegetative propagation is the production of plant **clones** from **non-reproductive tissues**, e.g. roots, leaves and stems. The table below describes some of the **natural vegetative propagation** methods that plants use:

Method	Description	Example of plant using method
Rhizomes	Rhizomes are stem structures that grow horizontally underground away from the parent plant. They have 'nodes' from which new shoots and roots can develop.	Bamboo
Stolons (also called runners)	Stolons are pretty similar to rhizomes. The main difference is that they grow above ground, on the surface of the soil. New shoots and roots can either develop from nodes (like in rhizomes) or form at the end of the stolon.	Strawberries
Suckers	Suckers are shoots that grow from sucker buds (undeveloped shoots) present on the shallow roots of a parent plant.	Elm trees
Tubers	Tubers are large underground plant structures that act as a food store for the plant. They're covered in 'eyes'. Each eye is able to sprout and form a new plant.	Potatoes
Bulbs	Bulbs are also underground food stores used by some plants. New bulbs are able to develop from the original bulb and form new individual plants.	Onions

Horticulturists (plant growers) use other 'natural' methods of **vegetative propagation** to produce **clones**. The methods include taking **cuttings** (see below), **grafting** (joining the **shoot** of **one plant** to the **growing stem** and **root** of **another plant**) and **layering** (**bending** a **stem** of a **growing plant** downwards so it **enters** the **soil** and grows into a **new plant**).

You Need to Know How to Produce a Clone From a Cutting

Growing plants from **cuttings** is a really simple way to make clones of a **parent plant**. You can take cuttings from **different parts** of a plant, e.g. a stem, root or leaf. Here's how a cutting can be taken and grown from a **stem**:

Example: Taking and growing a cutting from a stem

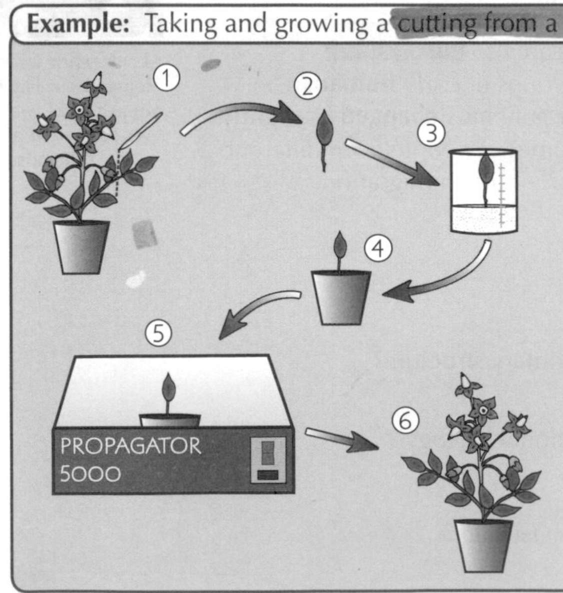

① Use a **scalpel** or **sharp secateurs** to **take** a **cutting**, between **5 cm** and **10 cm** long, from the end of a **stem** of your **parent plant**.

② **Remove** the **leaves** from the **lower** end of your cutting (if there are any), leaving just one at the tip.

③ **Dip** the **lower end** of the cutting in **rooting powder**, which contains **hormones** that induce **root formation**.

④ Then **plant** your **cutting** in a **pot containing** a suitable **growth medium** (e.g. well-drained compost).

⑤ Provide your cutting with a **warm** and **moist environment** by either covering the whole pot with a **plastic bag** or by putting it in a **propagator** (a specialised piece of kit that provides these conditions).

⑥ When your cutting has **formed** its **own roots** and is **strong enough**, you can **plant** it **elsewhere** to continue growing.

Here are examples of how you could take and grow cuttings from a **root** or **leaf**:

- To take a **root cutting**, cut a **piece** of root from the plant with a **straight cut** using a **scalpel** or **secateurs**. Then **remove** the **uncut** end of the root with a **slanted cut**. Dip the end of the cutting in **rooting powder** and **plant** it in a suitable **growth medium**. Then follow **steps 5** and **6** from the example above.
- A popular type of **leaf cutting** (known as a **split vein** cutting) involves **removing** a **complete leaf** and **scoring** the **large veins** on the **lower** leaf surface using a scalpel. You then put it **on top** of the **growth medium** with the **broken veins facing down** and then follow **steps 5** and **6** from above. A **new plant** should form from **each break** in the veins.

scalpel
scored vein

Plant Cloning

Plants can be Artificially Cloned using Tissue Culture

Plants can be **artificially cloned** from existing plants using a technique called **tissue culture**. Here's how it's done:

1) **Cells** are **taken from** the original **plant** that's going to be cloned.
2) Cells from the **stem** and **root tips** are used because they're **stem cells** — like in humans, plant stem cells can develop into **any type of cell**.
3) The cells are **sterilised** to kill any **microorganisms** — bacteria and fungi **compete** for nutrients with the **plant cells**, which **decreases** their **growth rate**.
4) The cells are placed on a **culture medium** containing plant **nutrients** (like **glucose** for **respiration**) and **growth hormones** (such as **auxins**).
5) When the cells have **divided** and **grown** into a **small plant** they're taken out of the medium and **planted in soil** — they'll develop into plants that are **genetically identical** to the **original plant**.

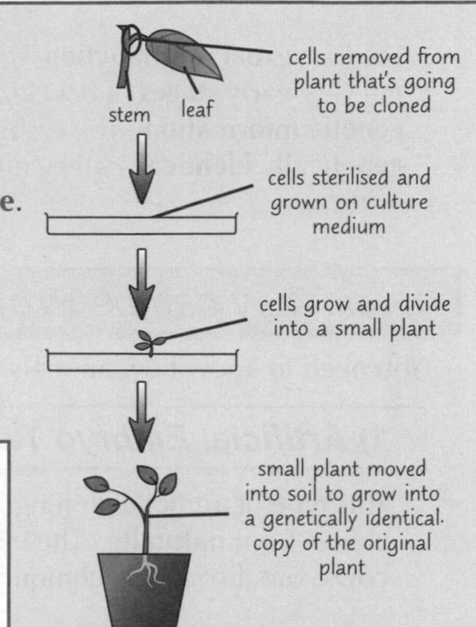

1) Tissue culture is used to clone plants that **don't readily reproduce** or are **endangered** or **rare**, e.g. British orchids.
2) It's also used to grow **whole plants** from **genetically engineered plant cells**.
3) **Micropropagation** is when **tissue culture** is used to produce **lots** of cloned plants **very quickly**. **Cells** are taken from developing cloned plants and **subcultured** (grown on another fresh culture medium) — repeating this process creates **large numbers of clones**. This technique is used extensively in **horticulture** and **agriculture**, e.g. to produce fields full of a crop that has been genetically engineered to be pest-resistant.

Agriculture and horticulture both involve cultivating plants — agriculture generally relates to farming (i.e. using land to grow crops for human use or consumption) whereas horticulture can involve the cultivation of any plant for any purpose, but usually on a smaller scale, e.g. for gardening.

There are Arguments For and Against Artificial Plant Cloning

You need to be able to **evaluate** the uses of **tissue culture** in **agriculture** and **horticulture** — this handy list of arguments **for** and **against** tissue culture should help you:

Arguments For

- **Desirable genetic characteristics** (e.g. high fruit production) are **always passed on** to clones. This **doesn't always** happen when plants **reproduce sexually**.
- Tissue culture allows plants to be reproduced in **any season** because the environment is controlled.
- **Less space** is required by **tissue culture** than would be needed to produce the **same** number of plants by conventional growing methods.
- It produces **lots** of plants **quickly** compared to the time it would take to **grow** them from **seeds**.

Arguments Against

- **Undesirable genetic characteristics** (e.g. producing fruit with lots of seeds) are **always passed on** to clones.
- **Cloned plant populations** have **no genetic variability**, so a **single disease** could **kill** them all.
- **Production costs** of tissue culture are **very high** due to **high energy use** and the **training** of skilled workers, so it's **unsuitable** for **small scale** production.
- **Contamination** by **microorganisms** during tissue culture can be **disastrous** and result in **complete loss** of the plants being cultured.

Practice Questions

Q1 What is vegetative propagation?

Exam Question

Q1 A scientist wants to produce a whole plant from a genetically engineered plant stem cell.
Describe how she could achieve this. [4 marks]

Plant cloning is a cheap way to fill up your garden...

... as long as you don't like variety. Make sure you know the many different methods that can be used to clone plants (both naturally and artificially) and are clued up on the arguments for and against using tissue culture.

Animal Cloning

It's not only plants that can be cloned — there are plenty of genetically identical animals knocking about too...

Animal Clones can Occur Naturally...

During **sexual reproduction**, once an egg has been **fertilised**, it's possible for it to **split** during the very **early stages** of development and **develop** into **multiple embryos** with the **same genetic information**. The embryos can develop as normal to produce **offspring** that are all **genetically identical** — they are **clones**. For example, **identical twins** are natural clones.

... or They can be Produced Artificially

You need to know how animals can be **artificially cloned** using these **two methods**:

1) Artificial Embryo Twinning

This type of artificial cloning is **similar** to what happens when animal clones form **naturally**. The example below shows how this is done in **cows**, but the **same** technique can be used for **other animals**:

① An **egg cell** is extracted from a female cow and **fertilised** in a Petri dish.

② The **fertilised egg** is left to **divide** at least once, forming an **embryo** *in vitro* (outside a living organism).

③ Next, the **individual cells** from the embryo are separated and each is put into a **separate** Petri dish. Each cell **divides** and **develops normally**, so an **embryo forms** in **each** Petri dish.

④ The embryos are then **implanted** into female cows, which act as **surrogate mothers**.

⑤ The **embryos continue to develop** inside the surrogate cows, and eventually the **offspring** are **born**. They're all **genetically identical** to each other.

The process could also be done using an early embryo extracted from a pregnant animal, rather than using an embryo created in the lab.

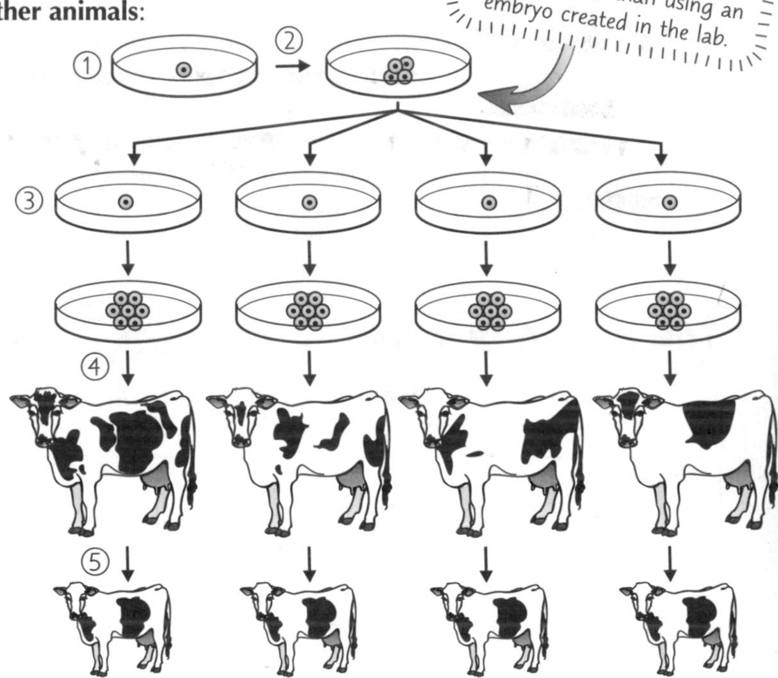

2) Somatic Cell Nuclear Transfer (SCNT)

This method is a bit more **high-tech**. This is how it's done in **sheep**, but again the method's the **same** for **other animals**:

1) A **somatic cell** (any cell that isn't a reproductive cell) is taken from sheep A. The **nucleus** is **extracted** and **kept**.
2) An **oocyte** (immature **egg cell**) is taken from sheep B. Its nucleus is **removed** to form an **enucleated oocyte**.
3) The nucleus from sheep A is **inserted** into the enucleated oocyte — the oocyte from **sheep B** now contains the **genetic information** from **sheep A**.
4) The nucleus and the enucleated oocyte are **fused together** and **stimulated** to **divide** (e.g. by electrofusion, where an electrical current is applied). This produces an **embryo**.
5) Then the embryo is **implanted** into a **surrogate mother** and eventually a **lamb** is born that's a **clone** of **sheep A**.

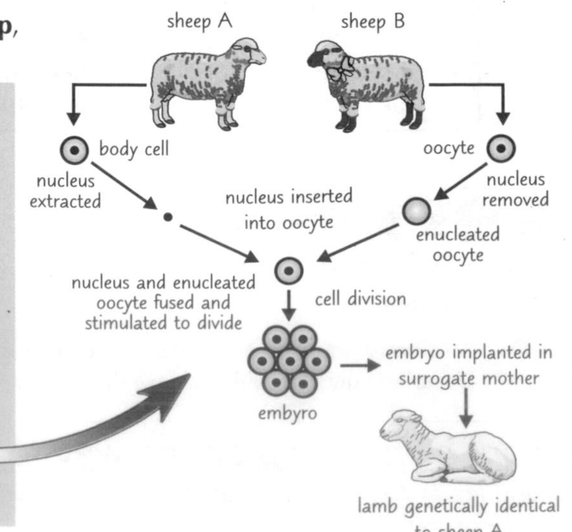

Animal Cloning

Animal Cloning has *Many Uses*

1) Scientists use cloned animals for **research purposes**, e.g. in the field of medicine they can **test new drugs** on cloned animals. They're all genetically identical, so the **variables** that come from **genetic differences** (e.g. the likelihood of developing cancer) are **removed**.
2) Cloning can be used to **save endangered animals** from **extinction** by cloning new individuals.
3) Cloning can also be used in agriculture so **farmers** can **increase** the **number** of animals with **desirable characteristics** to **breed from**, e.g. a prize-winning cow with high milk production could be cloned.
4) Animals that have been **genetically modified** (see page 90) to produce a **useful substance** that they wouldn't normally produce (e.g. a beneficial protein in their milk) could be cloned to produce **lots** of identical animals that all produce the same substance.
5) Cloning **doesn't** have to be used to make **whole** animals. Sometimes scientists only want the cloned **embryonic stem cells**. These cells are harvested from **young embryos** and have the **potential** to become **any cell type**, so scientists think they could be used to **replace damaged tissues** in a **range** of **diseases**, e.g. heart disease, spinal cord injuries, degenerative brain disorders like Parkinson's disease. If replacement tissue is made from cloned embryonic stem cells that are **genetically identical** to the **patient's own cells**, it **won't be rejected** by their immune system.

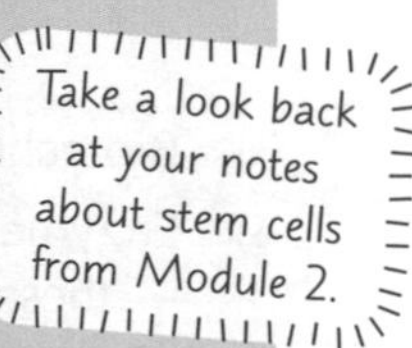

There are Arguments For and Against Animal Cloning

You might have to **evaluate** the **uses** of **animal cloning**, so you need to be aware of the arguments **for** and **against** the process:

Mirrors — the budget way to clone.

Arguments For

- **Desirable genetic characteristics** are **always passed on** to clones (e.g. high milk production in cows). This **doesn't always** happen with **sexual reproduction**.
- **Infertile animals** can be **reproduced**.
- **Increasing** the population of **endangered species** helps to **preserve biodiversity**.

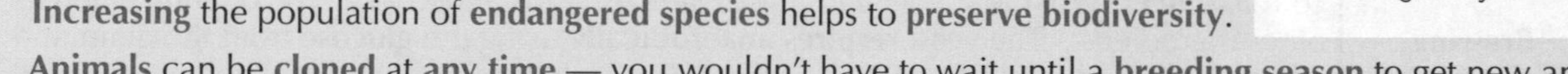

- **Animals** can be **cloned** at **any time** — you wouldn't have to wait until a **breeding season** to get new animals.
- Cloning can help us develop **new treatments** for disease, which could mean **less suffering** for some people.

- Animal cloning is very **difficult**, **time-consuming** and **expensive**.
- There's no **genetic variability** in cloned populations, so **undesirable genetic characteristics** (e.g. a weak immune system) are **always passed on** to clones. This means that all of the cloned animals in a population are **susceptible** to the **same diseases**. Potentially, a single disease could **wipe them all out**.
- Some evidence suggests that clones **may not live as long** as natural offspring. Some think this is **unethical**.
- Using **cloned human embryos** as a **source** of **stem cells** is controversial. The embryos are usually **destroyed** after the embryonic stem cells have been harvested — some people believe that doing this is **destroying a human life**.

Practice Questions

Q1 Describe how animal clones can occur naturally.

Q2 Describe how artificial embryo twinning is carried out.

Q3 Give three uses of animal cloning.

Exam Question

Q1 A team of scientists wants to create a herd of cloned alpacas from Alpaca A, which has particularly desirable characteristics for wool production.

a) Outline how they could create a clone of Alpaca A using somatic cell nuclear transfer. [4 marks]

b) Give two arguments against creating a cloned herd. [2 marks]

If you cloned yourself, you could be relaxing while the other you revised...

Unfortunately, that's not going to happen, so you should just get on with learning about how the different types of animal cloning are carried out, how cloning in animals is actually used and the arguments for and against it.

Biotechnology

The global biotechnology industry is humongous, but fortunately you've only got to learn a few pages about it...

Biotechnology is the Use of Living Organisms in Industry

1) **Biotechnology** is the **industrial use** of **living organisms** to produce **food**, **drugs** and **other products**.
2) The living organisms used are mostly **microorganisms** (bacteria and fungi). Here are a few reasons why:
   - Their **ideal growth conditions** can be **easily** created — microorganisms will generally grow successfully as long as they have the right **nutrients**, **temperature**, **pH**, **moisture levels** and **availability of gases** (e.g. some need oxygen).
   - Because of their **short life-cycle**, they grow **rapidly** under the right conditions, so **products** can be made **quickly**.
   - They can be grown on a **range** of **inexpensive** materials — this makes them **economical** to use.
   - They can be grown at **any time** of the year.
3) Biotechnology also **uses parts** of **living organisms** (such as **enzymes**) to make products.
4) Enzymes used in industry can be **contained within the cells** of organisms — these are called **intracellular enzymes.**
5) Enzymes are also used that **aren't contained within cells** — these are called **isolated enzymes**. **Some** are **secreted naturally** by microorganisms (called **extracellular enzymes**), but others have to be **extracted**.
6) **Naturally secreted** enzymes are **cheaper** to use because it can be **expensive** to **extract** enzymes from cells.

You can find out how isolated enzymes are used in biotechnology on pages 104-105.

Microorganisms are Used in a Wide Variety of Industrial Processes

Process	Role of Microorganisms
Brewing (making beer)	To make **beer**, **yeast** (e.g. *Saccharomyces cerevisiae)* is added to a type of **grain** (such as barley) and other ingredients. The yeast **respires anaerobically** using the **glucose** from the grain and produces **ethanol** (alcohol) and **CO_2**. (When anaerobic respiration produces ethanol, the process is called **fermentation**.)
Baking	Yeast is also the organism that makes **bread rise**. The **CO_2** produced by **fermentation** of sugars in the dough makes sure it doesn't stay flat. Many flat breads, like tortillas, are made **without** yeast.
Cheese Making	**Cheese** production used to rely on a substance called **rennet**. Rennet contains the enzyme **chymosin**, which **clots** the **milk** — a key process in cheese making. Traditionally we used to get chymosin by extracting rennet from the lining of **calves' stomachs**, but now chymosin can be obtained from **yeast cells** that have been **genetically modified** to produce the enzyme. Cheese making also involves **lactic acid bacteria** (e.g. ***Lactobacillus*** and ***Streptococcus***). These bacteria convert the **lactose** in milk into **lactic acid**, which makes it turn **sour** and contributes to it **solidifying**. The production of **blue cheeses** also involves the addition of **fungi** to make the characteristic blue veins.
Yoghurt Production	Just like cheese making, **yoghurt production** involves the use of **lactic acid bacteria** to **clot** the milk and cause it to **thicken**. This creates a basic yoghurt product and then any **flavours** and **colours** are added.
Penicillin Production	In times of **stress**, **fungi** from the ***Penicillium*** genus produce an **antibiotic**, **penicillin**, to stop **bacteria** from **growing** and **competing** for **resources**. Penicillin is one of the **most common** antibiotics used in **medicine**, so we produce it on a **massive scale**. The fungus (usually ***Penicillium chrysogenum***) is grown under stress in **industrial fermenters** (see next page) and the penicillin produced is **collected** and **processed** to be used in medicine.
Insulin Production	**Insulin** is a **hormone** that's crucial for treating people with **Type 1 diabetes**. Insulin is made by **genetically modified bacteria**, which have had the **gene** for **human insulin production** inserted into their **DNA** (see page 88). These bacteria are grown in an **industrial fermenter** on a massive scale and the insulin produced is **collected** and **purified**.
Bioremediation	**Bioremediation** is a posh name for the process of using organisms (usually microorganisms) to **remove pollutants**, like oil and pesticides, from **contaminated sites**. Most commonly, pollutant-removing bacteria that occur **naturally** at a site are provided with **extra nutrients** and enhanced **growing conditions** to allow them to multiply and thrive. These bacteria **break down** the **pollutants** into **less harmful products**, cleaning up the area. For example, bioremediation using bacteria has been used to clean up **oil spills** at sea.

Biotechnology

Using Microorganisms in Food Production has Pros and Cons

1) As you can see from the previous page, **microorganisms** play a **key role** in the **production** of lots of **different** foods.
2) Some **microorganisms** can also be grown as a **source** of **protein** (called **single-cell protein**), which can act as a valuable **food source** for **humans** and other **animals**.
3) Examples of microorganisms used to make single-cell protein include the **fungus** *Fusarium venenatum* (which is used to make the popular meat substitute Quorn™) and the **bacteria** *Methylophilus methylotrophus*.
4) There are **advantages** and **disadvantages** of producing **food for human consumption** using **microorganisms**:

Advantages

1) Microorganisms used to make single-cell protein can be grown using many different **organic substrates**, including **waste materials** such as **molasses** (a by-product of sugar processing). Production of single-cell protein could actually be used as a way of **getting rid of waste products**.
2) Microorganisms can be grown **quickly**, **easily** and **cheaply**. **Production costs** are **low** because microorganisms have **simple growth requirements**, can be grown on **waste products** and **less land** is **required** in comparison to growing crops or rearing livestock.
3) Microorganisms can be cultured anywhere if you have the right equipment. This means that a **food source** could be readily **produced** in places where growing **crops** and rearing **livestock** is **difficult** (e.g. very hot or cold climates). This could help tackle **malnutrition** in developing countries.
4) Single-cell protein is often considered a **healthier alternative** to animal protein

Disadvantages

1) Because the **conditions** needed to grow the **desired microorganism** are also **ideal** for **other microorganisms**, a lot of **effort** has to go into making sure that the food doesn't get **contaminated** with unwanted bacteria, which could be **dangerous** to humans or **spoil** the food.
2) People may **not** like the **idea** of eating food that has been grown using **waste products**.
3) Single-cell protein **doesn't** have the **same texture** or **flavour** as real meat.
4) If single-cell protein is consumed in high quantities, **health problems** could be caused due to the **high levels** of **uric acid** released when the large amounts of amino acids are **broken down**.

Microorganisms are Grown in Fermentation Vessels

1) Biotechnology uses **cultures** of microorganisms. A culture is a **population** of **one type** of **microorganism** that's been **grown** under **controlled conditions**.
2) Cultures are grown in **large containers** called **fermentation vessels** to either **obtain lots** of the **microorganism** (e.g. for production of single-celled protein) or to **collect** lots of a **useful product** that the microorganism **makes**.
3) There are **two** main **methods** for **culturing** microorganisms:

- **Batch fermentation** — This is where microorganisms are grown in **individual batches** in a fermentation vessel — when one culture **ends** it's **removed** and then a **different batch** of microorganisms is grown in the vessel. This is known as a **closed culture** — see next page.
- **Continuous fermentation** — This is where microorganisms are **continually grown** in a fermentation vessel **without stopping**. **Nutrients** are put **in** and **waste products** taken **out** at a **constant rate**.

4) The **conditions** inside the fermentation vessels are kept at the **optimum for growth** — this **maximises** the **yield** of microorganisms and **desirable products**. Here's how it's done:

Factor	How it's regulated	How it maximises yield
pH	Constantly monitored by a pH probe and kept at the optimum level.	Allows enzymes to work efficiently, so the rate of reaction is kept as high as possible.
Temperature	Kept constant by a water jacket that surrounds the entire vessel.	
Access to nutrients	Paddles constantly circulate fresh nutrient medium around the vessel.	Ensures that the microorganisms always have access to their required nutrients.
Volume of oxygen	Sterile air is pumped into the vessel when needed.	Makes sure that the microorganisms always have oxygen for respiration.
Vessel kept sterile	Superheated steam sterilises the vessel after each use.	Kills any unwanted organisms that may compete with the ones being cultured.

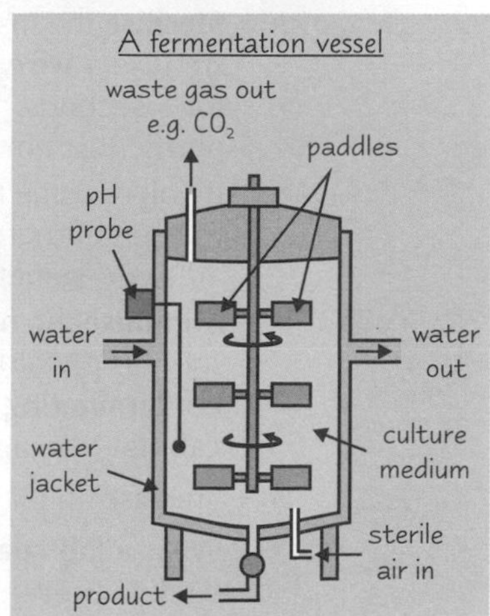

Biotechnology

Closed Cultures of Microorganisms follow a Standard Growth Curve

1) A **closed culture** is when growth takes place in a vessel that's **isolated** from the **external environment** — extra nutrients **aren't added** and waste products **aren't removed** from the vessel **during growth**.
2) In a closed culture (e.g. in batch fermentation) a population of microorganisms follows a **standard growth curve**:

(1) **Lag phase** — the population size **increases slowly** because the **microorganisms** have to make enzymes and other molecules before they can reproduce. This means the **reproduction rate** is **low**.

(2) **Exponential phase** — the population size **increases quickly** because the culture **conditions** are at their **most favourable** for **reproduction** (**lots of food** and **little competition**). The number of microorganisms **doubles** at **regular intervals**.

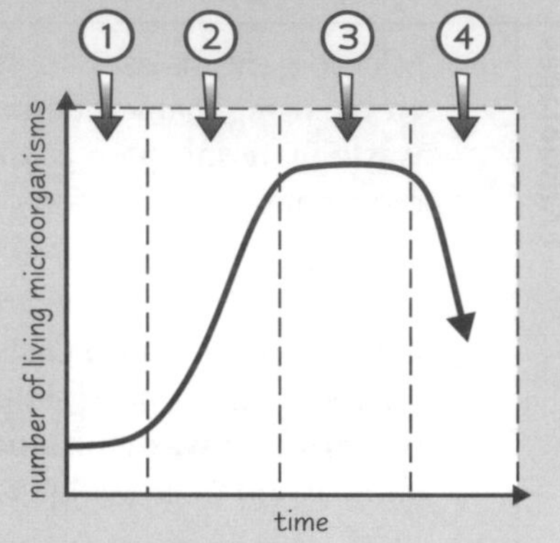

(3) **Stationary phase** — the population size **stays level** because the **death rate** of the microorganisms **equals** their **reproductive rate**. Microorganisms **die** because there's **not enough food** and poisonous **waste products build up**.

(4) **Decline phase** — the population size **falls** because the **death rate** is **greater** than the **reproductive rate**. This is because food is very **scarce** and waste products are at **toxic levels**.

You Need to Know How to Culture Microorganisms in the Lab

1) Cultures of microorganisms can be grown in the **lab**.
2) A common way to do this is on an **agar plate** — a sterile **Petri dish** containing **agar jelly**.
3) Microorganisms are **transferred** to the plate from a **sample** (e.g. bacteria in broth) using a **sterile** implement like a wire **inoculation loop** or a **sterile pipette** and **spreader**.
4) You then **incubate** the plates and allow the microorganisms to **grow**.
5) **Nutrients** can be **added** to the agar to help **improve** the **growing conditions**.

inoculation loop
agar plate
microorganism spread on the plate

Aseptic Techniques Are Used when Culturing Microorganisms

1) An important part of culturing microorganisms is using **aseptic techniques**. These are used to **prevent contamination** of cultures by **unwanted microorganisms**, which may **affect** the **growth** of the microorganism being cultured.
2) Contaminated cultures in **laboratory experiments** give **imprecise results** and may be **hazardous to health**.
3) Contamination on an **industrial scale** can be very **costly** because **entire cultures** may have to be **thrown away**.
4) Below are some **important** aseptic techniques that you should **follow** when culturing microorganisms in the lab:

- Regularly **disinfect** work surfaces to minimise contamination.
- Work near a **Bunsen flame**. Hot air rises, so any microorganisms in the air should be **drawn away** from your culture.
- **Sterilise** the instrument used to transfer cultures **before** and **after** each use, e.g. sterilise a **wire inoculation loop** by passing it through a **hot** Bunsen burner **flame** for 5 seconds. This will kill any microorganisms on the instrument. Pre-sterilised plastic instruments should only be used once and then safely discarded.
- If you're using broth, briefly pass the neck of the broth **container** through a Bunsen burner **flame** just after it's **opened** and just before it's **closed** — this causes air to move out of the container, preventing **unwanted** organisms from **falling in**.
- **Minimise** the time that the agar plate is open and put the lid on as soon as possible. This **reduces** the **chance** of **airborne** microorganisms **contaminating** the culture. You could even work in an **inoculation cabinet** (a chamber that has a flow of **sterile air** inside it).
- **Sterilise** all glassware before and after use, e.g. in an **autoclave**.
- Wear a **lab coat** and, if needed, **gloves**. **Tie long hair back** to prevent it from falling into anything.

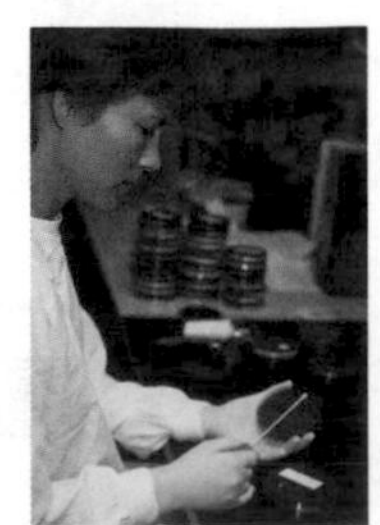

When Lynda found a tiny copy of Pride and Prejudice embedded in the agar, she knew she had cultured bacteria.

An autoclave is a machine which steams equipment at high pressure.

Biotechnology

Factors Affecting the *Growth* of *Microorganisms* can be *Investigated*

You can **investigate** the **effects of different factors** on the growth of microorganisms by growing them on **agar plates** under **different conditions**. The example below shows how you can investigate the effect of **temperature** on the growth of **bacteria** (although the same method can be used for other microorganisms, such as **fungi**).

Example: Measuring the Effects of **Temperature** on the Growth of **Bacteria**

Remember to use aseptic techniques when doing the experiment (see previous page).

1) You should be supplied with a **sample** of **bacteria** (e.g. *E. coli*) in **broth**. Using a sterile pipette, add a **set volume** (e.g. 0.1 cm^3) of your sample to an **agar plate**. Discard your pipette safely after use.

2) **Spread** the broth across the **entire surface** of the agar using a **sterile plastic spreader**. Discard the spreader safely after use.

3) Put the **lid** on the agar plate and **lightly tape it shut** using two small pieces of tape.

4) **Repeat steps 1-3** so that you have **six plates** in total.

5) Place three plates in a fridge at **4 °C** and put three in an incubator at **25 °C**. If you don't have access to an incubator, just leave the plates at room temperature, somewhere where the temperature is most likely to remain constant. The plates should be incubated **upside down**. This stops any **condensation** forming on the **lid** from **dropping** onto the **agar**.

5) Put another **lidded agar plate** in each of the two different temperature locations — these plates should be **uncultured** (i.e. you shouldn't have added any bacteria to them). These plates will act as **negative controls** (nothing should grow on them).

6) **Leave** all the plates for the **same** amount of time (e.g. 48 hours) then observe the results.

7) If **bacterial growth** has occurred, you should see **colonies** of bacteria on the surface of the agar.

8) **Count** the number of **colonies** that have formed on **each plate** and **record** your **results** in a table.

9) Work out the **mean** number of colonies formed at **each temperature**.

You might find that you have so many colonies that they overlap and you can't count them. If this happens, try making serial dilutions of your bacteria in broth and plate them on agar. One of these dilutions will give you a more manageable number of colonies.

This experiment can be **adapted** to investigate the effects of **different factors** on the growth of microorganisms. For example, you could:

- investigate the effect of **pH** by adding buffers at different pH levels to the broth.
- investigate the effects of **nutrient availability** by using different preparations of agar, which contain different nutrients.

You could also investigate the growth of microorganisms directly **in broth** (without the need to plate the broth on agar) using a **spectrophotometer**. This is a machine that measures the **turbidity** (**cloudiness**) of the **broth**. **Higher** turbidity means that **more** cells are **present** and, therefore, **more replication** has taken place.

Practice Questions

Q1 What is meant by 'biotechnology'?

Q2 What is bioremediation?

Q3 List two advantages and two disadvantages of the use of microorganisms in food production.

Q4 Give three ways in which growing conditions are optimised inside a fermentation vessel.

Q5 List the stages of the standard growth curve of microorganisms in a closed culture.

Exam Question

Q1 A scientist is plating *E. coli* bacterial cultures on agar to investigate the effects of pH on their growth.

a) Why must he carry out the experiment using aseptic techniques? [3 marks]

b) Outline three aseptic techniques that should be followed when culturing bacteria. [3 marks]

Calf stomachs, yeast and waste materials — biotechnology is sexy stuff...

Wow, biology and technology fused together... forget bionic arms, legs and eyes though — growing bacteria in a tank is where it's at. There's a lot of tough stuff to remember on these pages, but I promise you it's worth giving it the time.

Immobilised Enzymes

You might remember from page 100 that enzymes can be isolated from living organisms to be used in biotechnology. These pages tell you about how those enzymes can be immobilised for use in industrial processes. It's clever stuff.

Isolated Enzymes can be Immobilised

1) **Isolated enzymes** used in industry can become **mixed in** with the **products** of a reaction.
2) The **products** then need to be **separated** from this mixture, which can be **complicated** and **costly**.
3) This is **avoided** in large-scale production by using **immobilised enzymes** — enzymes that are **attached** to an **insoluble material** so they **can't** become mixed with the products.
4) There are **three main ways** that enzymes are **immobilised**:

① **Encapsulated** in jelly-like **alginate beads**, which act as a **semi-permeable membrane**.

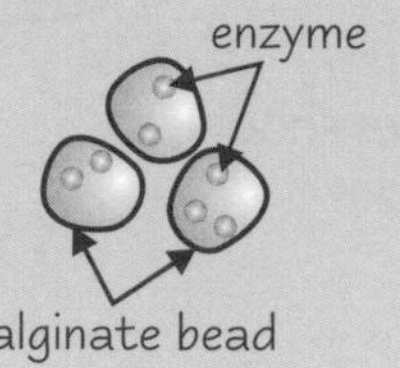

② **Trapped** in a **silica gel matrix**

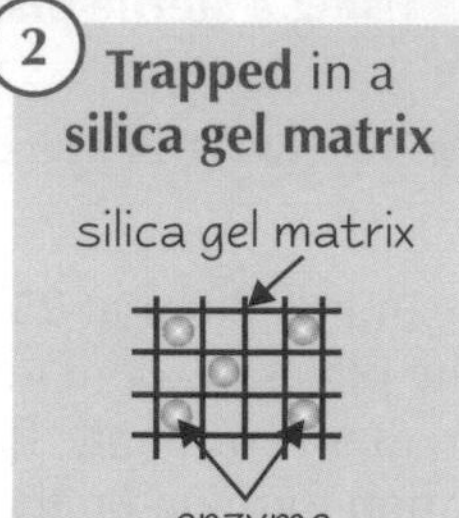

③ **Covalently bonded** to **cellulose** or **collagen fibres**

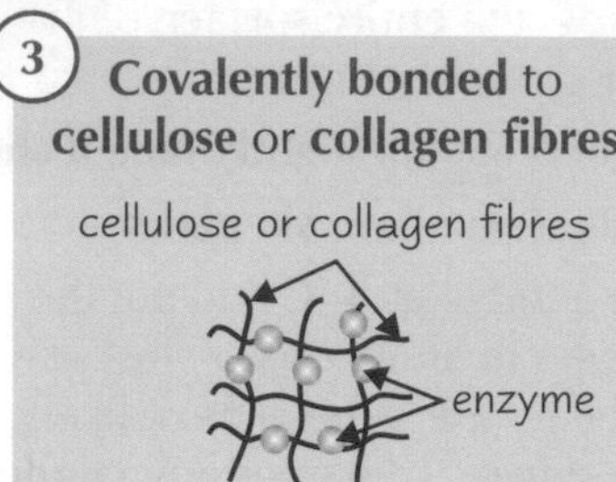

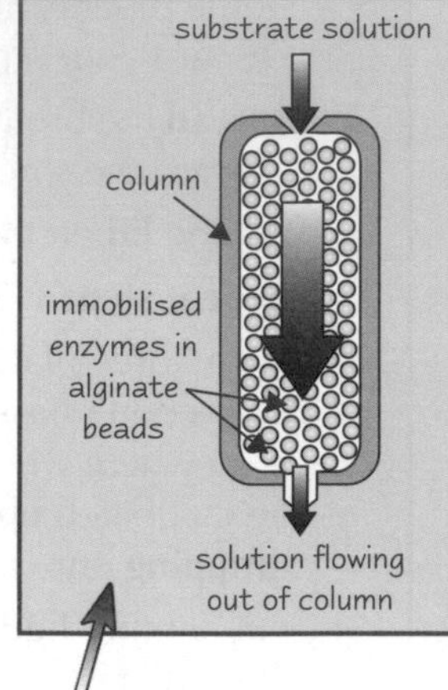

5) In industry, the **substrate solution** for a reaction is run through a **column** of **immobilised enzymes**.
6) The **active sites** of the enzymes are still **available** to **catalyse** the reaction but the solution flowing **out of** the column will **only** contain the **desired product**.
7) Here are some of the **advantages** of using **immobilised enzymes** in industry:

- Columns of immobilised enzymes can be **washed** and **reused** — this **reduces** the **cost** of running a reaction on an **industrial scale** because you don't have to **keep buying** new enzymes.
- The product **isn't mixed** with the enzymes — **no money** or **time** is **spent** separating them out.
- Immobilised enzymes are **more stable** than free enzymes — they're less likely to **denature** (become inactive) in **high temperatures** or **extremes** of **pH**.

8) There are **disadvantages** too:

- **Extra equipment** is required, which can be **expensive** to buy.
- **Immobilised enzymes** are **more expensive** to buy than **free enzymes**, so coupled with the equipment costs, they're **not** always **economical** for use in **smaller-scale** production.
- The immobilisation of the enzymes can sometimes lead to a **reduction** in the **enzyme activity** because they **can't** freely mix with their **substrate**.

Immobilised Enzymes are Used in a Wide Range of Industrial Processes

Conversion of Lactose to Glucose and Galactose

Some people are unable to digest **lactose** (a sugar found in milk) because they **don't** produce **enough** (or **any**) of the **enzyme lactase**. Lactase **breaks** lactose **down** into **glucose** and **galactose** via a **hydrolysis reaction**. Industrially, fresh milk can now be passed over **immobilised lactase** to produce **lactose-free milk** for use in the production of **lactose-free dairy products**.

Production of Semi-Synthetic Penicillins

Penicillin is a useful **antibiotic**, but some bacteria have become **penicillin resistant**. **Semi-synthetic penicillins** can now be produced, which have the **same** antibiotic properties as natural penicillin, but are **effective** against **penicillin-resistant** organisms. **Immobilised penicillin acylase** enzyme is used in their **production**.

Immobilised Enzymes

Conversion of Dextrins to Glucose

Glucose and **glucose syrup** are used in **massive amounts** in industry, e.g. they're used in the **food industry** to **sweeten** and **thicken** foods. Glucose can be **derived** from **starchy** foods, such as corn and potatoes, with the help of **immobilised enzymes**. Starch **breaks down** into **dextrins** (carbohydrate products), which are then **broken down** into **glucose** by the **immobilised enzyme glucoamylase**.

Conversion of Glucose to Fructose

Fructose is a sugar that's much **sweeter** than glucose. It's used as a **sweetener** in **food** — using fructose rather than glucose means that **less sugar** is needed to obtain the same level of sweetness in our foods. **Immobilised glucose isomerase** is used to convert **glucose** to **fructose** on an industrial scale.

Even though he eats your coursework and looks like a sultana, Doug is still even sweeter than fructose.

Production of Pure Samples of L-Amino Acids

Amino acids have **two chemical forms** (isomers) — L or D. Most amino acids **utilised** by the **body** need to be in the **L form**. Scientists are able to **chemically synthesise** amino acids, but end up with a **mix** of L and D forms. The enzyme **aminoacylase** separates them. **Immobilised aminoacylase** is used for the industrial production of **pure samples** of **L-amino acids**, which can be used for **many** purposes in the production of **animal** and **human food**, as well as in **dietary supplements**.

Conversion of Acrylonitrile to Acrylamide

Acrylamide is a chemical that is typically used in industry to produce **synthetic polymers** (e.g. plastics), which have a wide range of uses. For example, acrylamide is involved in the production of the polymer that's used in **disposable nappies** to make them **super-absorbent**. In industry, **immobilised nitrilase** is used to convert **acrylonitrile** (a man-made chemical) to **acrylamide**.

Practice Questions

Q1 List three advantages of using immobilised enzymes in industry.

Q2 Name a type of product that involves immobilised lactase in its production.

Q3 Name an industrial process that relies heavily on the action of immobilised penicillin acylase.

Q4 Name the immobilised enzyme used in the conversion of acrylonitrile to acrylamide.

Exam Questions

Q1 Aminoacylase is used industrially in the production of pure samples of L-amino acids.
- a) The aminoacylase can be immobilised. What does this mean? [1 mark]
- b) Give three ways in which aminoacylase could be immobilised. [3 marks]

Q2 A team of food technicians is designing a protocol for the mass production of glucose syrup. The enzyme glucoamylase plays a key role in this process. They are deciding whether to use immobilised or free enzyme.
- a) What role does glucoamylase play in the manufacture of glucose syrup? [1 mark]
- b) Give two disadvantages of using immobilised glucoamylase, rather than free glucoamylase, in the production of glucose syrup on an industrial scale. [2 marks]

Here's another way to immobilise an enzyme — run over it with a steamroller...

Some industrial processes can really benefit from the use of immobilised enzymes, but they have their drawbacks too. Make sure that you're able to give a balanced account of the pros and cons of immobilised enzyme usage in industry. You also need to know the different ways that enzymes can be immobilised and some examples of how great they are.

An Introduction to Ecosystems

All this ecology-type stuff is pretty wordy, so here are a nice few definitions to get you started. This way, you'll know what I'm banging on about throughout the rest of the section, and that always helps I think.

You Need to Learn Some Definitions to get you Started

Habitat — The **place** where an organism **lives**, e.g. a rocky shore or a field.
Population — **All** the organisms of **one species** in a **habitat**.
Producer — An organism that **produces organic molecules** using sunlight energy, e.g. plants.
Consumer — An organism that **eats other organisms**, e.g. animals and birds.
Decomposer — An organism that **breaks down dead** or **undigested organic material**, e.g. bacteria and fungi.
Trophic level — A **stage** in a **food chain** occupied by a particular **group** of organisms, e.g. producers are the first trophic level in a food chain.

Ecosystems Are Always Changing

1) An **ecosystem** is all the organisms living in a certain area and all the non-living conditions (factors) found there. It's a **dynamic system** — this means it's **changing all the time**.
2) An ecosystem includes both **biotic** and **abiotic factors**:
   - **Biotic factors** — The **living** features of an ecosystem. For example, the presence of **predators** or **food**.
   - **Abiotic factors** — The **non-living** features of an ecosystem. E.g. the **temperature**, **rainfall**, shape of the land (**topology**) and **soil nutrient availability**. In an aquatic ecosystem these may also include the **pH** and **salinity** (salt content) of the water.

The undead can find it hard to identify themselves as a living or a non-living feature of an ecosystem.

Biotic and Abiotic Factors Have an Impact on Ecosystems

Ecosystems cover different areas. They can be **small**, e.g. a pond, or **large**, e.g. an entire forest. Whatever size they are, ecosystems are **influenced** by **biotic** and **abiotic** factors. Here are some examples:

Rock pools

- **Biotic factors** — Seaweed can be a **food source** for **consumers** such as limpets that graze on this **producer**. Intense **competition** for food (such as seaweed) can **limit** the **number** of **organisms** that are present in a small rock pool ecosystem.
- **Abiotic factors** — Rock pools are heavily influenced by the **tides**. At **high** tide they are completely **submerged** by the ocean so experience **similar** abiotic factors (e.g. **pH**, **salinity**, **temperature**, etc.) to the ocean ecosystem. However, at **low** tide they experience more **extreme abiotic** conditions (e.g. **higher** salinity and temperatures) — only **some organisms** can **tolerate** these conditions.

Playing field

- **Biotic factors** — **Producers** include grass and other plants such as daisies, clover and dandelions. The large amount of these plants might attract a large number of organisms that use them as a **food** source (e.g. rabbits, caterpillars).
- **Abiotic factors** — **Rainfall** and **sunlight** affect the **growth** of the **producers** in the ecosystem. In a very **wet** year, the soil may become **waterlogged**, making it **difficult** for plants to grow. Poor plant growth may **decrease** the number of **consumers** the ecosystem is able to support.

Large tree

- **Biotic factors** — Insects, such as caterpillars, can use the **leaves** of a tree as a source of food. However, if they consume **all the leaves** on a tree (defoliation) they can **slow** tree growth and even lead to its **death**.
- **Abiotic factors** — **Drought conditions** (e.g. when there are prolonged periods of very **low rainfall**) can **negatively impact** the **growth** of a tree. In severe cases it can result in the whole tree (or parts of it) **dying**.

An Introduction to Ecosystems

Energy is Transferred Through Ecosystems

1) The **main route** by which energy **enters** an ecosystem is **photosynthesis** (e.g. by plants, see p. 44). (Some energy enters sea ecosystems when bacteria use chemicals from deep sea vents as an energy source.)
2) During photosynthesis plants **convert sunlight energy** into a form that can be **used** by other organisms — plants are called **producers** (see previous page). They store energy as **biomass**. **Biomass** is the **mass** of **living** material, e.g. the mass of plant material.
3) After producers store **sunlight energy** as **biomass**, you can then think of the following **energy transfers** through ecosystems as **biomass transfers**. You might come across energy transfers being called biomass transfers in your exam — don't panic, they refer to the same thing (energy transfer).
4) Energy is **transferred** through the **living organisms** of an ecosystem when organisms **eat** other organisms, e.g. producers are eaten by organisms called **primary consumers**. Primary consumers are then eaten by **secondary consumers** and secondary consumers are eaten by **tertiary consumers**.
5) **Food chains** and **food webs** show how energy is **transferred** through an ecosystem.
6) **Food chains** show **simple lines** of energy transfer.
7) **Food webs** show **lots** of **food chains** in an ecosystem and how they **overlap**.
8) Energy locked up in the things that **can't be eaten** (e.g. bones, faeces) gets recycled back into the ecosystem by **decomposers**.

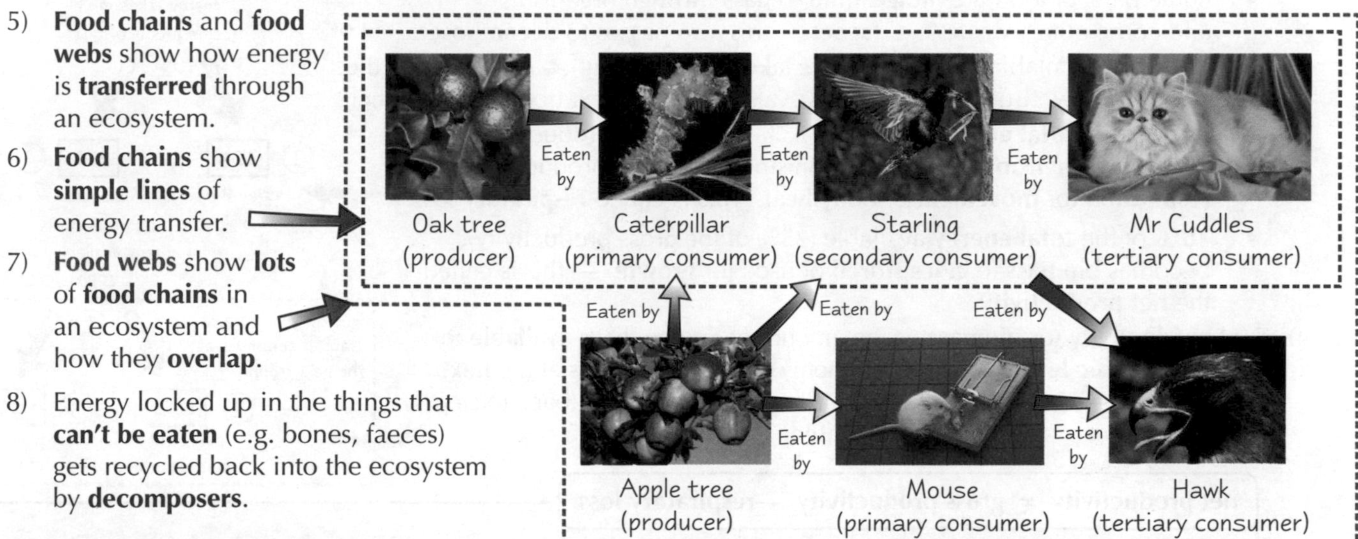

Practice Questions

Q1 Define ecosystem.
Q2 Why are ecosystems described as being dynamic?
Q3 What is a biotic factor?
Q4 What is biomass?
Q5 How is biomass related to energy?

Exam Questions

Q1 Which of the following is **not** an example of an abiotic factor.

A The amount of rainfall in a forest ecosystem.
B Sufficient space on a rocky surface for barnacles to attach themselves to in a seashore ecosystem.
C The presence of other plants that are competing for light in a woodland ecosystem.
D The salinity of water in an aquatic ecosystem. [1 mark]

Q2 In an orchard ecosystem, if there's a frost once the trees have started flowering, it can mean that the fruit doesn't develop properly.

a) Describe the effect that this might have on the rest of the organisms in the ecosystem. [2 marks]
b) Frost is an example of an abiotic factor in an ecosystem.
Suggest two other abiotic factors that might influence an orchard ecosystem. [2 marks]

Food chains — apparently there's more to them than candy necklaces...

Don't be taken in by the pretty pictures — this topic is not as easy as it might appear. Ecologists use very specific terms for things so you have to learn them and then be really careful that you use the right one. Take biomass and energy for instance. Biomass is energy stored in living material. Had me stumped for ages that one...

Energy Transfer Through an Ecosystem

Energy is lost along food chains (how careless, they should put it in a safe place if you ask me).

Not All Energy** gets **Transferred** to the **Next Trophic Level

1) **Not all** the energy (e.g. from sunlight or food) that's available to the organisms in a trophic level is **transferred** to the **next** trophic level — around **90%** of the **total available energy** is **lost** in various ways.
2) Some of the available energy (**60%**) is **never taken in** by the organisms in the first place. E.g.
    - Plants **can't use** all the light energy that reaches their **leaves**, e.g. some is the **wrong wavelength**, some is **reflected**, and some **passes straight through** the leaves.
    - Some sunlight can't be used because it hits parts of the plant that **can't photosynthesise**, e.g. the bark of a tree.
    - Some **parts** of food, e.g. **roots** or **bones**, **aren't eaten** by organisms so the energy isn't taken in — they pass to **decomposers**.
    - Some parts of food are **indigestible** so **pass through** organisms and come out as **waste**, e.g. **faeces** — this also passes to **decomposers**.
3) The rest of the available energy (**40%**) is **taken in** (**absorbed**) — this is called the **gross productivity**. But not all of this is available to the next trophic level either.
    - **30%** of the **total energy** available (75% of the gross productivity) is **lost to the environment** when organisms use energy produced from **respiration** for **movement** or body **heat**. This is called **respiratory loss**.
    - **10%** of the **total energy** available (25% of the gross productivity) becomes **biomass** (e.g. it's **stored** or used for **growth**) — this is called the **net productivity**.
4) **Net productivity** (or **biomass**) is the amount of energy that's **available** to the **next trophic level**. The **flow** of energy transfer **continues** at the **next trophic level** — the process starts again from the beginning (back to step 1). Here's how net productivity is **calculated**:

The percentages used are general figures — real values for a given ecosystem will vary.

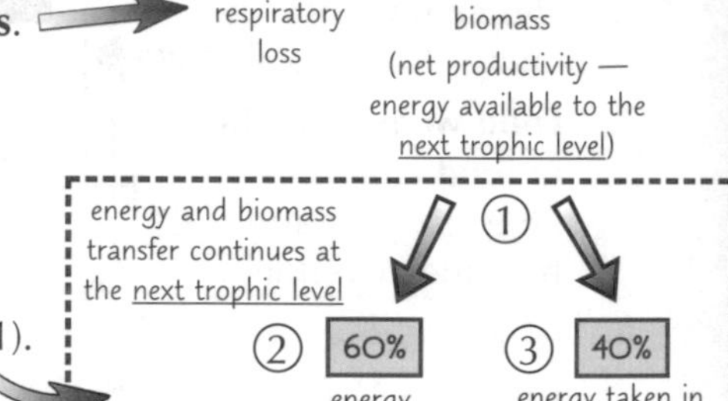

net productivity = gross productivity – respiratory loss

EXAMPLE: The rabbits in an ecosystem receive **20 000 kJm⁻²yr⁻¹** of energy, but don't take in **12 000 kJm⁻²yr⁻¹** of it, so their gross productivity is **8000 kJm⁻²yr⁻¹** (20 000 – 12 000). They lose **6000 kJm⁻²yr⁻¹** using energy from **respiration**. You can use this to **calculate** the **net productivity** of the rabbits:

net productivity = 8000 – 6000 = 2000 kJm⁻²yr⁻¹

5) You might be asked to **calculate** how **efficient energy transfer** from one trophic level to another is:

The rabbits receive **20 000 kJm⁻²yr⁻¹**, and their **net productivity** is **2000 kJm⁻²yr⁻¹**. So the **percentage efficiency of energy transfer** is:

(2000 ÷ 20 000) × 100 = 10%

Energy Transfer** Between **Trophic Levels** can be **Measured

1) To **measure** the **energy transfer** between two trophic levels you need to **calculate** the **difference** between the amount of **energy** in each level (the net productivity of each level).
2) You can **calculate** the **amount of energy** in a trophic level by measuring the **dry mass** of the organisms (their **biomass**). Remember, energy is stored as biomass, so it indicates **how much energy** an organism **contains**.
3) First you calculate the amount of biomass in a **sample** of the organisms, e.g. a 1 m^2 area of **wheat** or a single **mouse** that feeds on the wheat.
4) Then you **multiply** the results from the **sample** by the **size** of the **total population** (e.g. a 10 000 m^2 **field** of wheat or the **number** of mice in the population) to give the **total** amount of energy in the organisms at that **trophic level**.
5) The **difference** in **energy** between the trophic levels is the amount of energy **transferred**.
6) There are **problems** with this method though. For example, the consumers (mice) might have **taken in energy** from sources **other than** the producer measured (wheat). This means the difference between the two figures calculated **wouldn't** be an **accurate** estimate of the energy transferred between **only those two** organisms. For an **accurate estimate** you'd need to include **all** the individual organisms at each trophic level.

Energy Transfer Through an Ecosystem

Human Activities can Increase the Transfer of Energy

Some **farming methods increase productivity** by **increasing** the **transfer** of **energy** through an **ecosystem**:

1) **Herbicides** kill **weeds** that **compete** with agricultural crops for **energy**. Reducing competition means crops receive **more energy**, so they grow **faster** and become **larger**, **increasing** productivity.
2) **Fungicides** kill **fungal infections** that **damage** agricultural crops. The crops **use more** energy for **growth** and **less** for fighting infection, so they grow **faster** and become **larger**, **increasing** productivity.
3) **Insecticides** kill **insect** pests that **eat** and **damage** crops. Killing insect pests means **less biomass** is **lost** from crops, so they grow to be **larger**, which means productivity is **greater**.
4) **Natural predators** introduced to the ecosystem **eat** the pest species, e.g. ladybirds eat greenfly. This means the crops lose **less energy** and **biomass**, **increasing** productivity.
5) **Fertilisers** are chemicals that provide crops with **minerals** needed **for growth**, e.g. **nitrates**. Crops **use up** minerals in the soil as they **grow**, so their growth is **limited** when there **aren't enough** minerals. Adding fertiliser **replaces** the lost minerals, so **more energy** from the ecosystem can be used to grow, **increasing** the **efficiency** of energy conversion.
6) Rearing livestock **intensively** involves **controlling** the **conditions** they live in, so **more** of their **energy** is used for **growth** and **less** is used for **other activities** — the **efficiency** of energy conversion is increased so **more biomass** is produced and productivity is **increased**.
   Here are a couple of **examples**:

   1) Animals may be kept in **warm**, **indoor** pens where their **movement** is **restricted**. **Less energy** is **wasted** keeping **warm** and **moving around**.
   2) Animals may be given **feed** that's **higher in energy** than their natural food. This **increases** the **energy input**, so **more energy** is available for **growth**.

Increasing productivity was not an issue that was easy to raise with Herbert.

The benefits are that **more food** can be produced in a **shorter** space of time, often at **lower cost**. However, enhancing productivity by intensive rearing raises **ethical issues**. For example, some people think the **conditions** intensively reared animals are kept in cause the animals **pain**, **distress** or restricts their **natural behaviour**, so it **shouldn't be done**.

Practice Questions

Q1 What is the equation for net productivity?

Q2 What do you need to calculate to find the energy transfer between two trophic levels?

Q3 Give one example of how farmers increase the productivity of animals.

Exam Questions

Grass 13 883 $kJm^{-2}yr^{-1}$ → Arctic hare 2345 $kJm^{-2}yr^{-1}$ → Arctic fox 137 $kJm^{-2}yr^{-1}$

Q1 The diagram above shows the net productivity of different trophic levels in a food chain.

a) Explain why the net productivity of the Arctic hare is less than the net productivity of the grass. [4 marks]

b) Calculate the percentage efficiency of energy transfer from the Arctic hare to the Arctic fox. [2 marks]

Q2 A farmer grows cabbages in one of his fields.

a) Suggest how you could calculate the energy that the cabbages in the field contain. [2 marks]

b) The farmer wants to increase the productivity of his field.
Describe two ways he could do this and explain how they would help increase productivity. [4 marks]

I'm suffering from energy loss after those two pages...

So farming's not just about getting up early to feed the animals then — farmers are manipulating the transfer of energy to produce as much food as they can. And it's really important to remember that this transfer of energy isn't 100% efficient — most gets lost along the way so the next organisms don't get all the energy. Interesting, ve-ry interesting...

Recycling in Ecosystems

Bin day is Monday for the secondary consumers. Actually, ecosystems have developed a much better system to make sure necessary elements like carbon and nitrogen can be re-used and they don't run out.

*The **Carbon Cycle** shows how **Carbon** is **Passed On** and **Recycled***

All organisms need carbon to make **essential compounds**, e.g. plants use CO_2 in photosynthesis to make glucose. The **carbon cycle** is how carbon **moves** through **living organisms** and the **non-living environment**. The cycle includes processes that involve organisms (**photosynthesis**, **respiration**, and **decomposition**) and also chemical and physical processes such as **combustion** and **weathering**:

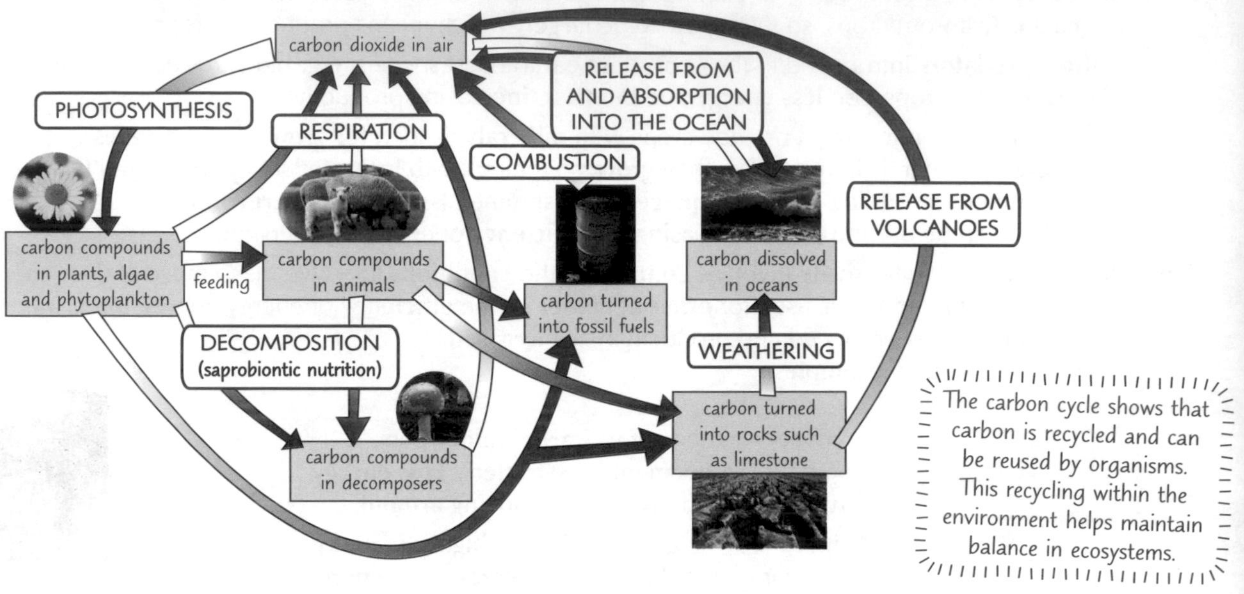

The carbon cycle shows that carbon is recycled and can be reused by organisms. This recycling within the environment helps maintain balance in ecosystems.

1) **Carbon** (in the form of CO_2 from **air** and **water**) is **absorbed** by plants when they carry out **photosynthesis** — it becomes carbon compounds in **plant tissues**.
2) Carbon is **passed on** to **primary consumers** when they **eat** the plants. It's passed on to **secondary** and **tertiary consumers** when they eat other consumers.
3) All living organisms **die** and the carbon compounds in the **dead organisms** are digested by **microorganisms** called **decomposers**, e.g. bacteria and fungi. Feeding on dead organic matter is called **saprobiontic nutrition**.
4) Carbon is **returned** to the air (and water) as **all living organisms** (including the decomposers) carry out **respiration**, which **produces CO_2**.
5) If dead organic matter ends up in places where there **aren't any** decomposers, e.g. deep oceans or bogs, their carbon compounds can be turned into **fossil fuels** over **millions of years** (by heat and pressure).
6) The carbon in fossil fuels (e.g. oil and coal) is **released** when they're **burnt** — this is called **combustion**.
7) As well as coal, other types of rock can be formed from dead organic matter deposited on the sea floor. For example, rocks such as **limestone** and **chalk** are mainly composed of **calcium carbonate** (**$CaCO_3$**). This comes from marine organisms like crabs, mussels, sea urchins and coral that utilise this compound in their development, e.g. to form **shells**.
8) One way carbon can be returned to the atmosphere from these rocks is by them being **drawn down** deep into the Earth's crust by the movement of **tectonic plates**. There they undergo chemical changes and release **carbon dioxide**, which is returned to the atmosphere by **volcanoes**.
9) The rocks can also eventually become **land**, which then is **weathered** (broken down by exposure to the atmosphere). This can happen **chemically** by **rainwater** (which is naturally slightly acidic due to the CO_2 dissolved in it) and **physically**, e.g. by plant roots, animals, etc. **Chemical weathering** causes **mineral ions** and **bicarbonate ions** (HCO_3^-) to be released from the rock in to solution and enter **groundwater**, from where they are transported into **rivers** and the **oceans**. There they **combine** to form carbon-containing compounds such as **$CaCO_3$**.
10) CO_2 can also **dissolve** directly into the **oceans** from the atmosphere and be transported in the ocean by **deep underwater currents** (a physical process). CO_2 can remain in these slow-moving currents for hundreds of years before returning to the surface and being **released** back into the **atmosphere**.

Recycling in Ecosystems

*The **Nitrogen Cycle** shows how **Nitrogen** is **Recycled** in **Ecosystems***

Plants and animals **need** nitrogen to make **proteins** and **nucleic acids** (DNA and RNA). The atmosphere's made up of about 78% nitrogen, but plants and animals **can't use it** in that form — they need **bacteria** to **convert** it into **nitrogen compounds** first. The **nitrogen cycle** shows how nitrogen is **converted** into a useable form and then **passed** on between different **living** organisms and the **non-living** environment.

The nitrogen cycle includes **food chains** (nitrogen is passed on when organisms are eaten), and four different processes that involve bacteria — **nitrogen fixation**, **ammonification**, **nitrification** and **denitrification**:

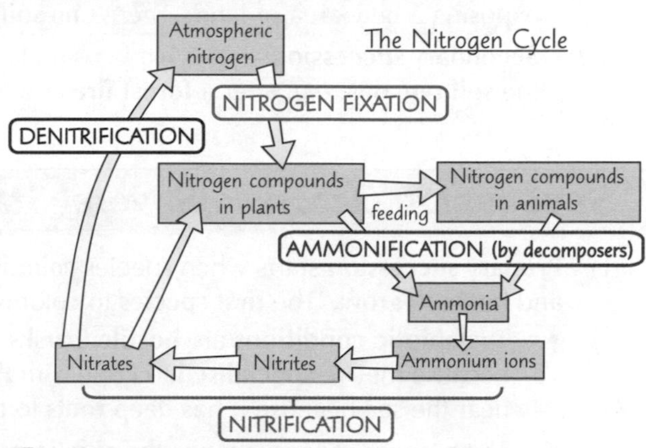

1 Nitrogen fixation

- **Nitrogen fixation** is when nitrogen **gas** in the atmosphere is turned into **ammonia** by **bacteria** such as ***Rhizobium*** and ***Azotobacter***. The ammonia can then be **used** by plants.
- *Rhizobium* are found inside **root nodules** (growths on the roots) of **leguminous** plants (e.g. peas, beans and clover).
- They form a **mutualistic** relationship with the plants — they provide the plant with **nitrogen compounds** and the plant provides them with **carbohydrates**.
- *Azotobacter* are found living in the **soil**. They **don't** form mutualistic relationships with plants.

2 Ammonification

- **Ammonification** is when nitrogen compounds from **dead organisms** are turned into **ammonia** by **decomposers**, which goes onto form **ammonium ions**.
- Animal **waste** (**urine** and **faeces**) also contains nitrogen compounds. These are also turned into ammonia by decomposers and go on to form ammonium ions.

3 Nitrification

- **Nitrification** is when **ammonium ions** in the soil are **changed** into **nitrogen compounds** that can then be **used** by plants (nitrates).
- First **nitrifying bacteria** called ***Nitrosomonas*** change **ammonium ions** into **nitrites**.
- Then other nitrifying bacteria called *Nitrobacter* change **nitrites** into **nitrates**.

4 Denitrification

- **Denitrification** is when nitrates in the soil are **converted** into **nitrogen gas** by **denitrifying bacteria** — they use nitrates in the soil to carry out **respiration** and produce nitrogen gas.
- This happens under **anaerobic conditions** (where there's **no** oxygen), e.g. in **waterlogged** soils.

Other ways that **nitrogen** gets into an **ecosystem** is by **lightning** (which **fixes atmospheric nitrogen**) or by **artificial fertilisers** (they're **produced from atmospheric nitrogen** on an **industrial scale** in the **Haber process**).

Practice Questions

Q1 Describe a chemical process that occurs in the carbon cycle.

Q2 Name the two groups of bacteria involved in nitrification.

Exam Questions

Nitrogen compounds in animals
Nitrogen compounds in decomposers
Nitrogen compounds in plants
B
A
C
Nitrogen compounds in the atmosphere
Leaching
Nitrogen compounds in the soil
Fertilisers

Q1 The diagram on the right shows the nitrogen cycle.

a) Name the processes labelled A and B in the diagram. [2 marks]

b) Name process C and describe the process in detail. [3 marks]

Q2 Cattle can be fed on silage (preserved grass) over winter months. Describe how carbon moves from carbon dioxide in the air to the formation of carbon compounds in cattle. [2 marks]

Nitrogen fixation — cheaper than a shoe fixation...

The nitrogen cycle's not as bad as it seems — divide up the four processes of nitrogen fixation, ammonification, nitrification and denitrification and learn them separately. Then before you know it, you'll have learnt the whole cycle.

Succession

The types of organisms in an ecosystem change over time, as does the environment itself...

Succession is the Process of Ecosystem Change

Succession is the process by which an **ecosystem changes** over **time**. The **biotic conditions** (e.g. **plant** and **animal communities**) change as the **abiotic conditions** change (e.g. **water** availability). There are **two** types of succession:

1) **Primary succession** — this happens on land that's been **newly formed** or **exposed**, e.g. where a **volcano** has erupted to form a **new rock surface**, or where **sea level** has **dropped** exposing a new area of land. There's **no soil** or **organic material** to start with, e.g. just bare rock.
2) **Secondary succession** — this happens on land that's been **cleared** of all the **plants**, but where the **soil remains**, e.g. after a **forest fire** or where a forest has been **cut down by humans**.

Succession Occurs in Several Stages

1) **Primary succession** starts when species **colonise** a new land surface. **Seeds** and **spores** are blown in by the **wind** and begin to **grow**. The **first species** to colonise the area are called **pioneer species** — this is the **first stage**.
   - The **abiotic conditions** are **hostile** (**harsh**), e.g. there's no soil to **retain water**. Only pioneer species **grow** because they're **specialised** to cope with the harsh conditions, e.g. **marram grass** can grow on sand dunes near the sea because it has **deep roots** to get water and can **tolerate** the salty environment.
   - The pioneer species **change** the **abiotic conditions** — they **die** and **microorganisms decompose** the dead **organic material** (**humus**). This forms a **basic soil**.
   - This makes conditions **less hostile**, e.g. the basic soil helps to **retain water**, which means **new organisms** can move in and grow. These then die and are decomposed, adding **more** organic material, making the soil **deeper** and **richer in minerals**. This means **larger plants** like **shrubs** can start to grow in the deeper soil, which retains **even more** water. As **more plants** move in they create **more habitats**, so **more animals** move in.
2) **Secondary succession** happens in the **same way**, but because there's already a **soil layer** succession starts at a **later stage** — the pioneer species in secondary succession are **larger plants**, e.g. shrubs.
3) At each stage, **different** plants and animals that are **better adapted** for the improved conditions move in, **out-compete** the plants and animals that are already there, and become the **dominant species** in the ecosystem.
4) As succession goes on, the ecosystem becomes **more complex**. New species move in **alongside** existing species, which means the **species diversity** (the number of **different species** and the **abundance** of each species) **increases**.
5) The amount of **biomass** also **increases** because plants at later stages are **larger** and **more dense**, e.g. **woody trees**.
6) The **final stage** is called the **climax community** — the ecosystem is supporting the **largest** and **most complex** community of plants and animals it can. It **won't change** much more — it's in a **steady state**.

This example shows primary succession on bare rock, but succession also happens on sand dunes, salt marshes and even in lakes.

Example of primary succession — bare rock to woodland

1) **Pioneer species colonise** the rocks. E.g. **lichens** grow **on** and **break down** rocks, **releasing minerals**.
2) The lichens **die** and are **decomposed** helping to form a **thin soil**, which thickens as more **organic material** is formed. This means other species such as **mosses** can **grow**.
3) **Larger plants** that need **more water** can move in as the soil **deepens**, e.g. **grasses** and **small flowering plants**. The soil **continues to deepen** as the larger plants die and are decomposed.
4) **Shrubs**, **ferns** and **small trees** begin to grow, **out-competing** the grasses and smaller plants to become the **dominant** species. **Diversity increases**.
5) Finally, the soil is **deep** and **rich** enough in **nutrients** to support **large trees**. These become the dominant species, and the **climax community** is formed.

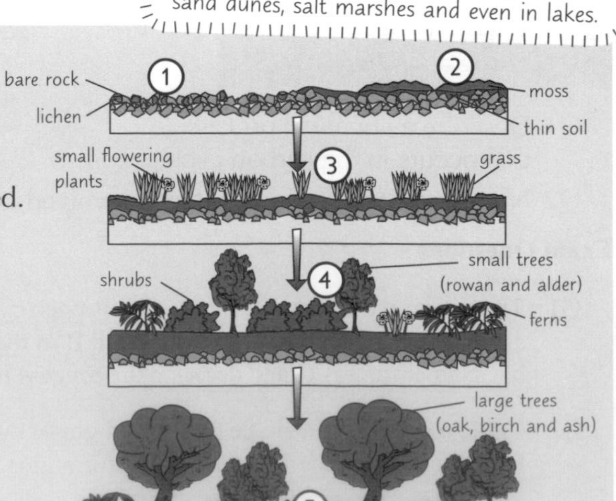

Succession

Different Ecosystems have Different Climax Communities

Which species make up the climax community depends on what the **climate's** like in an ecosystem. The climax community for a **particular** climate is called its **climatic climax**. For example:

In a **temperate climate** there's **plenty** of **available water**, **mild temperatures** and not much **change** between the seasons. The climatic climax will contain **large trees** because they **can grow** in these conditions once **deep soils** have developed. In a **polar climate** there's **not much available water**, temperatures are **low** and there are **massive changes** between the seasons. Large trees **won't ever** be able to grow in these conditions, so the climatic climax contains only **herbs** or **shrubs**, but it's still the **climax community**.

Succession can be Prevented or Deflected

Human activities can **prevent succession**, stopping the normal climax community from **developing**. When succession is stopped **artificially** like this, the climax community is called a **plagioclimax**. **Deflected succession** is when succession is prevented by human activity, but the plagioclimax that develops is one that's **different** to any of the **natural stages** of the ecosystem — the path of succession has been **deflected** from its natural course. For example:

1) A **regularly mown** grassy field **won't develop** woody plants, even if the climate of the ecosystem could support them.

2) The **growing points** of the woody plants are **cut off** by the lawnmower, so larger plants **can't establish** themselves — only the grasses can **survive** being mowed, so the **climax community** is a **grassy field**.

3) A grassy field isn't a **natural stage** — there should also be things like small flowering plants, so succession has been **deflected.**

Man had been given a mighty weapon with which they would tame the forces of nature.

Grazing and burning have the same effect as mowing.

Practice Questions

Q1 What is the difference between primary and secondary succession?

Q2 What is the name given to species that are the first to colonise an area during succession?

Q3 What is meant by a climax community?

Exam Questions

Q1 Which one of the following statements correctly describes deflected succession?

A When human intervention causes the natural climax community to form in an ecosystem.
B The process by which pioneer species change the abiotic conditions by forming a basic soil.
C A process that occurs on land that has been cleared but where soil remains.
D Where human activity has stopped the normal climax community from developing. [1 mark]

Q2 Succession occurs on sand dunes.
You can often see the different stages of succession as you move further inland from the sand dunes.

a) What type of succession is taking place when the first grasses start to appear on the dune? Give a reason for your answer. [2 marks]

b) Explain how the growth of grasses can lead to larger plants like shrubs becoming the dominant species on the sand dunes. [3 marks]

Revision succession — bare brain to a woodland of knowledge...

When answering questions on succession, examiners are pretty keen on you using the right terminology — that means saying "pioneer species" instead of "the first plants to grow there". If you can manage that, then you'll be just fine.

Investigating Ecosystems

Examiners aren't happy unless you're freezing to death in the rain in a field somewhere in the middle of nowhere. Still, it's better than being stuck in the classroom being bored to death learning about fieldwork techniques...

You need to be able to Investigate Populations of Organisms

Investigating **populations** of organisms involves looking at the **abundance** and **distribution** of **species** in a particular **area**.

1) **Abundance** — the **number of individuals** of **one species** in a **particular area**. The abundance of **mobile organisms** and **plants** can be estimated by simply counting the **number** of individuals in samples taken. **Percentage cover** can also be used to measure the abundance of plants — this is **how much** of the area you're investigating is **covered** by a species.
2) **Distribution** — this is **where** a particular species is within the **area you're investigating**.

You need to take a Random Sample from the Area You're Investigating

Most of the time it would be too **time-consuming** to measure the **number of individuals** and the **distribution** of every species in the **entire area** you're investigating, so instead you take **samples**:

1) **Choose** an **area** to **sample** — a **small** area **within** the area being investigated.
2) Samples should be **random** to **avoid bias**, e.g. by picking random sample sites.
3) Use an **appropriate technique** to take a sample of the population (see below and on the next page).
4) **Repeat** the process, taking as many samples as possible. This gives a more **precise** estimate for the **whole area**.
5) The **number of individuals** for the **whole area** can then be **estimated** by taking an **average** of the data collected in each sample and **multiplying** it by the size of the whole area. The **percentage cover** for the whole area can be estimated by taking the average of all the samples.

You'll have learnt more about random sampling in Module 4.

Finally! 26 542 981 poppies. What do you mean I didn't need to count them all?

When you are recording species it's important to identify them correctly. An identification key (a tool that allows you to identify species by their features) can help you do this.

Frame Quadrats can be used to Investigate Plant Populations

1) A **frame quadrat** is a **square** frame divided into a **grid** of 100 **smaller squares** by strings attached across the frame.
2) They're **placed on the ground** at **random points** within the area you're investigating. This can be done by selecting **random coordinates** (see above).
3) The **number of individuals** of each species is recorded in **each quadrat**.
4) The **percentage cover** of a species can also be measured by counting how much of the quadrat is **covered** by the species — you count a square if it's **more than half-covered**. Percentage cover is a **quick** way to investigate populations and you **don't** have to **count** all the **individual** plants.
5) Frame quadrats are useful for **quickly** investigating areas with species that **fit within** a **small quadrat** — most frame quadrats are **1 m by 1 m**.
6) Areas with **larger plants** and **trees** need **very large** quadrats. Large quadrats **aren't** always in a frame — they can be marked out with a **tape measure**.

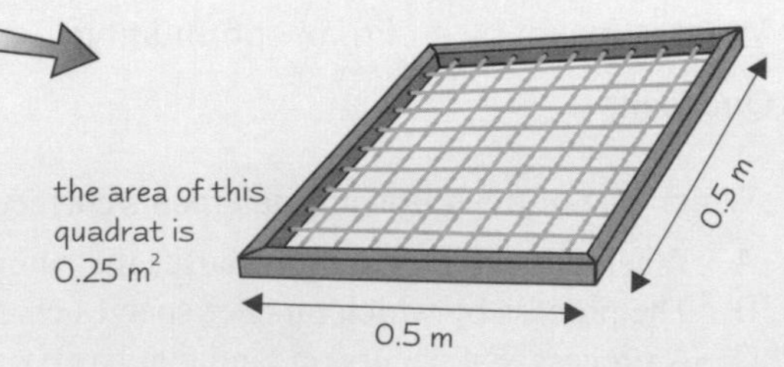

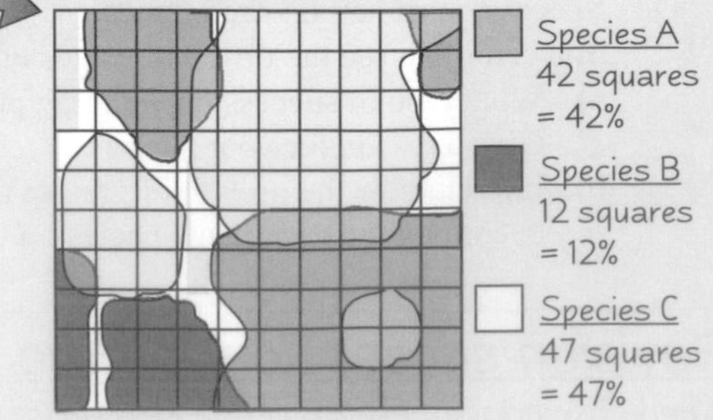

Investigating Ecosystems

Point Quadrats can also be used to *Investigate Plant Populations*

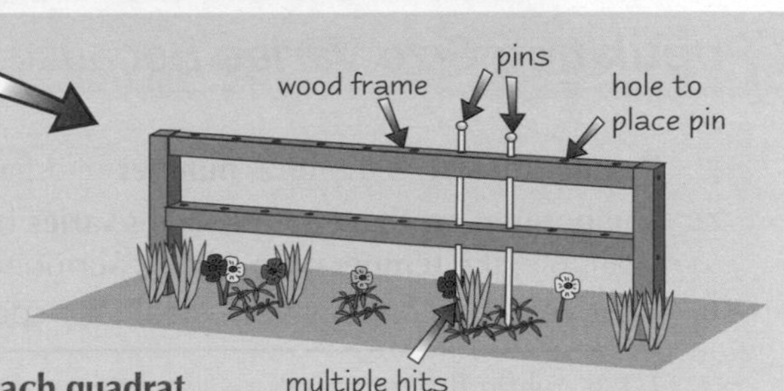

1) A **point quadrat** is a **horizontal bar** on **two legs** with a series of holes at set intervals along its length.
2) Point quadrats are **placed on the ground** at **random points** within the area you're investigating.
3) **Pins** are dropped through the holes in the frame and **every plant** that each pin **touches** is **recorded**. If a pin touches several **overlapping** plants, **all** of them are recorded.
4) The **number of individuals** of each species is recorded in **each quadrat**.
5) The **percentage cover** of a species can also be measured by calculating the **number of times** a pin has touched a species as a **percentage** of the **total number** of pins dropped.
6) Point quadrats are especially useful in areas where there's lots of **dense vegetation** close to the ground.

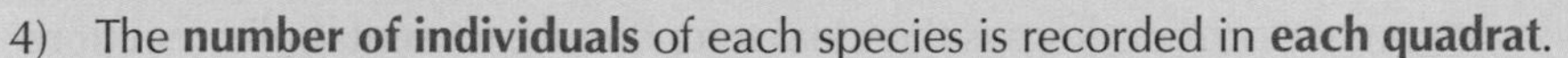
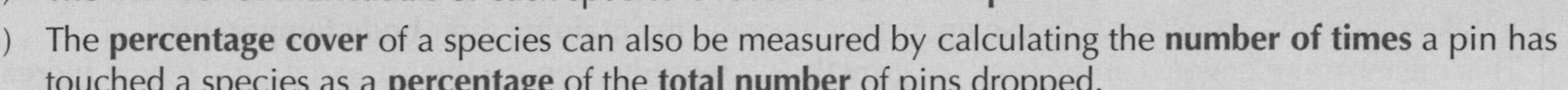

Transects are used to *Investigate* the *Distribution* of *Plant Populations*

You can use **lines** called **transects** to help find out how plants are **distributed across** an area, e.g. how species **change** from a hedge towards the middle of a field. You need to know about **three** types of transect:

1) **Line transects** — a **tape measure** is placed **along** the transect and the species that **touch** the tape measure are **recorded**.

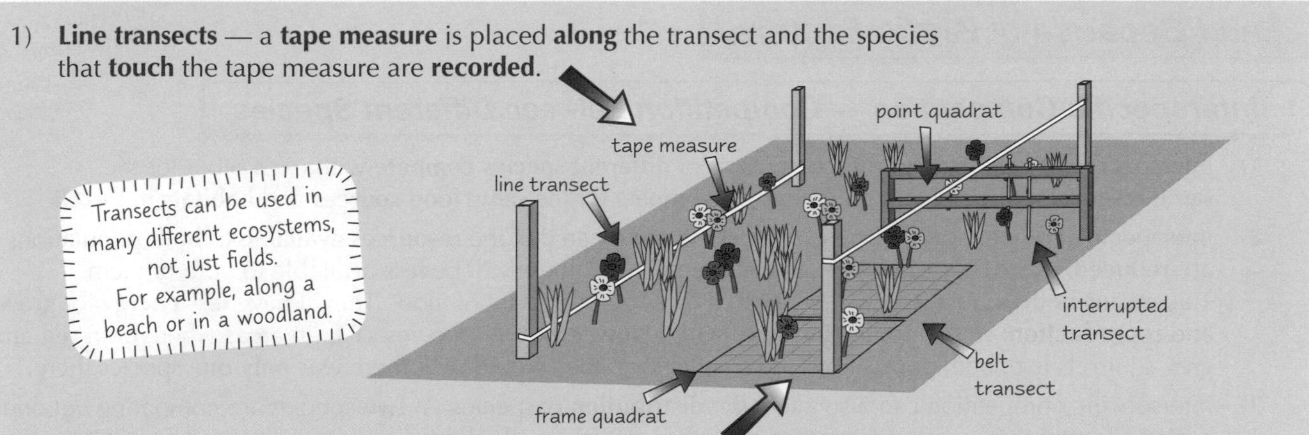

2) **Belt transects** — data is collected along the transect using **frame quadrats** placed **next to** each other.
3) **Interrupted transects** — instead of investigating the **whole transect** of either a line or a belt, you can take **measurements** at **intervals**. E.g. by placing **point quadrats** at **right angles** to the direction of the transect at **set intervals** along its length, such as **every 2 m**.

Practice Questions

Q1 Define abundance.

Q2 What does percentage cover show?

Q3 Explain why samples of a population are taken.

Q4 Briefly describe how belt transects are different from line transects.

Exam Question

Q1 A student wants to sample a population of daffodils in a field.

a) Describe a method she could use to avoid bias in her investigation. [1 mark]

b) Describe how she could investigate the percentage cover of daffodils in the field using frame quadrats. [3 marks]

c) Suggest how incorrect identification of plant species could lead to inaccuracies in the results. [1 mark]

What did the quadrat say to the policeman — I've been framed...

If you want to know what it's really like doing these investigations then read these pages outside in the pouring rain. Doing it while you're tucked up in a nice warm, dry exam hall won't seem so bad after that, take my word for it.

Factors Affecting Population Size

Uh-oh, anyone who loves cute little bunny-wunnys look away now — these pages are about how the population sizes of organisms fluctuate and the reasons why. One of the reasons, I'm sad to say, is because the little rabbits get eaten.

Population Size Varies Because of Abiotic Factors...

Remember — abiotic factors are the non-living features of an ecosystem.

1) **Population size** is the **total number** of organisms of **one species** in a **habitat**.
2) The **population size** of any species **varies** because of **abiotic** factors, e.g. the amount of **light**, **water** or **space** available, the **temperature** of their surroundings or the **chemical composition** of their surroundings.
3) When abiotic conditions are **ideal** for a species, organisms can **grow fast** and **reproduce successfully**.

E.g. when the temperature of a mammal's surroundings is the ideal temperature for **metabolic reactions** to take place, they don't have to **use up** as much energy **maintaining** their **body temperature**. This means more energy can be used for **growth** and **reproduction**, so their population size will **increase**.

4) When abiotic conditions **aren't ideal** for a species, organisms **can't** grow as **fast** or reproduce as **successfully**.

E.g. when the temperature of a mammal's surroundings is significantly **lower** or **higher** than their **optimum** body temperature, they have to **use** a lot of **energy** to maintain the right **body temperature**. This means less energy will be available for **growth** and **reproduction**, so their population size will **decrease**.

...and Because of Biotic Factors

Biotic factors are the living features of an ecosystem.

1 Interspecific Competition — Competition Between Different Species

1) Interspecific competition is when organisms of **different species compete** with each other for the **same resources**, e.g. **red** and **grey** squirrels compete for the same **food sources** and **habitats** in the **UK**.
2) Interspecific competition between two species can mean that the **resources available** to **both** populations are **reduced**, e.g. if they share the **same** source of food, there will be **less** available to both of them. This means both populations will be **limited** by a lower amount of food. They'll have less **energy** for **growth** and **reproduction**, so the population sizes will be **lower** for both species. E.g. in areas where both **red** and **grey** squirrels live, both populations are **smaller** than they would be if there was **only one** species there.
3) Interspecific competition can also affect the **distribution** of species. If **two** species are competing but one is **better adapted** to its surroundings than the other, the less well adapted species is likely to be **out-competed** — it **won't** be able to **exist** alongside the better adapted species. E.g. since the introduction of the **grey squirrel** to the UK, the native **red squirrel** has **disappeared** from large areas. The grey squirrel has a better chance of **survival** because it's **larger** and can store **more fat** over winter.

Plants compete for things like minerals and light.

2 Intraspecific Competition — Competition Within a Species

Intraspecific competition is when organisms of the **same species compete** with each other for the **same resources**.

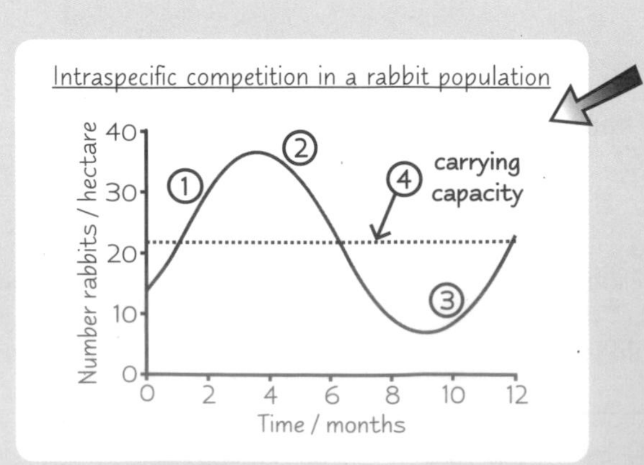

1) The **population** of a species (e.g. rabbits) **increases** when resources are **plentiful**. As the population increases, there'll be **more** organisms competing for the **same amount** of **space** and **food**.
2) Eventually, resources such as food and space become **limiting** — there **isn't enough** for all the organisms. The population then begins to **decline**.
3) A **smaller** population then means that there's **less competition** for space and food, which is **better** for **growth** and **reproduction** — so the population starts to **grow** again.
4) The **maximum stable population size** of a species that an ecosystem can **support** is called the **carrying capacity**.

Factors Affecting Population Size

3 Predation — Predator and Prey Populations are Controlled by Negative Feedback

Predation is where an organism (the predator) kills and eats another organism (the prey), e.g. lions kill and eat (**predate** on) buffalo. The **population sizes** of predators and prey are **controlled** by **negative feedback** (see page 3):

1) As the **prey** population **increases**, there's **more food** for predators, so the **predator** population **grows**. E.g. in the graph on the right the **lynx** population **grows** after the **snowshoe hare** population has **increased** because there's **more food** available.
2) As the **predator** population **increases**, **more prey** is **eaten** — so the **prey** population then begins to **fall**. E.g. **greater numbers** of lynx eat lots of snowshoe hares, so their population **falls**. This is an example of **negative feedback** — the **prey population** is restored to a more **stable size**.
3) This means there's **less food** for the **predators**, so their population **decreases** (more negative feedback), and so on. E.g. **reduced** snowshoe hare numbers means there's **less food** for the lynx, so their population **falls**.

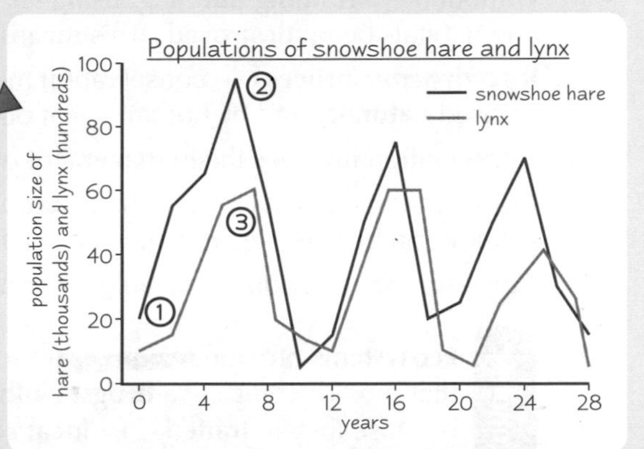

Predator-prey relationships are usually more **complicated** than this though because there are **other factors** involved, like availability of **food** for the **prey**. E.g. it's thought that the population of snowshoe hare initially begins to **decline** because there's **too many** of them for the amount of **food available**. This is then **accelerated** by **predation** from the lynx.

Limiting Factors Stop the Population Size of a Species Increasing

1) Limiting factors can be **abiotic**, e.g. the amount of **shelter** in an ecosystem **limits** the population size of a species because there's only enough shelter for a **certain number** of individuals.
2) Limiting factors can also be **biotic**, e.g. **interspecific competition limits** the population size of a species because the amount of **resources** available to a species is **reduced**.
3) Limiting factors determine the **carrying capacity** of an ecosystem.

Parasols and silk cushions were the limiting factors for Ralph's comfort.

Practice Questions

Q1 What is interspecific competition?

Q2 What will be the effect of interspecific competition on the population size of a species?

Q3 Define intraspecific competition.

Q4 What does 'carrying capacity' mean?

Q5 What is a limiting factor?

Exam Question

Q1* The graph on the right shows the population size of a predator species and a prey species over a period of 30 years.
Using the graph, describe and explain how the population sizes of the predator and prey species vary over the first 10 years.

population size / thousands
Years
Prey
Predator

[6 marks]

* You will be assessed on the quality of your written response in this question.

Predator-prey relationships — they don't usually last very long...

You'd think they could have come up with names a little more different than inter- and intraspecific competition. I always remember it as int-er means diff-er-ent species. The factors that affect population size are divided up nicely for you here — just like predators like to nicely divide up their prey into bitesize chunks.

Conservation of Ecosystems

It's important that ecosystems are conserved, so the resources we use from them don't run out.

*We Need to **Conserve Ecosystems***

1) **Conservation** is the **protection** and **management** of **ecosystems** so that the **natural resources** in them can be **used** without them **running out**. E.g. using rainforests for timber without any species becoming **extinct** and without any habitats being **destroyed**. This means the natural resources will still be available for **future generations**.
2) It's a **dynamic process** — conservation methods need to be **adapted** to the **constant changes** (caused **naturally** and by **humans**) that occur within ecosystems.
3) Conservation involves the **management** of ecosystems — controlling how **resources** are **used** and **replaced**.
4) Conservation can also involve **reclamation** — **restoring ecosystems** that have been **damaged** or **destroyed** so they can be **used again**, e.g. restoring **forests** that have been **cut down** so they can be used again.
5) Conservation is **important** for many reasons:

Economic

Ecosystems provide **resources** for lots of things that **humans need**, e.g. **rainforests** contain species that provide things like **drugs**, **clothes** and **food**. These resources are **economically important** because they're **traded** on a **local** and **global** scale. If the ecosystems **aren't** conserved, the resources that we use now will be **lost**, so there will be **less trade** in the future.

Social

Many ecosystems bring **joy** to lots of people because they're **attractive** to **look at** and people **use** them for **activities**, e.g. birdwatching and walking. The species and habitats in the ecosystems may be **lost** if they **aren't** conserved, so **future generations** won't be able to use and enjoy them.

Ethical

1) Some people think we should conserve ecosystems simply because it's the **right thing to do**, e.g. most people think organisms have a **right to exist**, so they shouldn't become extinct as a result of **human activity**.
2) Some people think we have a **moral responsibility** to conserve ecosystems for **future generations**, so they can enjoy and use them.

Cast your mind back to Module 4 — the reasons for conservation are similar to the reasons for conserving biodiversity.

6) **Preservation** is different from conservation — it's the **protection** of ecosystems so they're kept **exactly as they are**. Nothing is **removed** from a preserved ecosystem and they're only **used** for activities that **don't damage** them. For example, **Antarctica** is a preserved ecosystem because it's protected from **exploitation** by humans — it's only used for **limited tourism** and **scientific research**, not **mining** or other **industrial** activities.

Woodland Ecosystems** can **Provide Resources** in a **Sustainable Way

Ecosystems can be **managed** to provide resources in a way that's **sustainable** — this means enough resources are taken to meet the **needs** of people **today**, but without **reducing the ability** of people in the **future** to meet their own needs. **Temperate woodland** can be managed in a **sustainable way** — for every tree that's **cut down** for **timber**, a **new one** is planted in its place. The woodland should never become **depleted**. Cutting down trees and planting new ones needs to be done **carefully** to be **successful**:

Temperate woodland is between the tropics and the polar circles.

1) **Trees** are **cleared in strips or patches** — woodland **grows back more quickly** in smaller areas between bits of **existing woodland** than it does in larger, **open areas**.
2) The **cleared** strips or patches **aren't too large or exposed** — lots of **soil erosion** can occur on large areas of **bare ground**. If the soil is eroded, newly planted trees **won't** be able to **grow**.
3) **Timber** is sometimes **harvested by coppicing** — **cutting** down trees in a way that lets them **grow back**. This means new trees don't need to be planted.
4) **Native tree species** tend to be **planted in preference** to **non-native** species. This is **better** for **biodiversity** because native species have long-established **interactions** with other native species (e.g. plants, fungi, animals), so their presence should help species **thrive** in an area. Also some species might not adapt to the presence of non-native tree species.
5) Planted trees are attached to **posts** to provide **support**, and are grown in **plastic tubes** to stop them being **eaten** by grazing animals — this makes it **more likely** the trees will **survive** to become mature adults.
6) Trees **aren't planted too close together** — this means the trees aren't **competing** with each other for **space** or **resources**, so they're more likely to **survive**.

Conservation of Ecosystems

Fishing can also Provide Resources in a Sustainable Way

Fish stocks are **declining** because we're **overfishing**. This means there's **less fish** for us to **eat**, the ocean's **food chains** are affected and some species of fish may **disappear** altogether in some areas. To tackle this problem, we need to **maintain fish stocks** at a level where the fish **continue to breed**. This is **sustainable food production** — having enough food without using resources faster than they renew. Here are two examples of how fish stocks can be conserved:

Using Fishing Quotas

1) **Fishing quotas** are **limits** to the **amount** of certain fish species that fishermen are **allowed** to **catch**.
2) **Scientists** study different species and decide **how big** their populations need to be for them to **maintain** their numbers. Then they decide **how many** it's **safe** for fishermen to take without reducing the population **too much**.
3) **International agreements** are made (e.g. the Common Fisheries Policy in the EU) that state the **amount** of fish **each country** can take, and **where** they're allowed to take them from.
4) Fishing quotas are supposed to help to **conserve** fish species by **reducing** the numbers that are **caught** and **killed**, so the populations aren't **reduced** too much and the species aren't at risk from becoming **extinct**.
5) There are **problems** with fishing quotas though — e.g. fish of the **wrong** species or size are **still caught**, but they end up being **thrown back** into the sea, often **dead** or **dying**, because the restrictions don't allow the fishermen to bring them ashore. However, **new rules** for the Common Fisheries Policy are **banning** the discarding of fish like this and the whole catch will have to be brought ashore to be counted against the quota.

Controlling Mesh Size of Nets

1) There are different **limits** to the **mesh size** of the fish net, depending on what's being fished.
2) This is to **reduce** the number of **'unwanted'** and **discarded fish** that are **accidently caught**, e.g. shrimp caught along with cod. Using a **bigger mesh size** will let the 'unwanted' species **escape**.
3) It also means that **younger fish** will **slip through** the net, allowing them to reach **breeding age**.
4) However, it can be **difficult** to determine exactly **how big** the **mesh size** should be in areas where **several different fish species** are fished for at the same time. And **two nets**, each of which meets regulations, could be used **one inside the other** — effectively **reducing** the **reported mesh size**.

Practice Questions

Q1 How is preservation different from conservation?

Q2 What does managing an ecosystem in a sustainable way mean?

Q3 Give one way that fish stocks can be conserved in a sustainable way.

Exam Question

Q1 Some deciduous woodland in the UK is managed through a process called 'coppicing with standards'. The coppiced trees are cut down to the stump, and allowed to regrow from shoots which spring from the stump. The standards are trees that are not cut down and are left to grow and mature as normal.

a) Explain how coppicing allows woodland to be managed sustainably. [1 mark]

b) Suggest two benefits of not coppicing all the trees in a woodland. [2 marks]

c) It's recommended that only about 30% of the canopy is made up of standard trees. Suggest why it is necessary to restrict standard cover. [1 mark]

If I can sustain this revision it'll be a miracle...

Never mind ecosystems, I'm more interested in preserving my sanity after all this hard work. I know it doesn't seem all that sciencey, but you can still study Biology without a lab coat and some Petri dishes. Sustainability's a funny one to get your head around, but you need to know about how it applies to timber production and fishing.

Conservation of Ecosystems

Human activity can often come into conflict with conservation and preservation...

Conservation and Preservation can be Balanced with Human Needs

Areas can be **managed** to **reduce** the **conflict** between conservation and preservation, and human needs.

Example 1 — The Terai Arc

1) The **Terai Arc** is an area of **forest** and **grasslands** on the border between **Nepal** and **India**. A **variety** of **plants** and **animals** are found there, including **endangered species** like the **Bengal Tiger** and **Asian elephant**.
2) Nearly **7 million people** also live in this area and many of them depend on the **forest's resources** to survive.
3) Areas of the forest are also being **destroyed** to make way for **more housing** and **other development** — this **destruction of habitat** brings humans and animals into **closer contact** and **increases conflict** between the two. For example, **elephants** can **eat** and **trample crop fields** and **tigers** can **kill livestock**. This increases the likelihood of these animals being **shot** and **killed**.
4) Conservation charity the **WWF** has worked with **local people** to help **balance** their needs with conserving the forest and its wildlife. For example, the charity has provided people with things like **solar cookers** and **biogas generators**, so they **don't need** to use **wood** from the forest as **fuel**. Farmers are encouraged to plant **mint hedges** around their crops to **keep animals** (which don't like the taste of mint) **away**.

Example 2 — The Maasai Mara

1) The **Maasai Mara** is a national reserve in **Kenya**. It's a large area of **grassland** (**savannah**), which is home to huge populations of **wildebeest** and **zebra**, as well as **lions** and **cheetahs**. The Maasai Mara is named after the **Maasai people** who live in the area.
2) The Maasai people traditionally **earn a living** by raising **livestock**, such as **cattle**. This can bring them into **conflict** with conservationists — e.g. **overgrazing** by **livestock** can destroy grassland for **wildlife**.
3) Conservation trusts are working with the Maasai people to help them **make money** from their land through **conservation** and **ecotourism projects** rather than farming, and to **farm** in a **sustainable way**. So, the **economic needs** of the Maasai people are met, while still allowing the area to be conserved.

Example 3 — UK Peat Bogs

1) Lots of **upland** parts of the **UK** are home to **peat bogs** — areas of wet peat. These peat bogs **store water** and **carbon dioxide**, and are home to **lots of different plants** and **animals**, such as *Sphagnum* moss — these mosses actually help the peat bog form by retaining water.
2) Farmers use the peat bogs to **graze sheep** and **deer**. However, this can lead to **conflict** with conservationists because **overgrazing** causes **loss of moss species**, **soil compaction** (which increases **water runoff** down sheep paths, taking sediment with it) and general peat bog **erosion**.
3) Recent **government-funded programmes**, like the Environmental Stewardship Scheme, have given farmers **money** to use the peat bogs in a sustainable way, e.g. to carry out measures to **reduce water runoff**, to **lower** the **number** of **livestock** that use the peat bogs, and to **remove livestock** over **winter**.

Human Activities Affect Environmentally-Sensitive Ecosystems

The **animal** and **plant populations** in **important**, but **fragile**, **ecosystems** have been affected by **human activity**. Here are some examples, along with information on how these effects are being **controlled**:

1) The Galapagos Islands

The **Galapagos Islands** are a small group of islands in the **Pacific Ocean**. Many **rare species** of **animals** and **plants** have evolved there that **can't be found elsewhere**. In the past the islands have attracted **sailors**, **explorers** and **scientists**, but recently the number of **inhabitants** and **tourists** to the islands has increased considerably.

Effects of Human Activities:

1) **Non-native animals introduced** to the islands by humans **eat** some native species. This has caused a decrease in the populations of native species. E.g. non-native **dogs**, **cats** and **black rats** eat young **giant tortoises** and **Galapagos land iguanas**. **Goats** have eaten much of the **plant life** on some of the islands.
2) **Non-native plants** have also been introduced to the islands. These **compete** with native plant species, causing a decrease in their populations. For example, **quinine trees** are **taller** than some native plants — they **block out light** to the native plants, which then **struggle** to **survive**.

Conservation of Ecosystems

Methods of Control:

1) **Eradication programmes** have **removed wild goats** from some of the smaller islands and **wild dogs** from the largest island. **Quinine trees** are kept in check using **chemical herbicides** and by **uprooting** young trees.
2) When people visit the Galapagos National Park they are expected to follow a list of **rules**, which includes not bringing any **live plants** or **animals** onto the islands, or moving them between the islands. People are also only allowed to visit the Galapagos National Park in the company of a **licensed guide**.

2) Antarctica

Antarctica is the world's **southernmost continent**. It has a **unique icy landscape** with plants and animals that have adapted to its **harsh conditions**. For at least 200 years it has attracted **visitors**, e.g. research scientists and tourists.

Effects of Human Activities:

1) **Visitors** to Antarctica have caused **pollution** in the past by dumping **sewage** into the sea and leaving **rubbish**. **Shipping accidents** have lead to **oil spills**, which severely affect wildlife.
2) **Hunting**, **whaling** and **fishing** have all **reduced wildlife populations** in the area.

Methods of Control:

1) **All waste** apart from food waste and sewage must be **taken away by ship** for disposal in other countries. Many research stations now **treat** their **sewage** before releasing it, to reduce its effects on the environment.
2) **Ships** that use **thick oil** as a **fuel** are now **banned** from **Antarctic waters** — heavy oil spills are likely to cause more damage and be harder to clean up than spills of lighter fuels.
3) There are **tourist restrictions** — e.g. tourists are only allowed on land at **certain locations** for **a few hours**.
4) **Hunting** and **whaling** have been **banned** for some time now, although fishing still continues.

3) The **Lake District** and **Snowdonia National Parks**

The **Lake District** and **Snowdonia** are **beautiful national parks** — both are areas of **hills** and **lakes**, with the **Lake District** in North West England and **Snowdonia** in Wales. Both also attract **millions of visitors** per year.

Effects of Human Activities:

1) Many of the visitors to the Lake District go **walking** on the region's **footpaths**. This leads to the **erosion** of the footpaths and the **loss of soil** from **hillsides**. Soil that ends up in **waterways** and **lakes** can **disturb the pH** of the **water**, causing knock-on effects for wildlife. As the paths become harder to walk on, people can start to **trample** and **destroy** the **sensitive vegetation** either side of the paths.
2) It's a similar story in **Snowdonia** — a lot of **rain** falls in the Snowdonia hills, which leads to the **erosion** of the paths. Walkers often **trample the surrounding vegetation** as they try to walk around the floods.

Methods of Control:

1) Simple really — in the Lake District, conservation charities and the Lake District National Park Authority attempt to carry out **regular repair** and **maintenance work** on the paths and **encourage** the **regrowth** of **damaged vegetation**. Walkers are also **educated** about the importance of sticking to the paths and not taking short cuts, as these increase erosion.
2) In Snowdonia, volunteers have **dug drains** next to the paths to prevent them from flooding.

Practice Questions

Q1 Give one effect of human activity on the Galapagos Islands and an example of how this is being controlled.

Exam Question

Q1 Compare the ways in which the economic needs of humans have been balanced with conservation in three named areas of the world. [4 marks]

All I know is that exams affect my environmentally-sensitive system...

Ecosystems can be managed so that the needs of humans in the area can be met, but human activities also need to be controlled to protect ecosystems. Make sure you know all of the examples on these two pages. Off. By. Heart.

How To Do Well in Your Exams

The reason for learning all the lovely facts and diagrams in this book is so that you can ace your exams and get yourself an A-level in Biology. So, now it's a good idea to find out exactly what you'll be in for exam-wise...

*Make Sure You Know the **Structure** of Your **Exams***

It seems obvious, but if you know exactly what will be **covered** in each of the exams, how much **time** you'll have to do them and how they'll be **structured**, you can be better prepared. So let's take a look at the ins and outs of all the exams you'll be facing for **A-level Biology**...

	Paper	No. of marks	Time	Modules assessed	Type of questions in paper	
01	Biological Processes	100	2 hrs 15 mins	1, 2, 3, 5	Section A (15 marks) — multiple choice	Section B (85 marks) — short answer and extended response
02	Biological Diversity	100	2 hrs 15 mins	1, 2, 4, 6	Section A (15 marks) — multiple choice	Section B (85 marks) — short answer and extended response
03	Unified Biology	70	1 hr 30 mins	1, 2, 3, 4, 5, 6	No multiple choice. Short answer or extended response throughout.	

As you can see from the table...

1) **All three papers** cover theory from **both years** of your course — this means you need to make sure you **revise** your **Year 1 notes** for **modules** (**1-4**) as well as the **Year 2 modules** (**5-6**) covered in **this book** for these exams. The papers will contain some **synoptic** questions, which **connect** and **test** different areas of Biology from Years 1 and 2.
2) For each paper you get **just over a minute per mark**. This means if you get stuck on a short question it's sometimes worth moving onto another one and then coming back to it if you have time. However, bear in mind that you might want to spend a **bit longer** on the **extended response** questions, in which case you'll have to spend **less time** on the multiple choice and short answer questions.
3) In **Section A** of the **Biological Processes** and **Biological Diversity** papers you'll have **15 multiple choice questions**. Each question will have four possible answers (**A-D**) but only one will be correct.
4) All three papers include **short answer** and **extended response** questions. Short answer questions may involve **problem solving**, **calculations** or a **practical context** (see next page). There's more about extended response questions below...

Julie had heard of multiple choice, but this just took the biscuit...

***All** of Your Exams Will Contain **Extended Response** Questions*

1) In each of your three papers there will be **one** or **more extended response** questions.
2) These questions are worth **6** or **9 marks** and will require a **long answer**.
3) The questions are shown with an **asterisk** (*) next to their number.
4) You'll be awarded marks for the **quality** of your extended response as well as the **content** of your answer, so your answer needs to:
   - Be **legible** (the same goes for all your written answers).
   - Have a **clear** and **logical structure**.
   - Show **good reasoning** — i.e. show that you have thought about and understood the question, and can justify your answer.
   - Include information that's **relevant** to the question.
5) You can gain **practice** at extended response questions by doing the exam questions marked with an asterisk in this book.

These questions often want you to use a source (such as some text or a diagram, table or graph) to help you answer the question.

How To Do Well in Your Exams

Command Words Tell You What You Need to do in a Question

Command words are just the bits of a question that tell you **what to do**. You'll find answering exam questions much easier if you understand exactly what they mean, so here's a brief summary table of the **most common** ones:

Command word:	What to do:
Give / Name / State	Give a brief one or two word answer, or a short sentence.
Identify	Pick out information or say what something is.
Describe	Write about what something's like, e.g. describe the structure of fish gills.
Explain	Give reasons for something.
Suggest	Use your scientific knowledge to work out what the answer might be.
Compare	Give the similarities and differences between two things.
Outline	Write about the main points of a topic.
Calculate	Work out the solution to a mathematical problem.
Discuss	Write about a topic, considering different issues or ideas.

Even though you're taking an A-level in Biology, you'll still need to do some maths in the exams — but it'll be set in a biological context.

Some questions will also ask you to answer '**using the information/data provided**' (e.g. a graph, table or passage of text) or '**with reference to figure X**' — if so, you must **refer to** the information, data or figure you've been given or you won't get the marks. Some questions may also ask you to answer '**using your calculation**' — it's the same here, you need to use **your answer** to a particular **calculation**, otherwise you won't get the marks.

Not all of the questions will have command words, e.g. the multiple choice questions — instead they may just ask a which / why / what type of question.

Solving Problems in a Practical Context

Make sure you learn the language that goes with experiments too, e.g. precision, accuracy, validity.

In the exams, you'll get plenty of questions set in a 'practical context'. As well as answering questions about the **methods** used or the **conclusions** drawn, you'll need to be able to **apply** your **scientific knowledge** to **solve problems** set in these contexts. For example:

Q1 A scientist is investigating the effect on plant growth of adding additional CO_2 to the air in a greenhouse. The results are shown in the graph.

a) Explain the difference in the two curves shown on the graph. [3 marks]

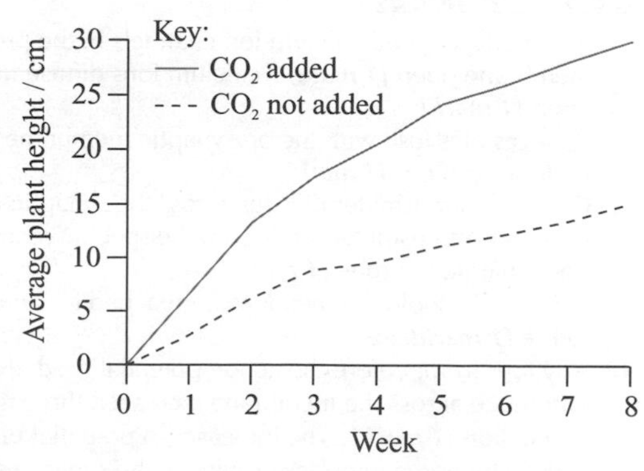

You should remember from Module 5 that plants use carbon dioxide to **produce glucose** by **photosynthesis**. The more carbon dioxide plants have, the **more glucose** they can produce (until something other than CO_2 becomes a limiting factor), meaning they can also **respire** more. This gives them more **ATP** for **DNA replication, cell division** and **protein synthesis**, leading to **increased plant growth.**

You might think you need your head examined for picking A-level Biology...

... because there's a lot to learn and three big exams to do. But let me just stop you right there... instead of worrying, just work through this book, including having a go at all of the questions, and you'll be well and truly prepped for the exams. Then re-read these pages to make sure you know what's coming. After that, all there is to say is... good luck.

Answers

Module 5: Section 1 — Communication and Homeostasis

Page 3 — Communication and Homeostasis Basics

1 a) The maintenance of a constant internal environment ***[1 mark]***.
b) Receptors detect when a level is too high or too low ***[1 mark]***, and the information's communicated via the nervous system or the hormonal system to effectors ***[1 mark]***. Effectors respond to counteract the change / to bring the level back to normal ***[1 mark]***.

Page 5 — Receptors and Neurones

1 a) They convert the energy from the stimulus into another form/ electrical energy ***[1 mark]***.
b) When a Pacinian corpuscle is stimulated, the lamellae/layers of connective tissue are deformed and press on the sensory nerve ending ***[1 mark]***. This causes deformation of stretch-mediated sodium channels in the sensory neurone's cell membrane ***[1 mark]***. The sodium ion channels open and sodium ions diffuse into the cell ***[1 mark]***, creating the generator potential ***[1 mark]***.
c) Once the threshold level is reached an action potential/nerve impulse will travel along the sensory neurone to a relay neurone in the CNS ***[1 mark]***. An action potential/nerve impulse will then travel from the relay neurone to a motor neurone, which carries the action potential/nerve impulse to effector cells ***[1 mark]***.

Page 7 — Action Potentials

1 a) A stimulus causes sodium ion channels in the neurone cell membrane to open ***[1 mark]***. Sodium ions diffuse into the cell, so the membrane becomes depolarised ***[1 mark]***.
b) The first action potential fired at 0.5 ms. If the second one fired at 4.5 ms, this means an action potential is fired every (4.5 – 0.5) = 4 ms. Number of ms in one hour = 60 × 60 × 1000 = 3 600 000. There is one action potential every 4 ms, so in one hour there will be 3 600 000 ÷ 4 = 900 000 = $\mathbf{9 \times 10^5}$ action potentials. ***[2 marks for the correct answer, allow 1 mark for the correct calculation of 3 600 000 ÷ 4.]***
c) 30 mV ***[1 mark]***
This is the same as the maximum potential difference shown on the graph. Remember, action potentials always fire with the same change in voltage no matter how big the stimulus is.

2 Transmission of action potentials will be slower in neurones with damaged myelin sheaths ***[1 mark]***. This is because myelin is an electrical insulator, so increases the speed of action potential conduction ***[1 mark]***. The action potentials 'jump' between the nodes of Ranvier/between the myelin sheaths, where sodium ion channels are concentrated ***[1 mark]***.

Page 9 — Synapses

1 A — voltage-gated calcium ion channels in the presynaptic membrane open ***[1 mark]*** / calcium ions diffuse into the synaptic knob ***[1 mark]***
B — vesicles fuse with the presynaptic membrane and release neurotransmitter ***[1 mark]***
C — neurotransmitter diffuses across the synaptic cleft ***[1 mark]***
D — neurotransmitter binds with the specific receptors on the postsynaptic neurone ***[1 mark]***

2 a) It is the threshold that needs to be reached for an action potential to fire ***[1 mark]***.
b) Any four from: before the action potential fired, the potential difference across the membrane increased three times in quick succession ***[1 mark]***. The increases in potential difference were caused by nerve impulses arriving at the synapse and releasing neurotransmitter ***[1 mark]***, which caused sodium ion channels to open on the postsynaptic membrane ***[1 mark]***. This allowed an influx of sodium ions into the postsynaptic membrane, which increased the potential difference across the membrane ***[1 mark]***. It was not until the arrival of the third impulse that enough neurotransmitter was acting on the membrane to allow the threshold level to be reached and the action potential to be fired ***[1 mark]***. ***[Maximum of 4 marks available.]***

Page 11 — The Hormonal System and Glands

1 The cortex secretes steroid hormones, such as cortisol and aldosterone ***[1 mark]***. Any two from: The hormones stimulate the breakdown of fats and proteins into glucose to make more energy available ***[1 mark]***. / They increase blood volume and pressure by increasing the uptake of sodium ions and water by the kidneys ***[1 mark]***. / They suppress the immune system ***[1 mark]***.

2 Any three from: The medulla secretes adrenaline ***[1 mark]***. Adrenaline binds to specific receptors on cell membranes ***[1 mark]*** and activates adenylyl cyclase ***[1 mark]***. This catalyses the production of cyclic AMP from ATP ***[1 mark]***, which activates a cascade of reactions including the conversion of glycogen into glucose ***[1 mark]***. ***[Maximum of 3 marks available.]***
Noradrenaline (secreted by the medulla) can also catalyse the production of cyclic AMP from ATP, but you need to know specifically about **adrenaline** for your exam.

Page 13 — Homeostasis — Control of Body Temperature

1 Peripheral temperature receptors/thermoreceptors in the skin detect a higher external temperature than normal ***[1 mark]***. The peripheral temperature receptors/thermoreceptors send impulses along sensory neurones to the hypothalamus ***[1 mark]***.

2 Snakes are ectotherms so they can't control their body temperature internally and depend on the temperature of their external environment ***[1 mark]***. In cold climates, snakes will be less active ***[1 mark]***, which makes it harder to catch prey, avoid predators, find a mate, etc. ***[1 mark]***.
You need to use a bit of common sense to answer this question — you know that the activity level of an ectotherm depends on the temperature of the surroundings, so in a cold environment it won't be very active. And if it can't be very active it'll have trouble surviving.

3 Maximum of four marks available. 1 mark for each method, up to a maximum of 2 marks. 1 mark for the correct explanation of the method, up to a maximum of 2 marks.
Vasoconstriction of blood vessels ***[1 mark]*** reduces heat loss because less blood flows through the capillaries in the surface layers of the dermis ***[1 mark]***. / Erector pili muscles contract to make hairs stand on end ***[1 mark]***, trapping an insulating layer of air to prevent heat loss ***[1 mark]***. / Muscles contract in spasms to make the body shiver ***[1 mark]***, so more heat is produced from increased respiration ***[1 mark]***. / Adrenaline and thyroxine are released ***[1 mark]***, which increase metabolism so more heat is produced ***[1 mark]***.

Page 15 — Homeostasis — Control of Blood Glucose

1 a) Negative feedback because the pancreas secretes hormones that return blood glucose concentration to normal if it is detected as being too high or too low ***[1 mark]***.
b) Any four from: Insulin is released when blood glucose concentration is too high ***[1 mark]***. It binds to specific receptors on muscle and liver cells ***[1 mark]*** causing them to become more permeable to glucose so more is absorbed from the blood ***[1 mark]***. Insulin activates glycogenesis so that glucose can be stored ***[1 mark]***. Insulin also causes the rate of respiration of glucose to increase so that more is used up ***[1 mark]***.
[Maximum of 4 marks available.]

2 No insulin would be secreted ***[1 mark]*** because ATP wouldn't be produced, so the potassium ion channels in the β cell plasma membrane wouldn't close / the plasma membrane of β cell wouldn't be depolarised ***[1 mark]***.

Page 17 — Diabetes

1 Any two from: It's cheaper to produce insulin using GM bacteria than to extract it from animal pancreases ***[1 mark]***. Large amounts of insulin can be made using GM bacteria, so there's enough insulin to treat everyone with Type I diabetes ***[1 mark]***. GM bacteria make real human insulin, which is more effective and less likely to trigger an allergic response or be rejected by the immune system ***[1 mark]***. Some people prefer insulin from GM bacteria for ethical or religious reasons ***[1 mark]***.

Answers

2 a) Any two from: Person A's blood glucose concentration is initially at a higher level than person B's blood glucose concentration. / Person A's blood glucose concentration reaches a much higher level than person B's blood glucose concentration. / It takes longer for person A's blood glucose concentration to start to decrease than it does for person B's blood glucose concentration to start to decrease. / Person A's blood glucose concentration decreases at a much slower rate than person B's blood glucose concentration. / Person A experiences a greater range of blood glucose concentration than person B. ***[2 pieces of evidence for 1 mark.]***

b) The insulin receptors on person A's cell membranes don't work properly / person A does not produce enough insulin, so their cells don't take up enough glucose ***[1 mark]***. This means their blood glucose concentration remains higher than normal ***[1 mark]***.

c) i)

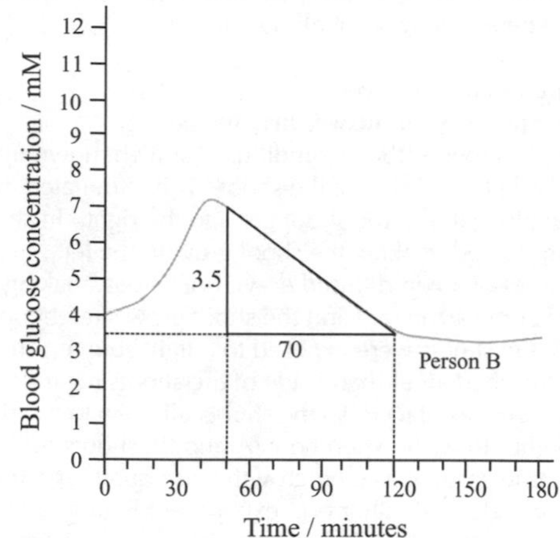

Rate of decrease = $\frac{3.5}{70}$ = **0.05 mM min^{-1}** ***[1 mark]***.

ii) Person A has diabetes so they don't produce enough insulin or they are unable to respond to insulin properly, which means their body can't take up all of the glucose as quickly as person B ***[1 mark]***.

d) Metformin acts on liver cells to reduce the amount of glucose that they release into the blood ***[1 mark]***. It also acts to increase the sensitivity of cells to insulin so more glucose can be taken up with the same amount of insulin ***[1 mark]***. This means that person A's blood glucose concentration would decrease much more quickly after taking the glucose drink if they did the test again ***[1 mark]***.

Module 5: Section 2 — Excretion

Page 20 — The Liver and Excretion

1 central vein ***[1 mark]***

2 B ***[1 mark]***

3 ***5-6 marks:***
The answer explains fully why there would be an increased concentration of urea in the urine, with a detailed description of deamination and the production of urea in the ornithine cycle.
The answer has a clear and logical structure. The information given is relevant and detailed.
3-4 marks:
The answer explains briefly why there would be an increased concentration of urea in the urine, with some mention of the break down of amino acids into ammonia and the production of urea in ornithine cycle.
The answer has some structure. Most of the information given is relevant and there is some detail involved.
1-2 marks:
The answer includes a basic explanation as to why there would be an increased concentration of urea in the urine.
The answer has no clear structure. The information given is basic and lacking in detail. It may not all be relevant.
0 marks:
No relevant information is given.
Here are some points your answer may include:
The protein would be digested, producing amino acids. Amino acids contain nitrogen in their amino groups, but the body can't usually store nitrogenous substances, so if a lot of protein is eaten there could be an excess of amino acids that will need to be used or broken down and excreted. Excess amino acids are broken down in the liver into ammonia and organic acids in a process called deamination. Ammonia is then combined with CO_2 in the ornithine cycle to produce urea. Urea is then released into the blood and filtered out at the kidneys to produce urine. So if a large amount of protein is eaten, there may be excess amino acids that are broken down by the liver, producing a large amount of urea that's excreted in the urine.
Don't forget to say that only excess amino acids are broken down.

Page 23 — The Kidneys and Excretion

1 a) C (loop of Henle) ***[1 mark]***

b) Point C because glucose is reabsorbed in the PCT so by the time the filtrate reaches point C there will be no glucose remaining/ the concentration of glucose will be much lower than at point B ***[1 mark]***.

c) Ultrafiltration is when substances are filtered out of the blood and enter the tubules in the kidneys ***[1 mark]***. Blood enters a glomerulus, a bundle of capillaries looped inside a hollow ball called a Bowman's capsule ***[1 mark]***. The blood in the glomerulus is under high pressure because it enters through the afferent arteriole and leaves through the smaller efferent arteriole ***[1 mark]***. The high pressure forces liquid and small molecules in the blood out of the capillary and into the Bowman's capsule ***[1 mark]***. The liquid and small molecules pass through the capillary wall, the basement membrane and slits in the epithelium of the Bowman's capsule. But larger molecules like proteins and blood cells can't pass through and stay in the blood ***[1 mark]***.

Page 25 — Controlling Water Potential

1 a) Strenuous exercise causes more water to be lost from the body (through sweating), which decreases the water potential of the blood ***[1 mark]***. This is detected by osmoreceptors in the hypothalamus ***[1 mark]***, which stimulates the posterior pituitary gland to release more ADH ***[1 mark]***.

b) ADH increases the permeability of the walls of the distal convoluted tubule and collecting duct ***[1 mark]***. This means more water is reabsorbed into the medulla and into the blood by osmosis, so a small amount of concentrated urine is produced ***[1 mark]***.

2 Gerbils have longer loops of Henle than mice or rats ***[1 mark]***. A longer ascending limb means more ions are actively pumped out into the medulla ***[1 mark]***, which creates a very low water potential in the medulla ***[1 mark]***. This means more water moves out of the nephron into the capillaries, giving very concentrated/a very low volume of urine ***[1 mark]***.

Page 27 — Kidney Failure and Detecting Chemicals

1 E.g. Advantages, any two from: Kidney transplants are cheaper in the long term than renal dialysis ***[1 mark]***. / Having a kidney transplant is more convenient for a person than regular dialysis sessions ***[1 mark]***. / A patient who has had a kidney transplant won't feel unwell between dialysis sessions ***[1 mark]***.
Disadvantages: A transplant means the patient has to undergo a major operation, which is risky ***[1 mark]***. The patient also has to take drugs to suppress the immune system so it doesn't reject the transplant ***[1 mark]***.

Module 5: Section 3 — Animal Responses

Page 29 — The Nervous System

1 a) Hypothalamus ***[1 mark]***.

b) Control of breathing rate and heart rate ***[1 mark]***.

Answers

c) Lack of coordinated movement / balance / posture *[1 mark]*.
You know that the cerebellum normally coordinates muscles, balance and posture, so damage to it is likely to cause a lack of coordinated movement, balance or posture.

2 a) It helps to maintain posture and balance *[1 mark]*.
b) Any four from: Stretch receptors in the quadriceps muscle detect that the muscle is being stretched *[1 mark]*. A nerve impulse is passed along a sensory neurone *[1 mark]*, which communicates directly with a motor neurone in the spinal cord *[1 mark]*. The motor neurone carries the nerve impulse to the effector/quadriceps muscle *[1 mark]*, causing it to contract and the lower leg to move forward quickly *[1 mark]*. ***[Maximum of 4 marks available.]***

Page 31 — 'Fight or Flight' Response and Heart Rate

1 a) High blood pressure is detected by pressure receptors in the aorta called baroreceptors *[1 mark]*. Impulses are sent along sensory neurones to the medulla *[1 mark]*. Impulses are then sent from the medulla to the SAN along the vagus nerve *[1 mark]*. The vagus nerve secretes acetylcholine, which binds to receptors on the sinoatrial node/SAN *[1 mark]*. This slows the heart rate (reducing blood pressure) *[1 mark]*.
b) No impulses sent from the medulla would reach the SAN *[1 mark]*, so the heart rate wouldn't increase or decrease/control of the heart rate would be lost *[1 mark]*.

Page 34 — Muscle Contraction

1 Drawing number 3 *[1 mark]* because the M-line connects the middle of the myosin filaments *[1 mark]*. The cross-section would only show myosin filaments, which are the thick filaments *[1 mark]*.
The answer isn't drawing number 1 because all the dots in the cross-section are smaller, so the filaments shown are thin actin filaments — which aren't found at the M-line.

2 The A-bands stay the same length during contraction *[1 mark]*. The I-bands get shorter *[1 mark]*.

3 Muscles need ATP to relax because ATP provides the energy to break the actin-myosin cross bridges *[1 mark]*. If the cross bridges can't be broken, the myosin heads will remain attached to the actin filaments *[1 mark]*, so the actin filaments can't slide back to their relaxed position *[1 mark]*.

4 The muscles won't contract *[1 mark]* because calcium ions won't be released into the sarcoplasm, so troponin won't be removed from its binding site *[1 mark]*. This means no actin-myosin cross bridges can be formed *[1 mark]*.

Page 37 — Muscle Contraction

1 a) Creatine phosphate is split into creatine and phosphate *[1 mark]*. The phosphate group combines with ADP to make ATP *[1 mark]*.
b) Short burst of vigorous activity, such as a tennis serve (or similar example) *[1 mark]* because it is used up in a few seconds / very quickly *[1 mark]*.

2 Any four from: When an action potential arrives at a neuromuscular junction, it triggers the release of the neurotransmitter acetylcholine *[1 mark]*. This should bind to nicotinic cholinergic receptors on the postsynaptic membrane *[1 mark]* and trigger depolarisation in the muscle cell causing it to contract *[1 mark]*. If some of the nicotinic cholinergic receptors are damaged or blocked, the muscle cells won't be depolarised and won't contract *[1 mark]*. Fewer muscle cells working properly will lead to muscle fatigue *[1 mark]*. ***[Maximum of 4 marks available.]***

Module 5: Section 4 — Plant Responses and Hormones

Page 40 — Plant Responses

1 a) Because auxins are made in the shoot tip, so removing the tip means that any effects caused by auxins will only be due to the auxins added in the experiment *[1 mark]*.
b) To provide the shoots with the energy they needed to grow *[1 mark]*.
c) They are a (negative) control *[1 mark]*. They show that it is the auxin having the effect and nothing else about the sponges *[1 mark]*.
d) ***5-6 marks:***
The answer fully explains all the results for shoots A-C for each experiment, with reference to the movement of auxin and the effect of auxin on the shoot cells.
The answer has a clear and logical structure. The information given is relevant and detailed.
3-4 marks:
The answer explains some of the results for shoots A-C, with some reference to either the movement of auxin or its effect on the shoot cells.
The answer has some structure. Most of the information given is relevant and there is some detail included.
1-2 marks:
One or two results are described with little or no explanation.
The answer has no clear structure. The information given is basic and lacking in detail. It may not all be relevant.
0 marks:
No relevant information is given.
Here are some points your answer may include:
In experiment A, shoot A, the auxin diffused straight down from the sponge into the left-hand side of the shoot. This stimulated the cells on this side to elongate, so the shoot grew to the right. In shoot B, the opposite occurred, making the shoot grow to the left. In shoot C, equal amounts of auxin diffused down both sides, making all the cells elongate at the same rate and the shoot grow straight up. In experiment B, the shoots were exposed to a light source. The auxin diffused into the shaded/left-hand side of the shoots regardless of where the sponge was placed, so the shoots all grew to the right/ towards the light. In each experiment (A and B), shoots A, B and C all grew the same amount as their growth was equally stimulated by the auxin and glucose. Shoots in experiment B grew 2 mm more than the shoots in experiment A because they were exposed to light. This meant they were able to carry out photosynthesis, which allowed them to put more energy into growth compared to the shoots in experiment A, which were in the dark and not photosynthesising.

Page 43 — The Effects of Plant Hormones

1 A *[1 mark]*

2 a) ethene *[1 mark]*
b) Ethene stimulates enzymes that break down cell walls, break down chlorophyll and convert starch to sugars *[1 mark]*.
c) E.g. the tomatoes are less likely to be damaged in transport *[1 mark]*.

3 Abscisic acid/ABA triggers stomatal closure *[1 mark]*. This helps the plant to conserve water, by reducing water loss through transpiration *[1 mark]*.

Module 5: Section 5 — Photosynthesis

Page 45 — Photosynthesis and Respiration

1 C *[1 mark]*.

Page 49 — Photosynthesis

1 a) The thylakoid membranes *[1 mark]*.
b) Photosystem II *[1 mark]*.
c) Light energy splits water *[1 mark]*.
H_2O *[1 mark]* $\rightarrow 2H^+ + \frac{1}{2}O_2$ *[1 mark]*.
The electrons from the water replace the electrons lost from chlorophyll *[1 mark]*.
The question asks you to explain the purpose of photolysis, so make sure you include why the water is split up — to replace the electrons lost from chlorophyll.
d) NADP *[1 mark]*.

2 a) ***5-6 marks:***
The answer describes the full process of triose phosphate production, including the reactants and products of each step, and the roles of RuBisCO, ATP and reduced NADP.
The answer has a clear and logical structure. The information given is relevant and detailed.

Answers

3-4 marks:
The answer describes most of the process of triose phosphate production, including most of the reactants and products of each step and gives some mention of the roles of RuBisCO, ATP and reduced NADP.
The answer has some structure. Most of the information given is relevant and there is some detail involved.
1-2 marks:
Only one of the steps in the process of triose phosphate production is mentioned. There may be some mention of the role of one of either RuBisCO, ATP or reduced NADP.
The answer has no clear structure. The information given is basic and lacking in detail. It may not all be relevant.
0 marks:
No relevant information is given.
Here are some points your answer may include:
Ribulose bisphosphate/RuBP and carbon dioxide/CO_2 join together to form an unstable 6-carbon compound. This reaction is catalysed by the enzyme RuBisCO/ribulose bisphosphate carboxylase.
The compound breaks down into two molecules of a 3-carbon compound called glycerate 3-phosphate/GP. Two molecules of glycerate 3-phosphate are then converted into two molecules of triose phosphate/TP. The energy for this reaction comes from ATP and the H^+ ions come from reduced NADP.

b) Ribulose bisphosphate is regenerated from triose phosphate/TP molecules ***[1 mark]***. ATP provides the energy to do this ***[1 mark]***.
This question is only worth two marks so only the main facts are needed, without the detail of the number of molecules.

c) No glycerate 3-phosphate/GP would be produced ***[1 mark]***, so no triose phosphate/TP would be produced ***[1 mark]***. This means there would be no glucose produced ***[1 mark]***.

Page 51 — Limiting Factors in Photosynthesis

1 25 °C ***[1 mark]***. This is because photosynthesis involves enzymes ***[1 mark]***, which become inactive at low temperatures/10 °C ***[1 mark]*** and denature at high temperatures/45 °C ***[1 mark]***.

Page 53 — Limiting Factors in Photosynthesis

1 a) The level of GP will rise and levels of TP and RuBP will fall ***[1 mark]***. This is because there's less reduced NADP and ATP from the light-dependent reaction ***[1 mark]***, so the conversion of GP to TP and RuBP is slow ***[1 mark]***.

b) The levels of RuBP, GP and TP will fall ***[1 mark]***. This is because the reactions in the Calvin cycle are slower ***[1 mark]*** due to all the enzymes working more slowly ***[1 mark]***.

2 ***5-6 marks:***
A full description of the method used to investigate how temperature affects photosynthesis in Canadian pondweed is given, including all the apparatus needed.
The answer has a clear and logical structure. The information given is relevant and detailed.
3-4 marks:
A description of the method used to investigate how temperature affects photosynthesis in Canadian pondweed is given, with one or two steps missing. Most of the apparatus needed is included.
The answer has some structure. Most of the information given is relevant and there is some detail involved.
1-2 marks:
Only one or two of the steps in the method used to investigate how temperature affects photosynthesis in Canadian pondweed are given. There may be mention of some of the apparatus needed.
The information given is basic and lacking in detail. It may not all be relevant.
0 marks:
No relevant information is given.
Here are some points your answer may include:
A sample of pondweed would be placed in a test tube of water. The test tube would be placed in a beaker containing water at a known temperature. The test tube would be connected to a capillary tube of water and the capillary tube connected to a syringe. The pondweed would be allowed to photosynthesise for a set period of time. Afterwards, the syringe would be used to draw the bubble of oxygen produced up the capillary tube where its length would be measured using a ruler. The experiment is repeated and the mean length of gas bubble is calculated. Then the whole experiment is repeated at several different temperatures.

Module 5: Section 6 — Respiration

Page 55 — Aerobic Respiration

1 a) A = CO_2 ***[1 mark]***, D = acetate ***[1 mark]***, E = acetyl CoA ***[1 mark]***

b) Compound B (NAD) is reduced — it collects hydrogen from pyruvate, changing pyruvate into acetate ***[1 mark]***.

c) mitochondrial matrix ***[1 mark]***

2 C - A 2 carbon molecule that is the product of the link reaction and feeds into the Krebs cycle ***[1 mark]***.

3 D — Only 1 ***[1 mark]***.

4 ***5-6 marks:***
The answer describes the full process of glycolysis, including correct references to all the intermediate molecules, as well as the number of ATP and reduced NAD molecules made or used at each stage.
The answer has a clear and logical structure. The information given is relevant and detailed.
3-4 marks:
The answer describes part of the process of glycolysis, including correct references to some of the intermediate molecules. There is some mention of the either the number of ATP or reduced NAD molecules made or used.
The answer has some structure. Most of the information given is relevant and there is some detail involved.
1-2 marks:
The answer mentions at least one of the stages of glycolysis, but lacks correct reference to the intermediate molecules or the involvement of ATP and NAD.
The answer has no clear structure. The information given is basic and lacking in detail. It may not all be relevant.
0 marks:
No relevant information is given.
Here are some points your answer may include:
First, the 6-carbon glucose molecule is phosphorylated by adding two phosphates from two molecules of ATP. This creates one molecule of 6-carbon hexose bisphosphate and two molecules of ADP. Then, the hexose bisphosphate is split up into two molecules of 3-carbon triose phosphate. Triose phosphate is oxidised (by removing hydrogen) to give two molecules of 3-carbon pyruvate. The hydrogen is accepted by two molecules of NAD, producing two molecules of reduced NAD. During this step, four molecules of ATP are produced.

Page 57 — Aerobic Respiration

1 a) The transfer of electrons down the electron transport chain stops ***[1 mark]***. So there's no energy released to phosphorylate ADP/produce ATP ***[1 mark]***.

b) The Krebs cycle stops ***[1 mark]*** because there's no oxidised NAD/FAD coming from the electron transport chain ***[1 mark]***.
Part b is a bit tricky — remember that when the electron transport chain is inhibited, the reactions that depend on the products of the chain are also affected.

Page 59 — Anaerobic Respiration and RQs

1 Because lactate fermentation doesn't involve electron carriers/the electron transport chain/oxidative phosphorylation ***[1 mark]***.

2 RQ = $CO_2 \div O_2$ ***[1 mark]***
So the RQ of triolein = 57 ÷ 80 = 0.71 ***[1 mark]***
Award 2 marks for the correct answer of 0.71, without any working.

Answers

Page 61 — Respiration Experiments

1 ***5-6 marks:***
A full description of the method is given, making it clear how the effect of temperature should be investigated. It includes all the apparatus required, states any variables that should be controlled, and outlines any repeats and control experiments that are needed. The answer has a clear and logical structure. The information given is relevant and detailed.
3-4 marks:
A brief description of the method is given that shows how the effect of temperature should be investigated. However, full details about the apparatus required, variables that should be controlled or repeats and control experiments needed aren't included.
The answer has some structure. Most of the information given is relevant and there is some detail involved.
1-2 marks:
There is some description of the method, but it's not clear how the effect of temperature should be investigated. There is limited mention of the apparatus required, variables that should be controlled or repeats and control experiments needed.
The answer has no clear structure. The information given is basic and lacking in detail. It may not all be relevant.
0 marks:
No relevant information is given.
Here are some points your answer may include:
The respirometer should be set up in a water bath at one of the temperatures under investigation. In one of the tubes of the respirometer, a known mass of germinating mung beans should be placed on top of the gauze. The other tube should be set up as a control tube by placing glass beads, of the same mass as the mung beans, on top of the gauze. The syringe should be used to adjust the level of the fluid in the manometer to a known level. The apparatus should then be left for a set period of time (e.g. 20 minutes) with the tap closed. After this time, the distance moved by the liquid should be measured and used to calculate the volume of oxygen taken up by the mung beans per minute. Any other variables that could affect the results, e.g. light intensity, should be kept constant. The experiment should then be repeated at each of the temperatures under investigation several times and the mean results calculated.

Module 6: Section 1 — Cellular Control

Page 63 — Regulating Gene Expression

1 The introns from primary mRNA (pre-mRNA) are removed in a process called splicing ***[1 mark]***. This makes mature mRNA, which consists only of the exons ***[1 mark]***.

2 When no lactose is present, the lac repressor binds to the operator site and blocks transcription ***[1 mark]***. When lactose is present, it binds to the lac repressor ***[1 mark]***, changing its shape so that it can no longer bind to the operator site ***[1 mark]***. RNA polymerase can now begin transcription of the structural genes, including the ones that code for ß-galactosidase and lactose permease ***[1 mark]***.

Page 65 — Regulating Gene Expression

1 Insertion ***[1 mark]***.

2 Because they all have similar genes called Hox genes, which control body plan development ***[1 mark]***. These Hox genes contain homeobox sequences, which are highly conserved between different organisms ***[1 mark]***.

Module 6: Section 2 — Patterns of Inheritance

Page 67 — Types and Causes of Variation

1 a) Coat colour — because it shows discontinuous variation ***[1 mark]***.
You can tell the variation is discontinuous because there are no intermediate categories of coat colour — puppies are either yellow, chocolate or black and nothing inbetween (like yellowy-black). Discontinuous variation is usually controlled by only a small number genes (or a single gene).

b) Mass — because it shows continuous variation ***[1 mark]***.

c) 18.99 – 9.25 = **9.74 kg** ***[1 mark]***

Page 70 — Inheritance

1 Parents' genotypes identified as RR and rr ***[1 mark]***. Correct genetic diagram drawn with gametes' alleles identified as R, R and r, r ***[1 mark]*** and gametes crossed to show Rr as the only possible genotype in the offspring ***[1 mark]***.
The question specifically asks you to draw a genetic diagram, so make sure that you include one in your answer, e.g.

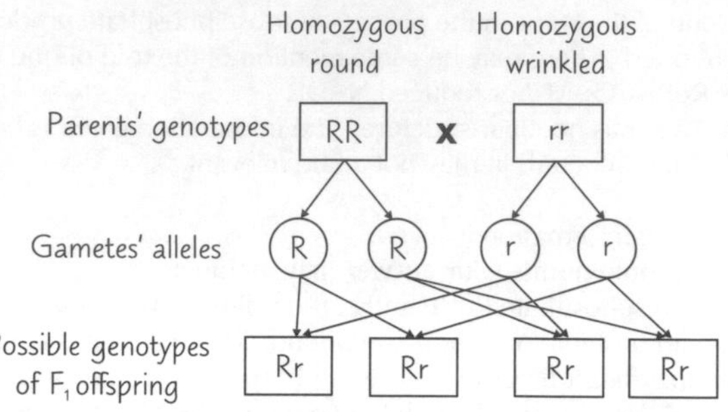

2 a) Because the alleles for red and white coats are codominant, so they are both expressed in the phenotype ***[1 mark]***.

b) Parents' genotypes identified as C^WC^W and C^RC^W ***[1 mark]***. Correct genetic diagram drawn with gametes' alleles identified as C^W, C^W and C^R, C^W ***[1 mark]*** and gametes crossed to show two offspring with genotype C^WC^W and two with genotype C^RC^W ***[1 mark]***. The phenotypes of the offspring are stated as two white and two roan ***[1 mark]***.
The question specifically asks you to draw a genetic diagram, so make sure that you include one in your answer, e.g.

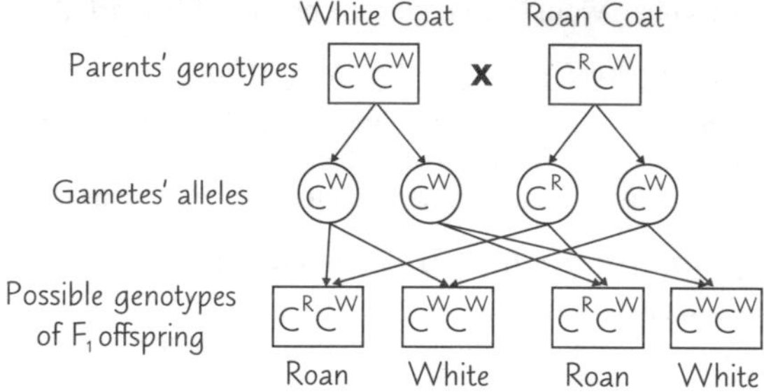

Page 73 — Linkages and Epistasis

1 a) Parents' genotypes identified as X^HX^h and X^hY ***[1 mark]***.
Correct genetic diagram drawn with gametes' alleles identified as X^H, X^h and X^h,Y ***[1 mark]*** and gametes crossed to show X^HX^h, X^HY, X^hX^h and X^hY as the possible genotypes of the offspring ***[1 mark]***.
The question specifically asks you to draw a genetic diagram, so make sure that you include one in your answer, e.g.

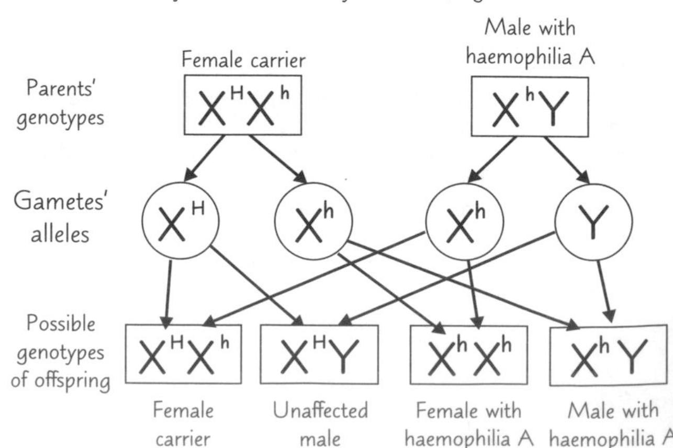

b) Men only have one copy of the X chromosome (XY) but women have two (XX) ***[1 mark]***. Haemophilia A is caused by a recessive allele, so females would need two copies of the allele for them to have haemophilia A ***[1 mark]***. As males only have one X chromosome they only need one recessive allele to have haemophilia A, which makes them more likely to have haemophilia A than females ***[1 mark]***.

Answers

2 A cross between CCGG and ccgg will produce a 9 : 3 : 4 phenotypic ratio in the F_2 generation ***[1 mark]*** of coloured grey : coloured black : albino ***[1 mark]***. This is because gene 1 has a recessive epistatic gene (c) ***[1 mark]***, and two copies of the recessive epistatic gene (cc) will mask the expression of the colour gene ***[1 mark]***.
You don't need to draw a genetic diagram to explain the phenotypic ratio that you'd expect from this cross. You can just state the ratio and explain it using your own knowledge.

3 The table shows that a cross between hhss and HHSS produces a 36 : 9 : 3 or 12 : 3 : 1 phenotypic ratio in the F_2 generation of bald : straight hair : curly hair ***[1 mark]***. This is because the hair gene has a dominant epistatic allele (H) ***[1 mark]***, which means having at least one copy of the dominant epistatic gene (Hh or HH) will result in a bald phenotype that masks the expression of the type of hair gene ***[1 mark]***.

Page 75 — The Chi-Squared Test

1 a) ***[3 marks]*** for a correct answer of 3.81. Otherwise, allow ***[1 mark]*** for each of the O–E-^{2} and (O–E)^2/E columns correctly filled in.

Phenotype	Ratio	Expected Result (E)	Observed Result (O)	O – E	O – E^2	$\frac{(O-E^2)}{E}$
Blue with white spots	9	135	131	–4	16	0.12
Purple with white spots	3	45	52	7	49	1.09
Blue with yellow spots	3	45	48	3	9	0.2
Purple with yellow spots	1	15	9	–6	36	2.4
						3.81

b) The χ^2 value does support the null hypothesis ***[1 mark]*** because it's smaller than the critical value ***[1 mark]***.

Module 6: Section 3 — Evolution

Page 78 — Evolution by Natural Selection and Genetic Drift

1 The northern elephant seals underwent a genetic bottleneck ***[1 mark]***. Hunting reduced their population size, which led to a reduction in their gene pool ***[1 mark]***. Southern elephant seals did not undergo the same reduction in population size/reduction of their gene pool ***[1 mark]***.

2 a) The graph shows stabilising selection ***[1 mark]***. The initial sample shows a fairly wide range of shell colours from light to dark ***[1 mark]***. Over time, the average colour of oyster shell has shifted towards the middle of the range, so more oysters have a mid-range coloured shell by the final sample ***[1 mark]***.

b) Oyster shells at the extremes of light and dark are less likely to survive because they can be more easily seen by predators against the sand ***[1 mark]***. This means that the mid-range coloured oysters have an advantage and are more likely to survive and reproduce ***[1 mark]***. The advantageous alleles for mid-range coloured oysters are more likely to be passed on to the next generation ***[1 mark]*** leading to an increase in mid-range coloured oysters in the population ***[1 mark]***.

Page 81 — Hardy-Weinberg Principle and Artificial Selection

1 Farmers could have selected a male and female with a high meat yield and bred these two together ***[1 mark]***. Then they could have selected the offspring with the highest meat yields and bred them together ***[1 mark]***. This process could have been continued over several generations to produce cattle with a very high meat yield ***[1 mark]***.

2 q = 0.23
p + q = 1
so p = 1 – 0.23 = 0.77
The frequency of the heterozygous genotype = 2pq
= 2(0.77 × 0.23) = **0.35** ***[2 marks for the correct answer or 1 mark for p = 0.77 or 2(p × 0.23)]***

3 a) Frequency of genotype CC = p^2 = 0.14
So the frequency of the dominant allele = p = $\sqrt{0.14}$ = 0.37
The frequency of the recessive allele = q
q = 1 – p
q = 1 – 0.37 = **0.63** ***[2 marks for the correct answer or 1 mark for 1 – √0.14]***

b) Frequency of the homozygous recessive genotype = q^2
= 0.63^2 = **0.4** ***[1 mark for the correct answer. Allow 1 mark for evidence of correct calculation using incorrect answer to part a)]***

Page 83 — Speciation

1 a) The new species could not breed with each other ***[1 mark]***.

b) Different populations of flies were isolated and fed on different foods ***[1 mark]***. This led to changes in allele frequencies between the populations ***[1 mark]***, which made them reproductively isolated and eventually resulted in speciation ***[1 mark]***.

c) Any two from: e.g. seasonal changes (become sexually active at different times) ***[1 mark]*** / mechanical changes (changes to genitalia) ***[1 mark]*** / behavioural changes (changes in behaviour that prevent mating) ***[1 mark]***.

d) E.g. geographical barrier ***[1 mark]*** / flood ***[1 mark]*** / volcanic eruption ***[1 mark]*** / earthquake ***[1 mark]*** / polyploid organisms are formed ***[1 mark]***.

Module 6: Section 4 — Manipulating Genomes

Page 86 — Common Techniques

1 ***5-6 marks:***
The answer describes and explains the full process of PCR, including correct references to all the molecules and temperatures involved. The answer has a clear and logical structure. The information given is relevant and detailed.
3-4 marks:
The answer describes the full process of PCR including the molecules involved, but gives limited explanation of the process or detail of the temperatures involved.
The answer has some structure. Most of the information given is relevant and there is some detail involved.
1-2 marks:
The answer mentions at least one of the molecules involved in PCR and gives a basic description of the process, but lacks any explanation of the process or detail of the temperatures involved. The answer has no clear structure. The information given is basic and lacking in detail. It may not all be relevant.
0 marks:
No relevant information is given.
Here are some points your answer may include:
The DNA sample from the hair is mixed with free nucleotides, primers and DNA polymerase. The mixture is heated to 95 °C to break the hydrogen bonds. The mixture is then cooled to between 50-65 °C to allow the primers to bind/anneal to the DNA. The primers bind/anneal to the DNA because they have a sequence that's complementary to the sequence at the start of the DNA fragment. The mixture is then heated to 72 °C and DNA polymerase lines up free nucleotides along each template strand, producing new strands of DNA. The cycle would be repeated over and over to produce lots of copies.
This question asks you to describe and explain, so you need to give the reasons why each stage is done to gain full marks.

Page 87 — DNA Profiling

1 a) DNA is isolated from all the samples ***[1 mark]***. PCR is used to amplify multiple areas containing different sequence repeats ***[1 mark]***. The DNA mixture undergoes electrophoresis to separate out the bands according to size ***[1 mark]***.

b) The blood is most likely to belong to missing person B because all of the bands on this DNA profile match that of the blood sample ***[1 mark]***.

Answers

Page 89 — Genetic Engineering

1 C *[1 mark]*

2 a) Colony A is shown on the plate under UV light, whereas colony B isn't *[1 mark]*, which shows that colony A contains the YFP gene, so it contains transformed cells *[1 mark]*.

b) The plasmid vector DNA would have been cut open with the same restriction endonuclease that was used to isolate the DNA fragment containing the YFP gene *[1 mark]*. The plasmid DNA and gene (DNA fragment) would have been mixed together with DNA ligase *[1 mark]*. DNA ligase joins the sugar-phosphate backbone of the two bits of DNA *[1 mark]*.

c) A suspension of unmodified bacterial cells would have been mixed with plasmids containing the YFP gene *[1 mark]*. Then the mixture would have been put into an electroporator where an electrical field increased the permeability of the bacterial cell membranes *[1 mark]*. This would have been done to allow the bacterial cells to take in the plasmids *[1 mark]*.

Page 91 — Genetically Modified Organisms

1 ***5-6 marks:***

The answer fully describes how genetic engineering could be used to create a bromoxynil-resistant cotton plant (including the use of restriction enzymes) and fully explains several ethical issues (both positive and negative) surrounding bromoxynil-resistant cotton plants.

The answer has a clear and logical structure. The information given is relevant and detailed.

3-4 marks:

The answer briefly describes how genetic engineering could be used to create a bromoxynil-resistant cotton plant and explains some of the positive and negative ethical issues surrounding bromoxynil-resistant cotton plants.

The answer has some structure. Most of the information given is relevant and there is some detail involved.

1-2 marks:

The answer gives a basic description of how genetic engineering could be used to create a bromoxynil-resistant cotton plant and references one positive and one negative ethical issue surrounding bromoxynil-resistant cotton plants.

The answer has no clear structure. The information given is basic and lacking in detail. It may not all be relevant.

0 marks:

No relevant information is given.

Here are some points your answer may include:

The gene responsible for the enzyme that converts bromoxynil to a harmless substance could be isolated using restriction enzymes, and then inserted into a bacterial plasmid. The plasmid could be reinserted into the bacteria and then the cotton plant infected with the transformed bacteria.

The creation of bromoxynil-resistant cotton plants raises positive ethical issues. For example, it should reduce the amount of chemical weedkillers used by farmers, which can harm the environment. The patenting of the gene could also be seen as a positive ethical issue, as sale of the genically modified cotton plant seeds will generate money for the company that owns the patent and they could then use this money to research and develop other beneficial genetically modified products.

However, the creation of bromoxynil-resistant cotton plants also raises negative ethical issues. For example, it could encourage monoculture, which decreases biodiversity. Also, the patenting of the gene may mean that some farmers in poorer countries cannot afford to produce bromoxynil-resistant cotton plants year on year.

Page 92 — Gene Therapy

1 a) Gene therapy involves altering/supplementing defective genes (mutated alleles) inside cells to treat genetic disorders *[1 mark]*.

b) Somatic gene therapy *[1 mark]*.

Page 95 — Sequencing Genes and Genomes

1 a) DNA polymerase *[1 mark]*, DNA primer *[1 mark]*, free nucleotides *[1 mark]* and fluorescently-labelled modified nucleotides *[1 mark]*.

b) E.g. it's faster/more bases can be sequenced in a given time/whole genomes can be sequenced more quickly *[1 mark]*, it is much cheaper *[1 mark]*.

2 They could sequence the genome of each bacterial species *[1 mark]* and then compare the genomes using computer software/bioinformatics/computational biology to establish how closely related they are *[1 mark]*.

Module 6: Section 5 — Cloning and Biotechnology

Page 97 — Plant Cloning

1 She could use tissue culture *[1 mark]*. The cell would be sterilised, to kill off any contaminating microorganisms *[1 mark]*, then placed on a culture medium containing nutrients and growth factors *[1 mark]*. The cell would then divide and grow into a small plant *[1 mark]*.

Page 99 — Animal Cloning

1 a) The nucleus from a somatic cell from Alpaca A *[1 mark]* is inserted into an enucleated oocyte taken from another individual *[1 mark]*. The host cell containing its new nucleus is stimulated by electrofusion to divide and produce an embryo *[1 mark]* and the embryo is implanted into a surrogate mother, where it develops into a clone of Alpaca A *[1 mark]*.

b) Any two from: e.g. any undesirable genetic characteristics from Alpaca A will be passed on to all the herd *[1 mark]*. / Animal cloning is a time-consuming, difficult and expensive process *[1 mark]*. / There is a risk that the cloned herd may have a shorter life-span than conventionally bred alpacas *[1 mark]*. / There is no genetic variability within the herd, which could make the entire herd susceptible to being wiped out by a single disease *[1 mark]*.

Page 103 — Biotechnology

1 a) Using aseptic techniques can prevent contamination of cultures by unwanted microorganisms *[1 mark]*. This is important because contamination could affect the growth of *E. coli*, which would reduce the precision of his results *[1 mark]* or allow the growth of microorganisms that could be harmful to health *[1 mark]*.

b) Any three from: e.g. regularly disinfect work surfaces to minimise contamination *[1 mark]*. / Work near a Bunsen flame to ensure that microorganisms in the air are drawn away from your culture *[1 mark]*. / Sterilise equipment before and after use to kill any unwanted microorganisms *[1 mark]*. / Minimise the time that the culture medium is open/put the lid on the agar plate as soon as possible/work in an inoculation cabinet to reduce the chances of airborne microorganisms from contaminating the culture *[1 mark]*. / If the bacterial sample is in broth, briefly pass the neck of the container through a Bunsen burner flame just after it's opened and just before it's closed so that air moves out of the container and unwanted microorganisms are prevented from falling in *[1 mark]*. / Wear a lab coat and ,if needed, gloves *[1 mark]*. / Tie long hair back to prevent it from falling into anything *[1 mark]*.

Page 105 — Immobilised Enzymes

1 a) Immobilised means that the enzyme is attached to an insoluble material *[1 mark]*.

b) By being encapsulated in alginate beads *[1 mark]*, trapped in a silica gel matrix *[1 mark]* or covalently bonded to cellulose or collagen fibres *[1 mark]*.

2 a) Glucoamylase catalyses the conversion of dextrins to glucose *[1 mark]*.

b) Any two from: e.g. the extra equipment needed to use immobilised enzymes can be expensive to buy *[1 mark]*. /Immobilised enzymes are more expensive to buy than free enzymes *[1 mark]*. / The activity of immobilised enzymes can be lower in comparison to free enzymes *[1 mark]*.

Module 6: Section 6 — Ecosystems

Page 107 — An Introduction to Ecosystems

1 C *[1 mark]*

Answers

2 a) If the fruit does not develop properly there will be less food available for the consumers *[1 mark]*. If the primary consumers don't get enough food, fewer of them will survive so there will be less food available for the secondary consumers, and likewise for the tertiary consumers *[1 mark]*.
b) Any two from: e.g. rainfall/precipitation *[1 mark]* / shape of land/topology *[1 mark]* / soil nutrient availability *[1 mark]*.

Page 109 — Energy Transfer Through an Ecosystem

1 a) Not all of the energy available from the grass is taken in by the Arctic hare *[1 mark]*. This is because some parts of the grass aren't eaten, so the energy they contain isn't taken in *[1 mark]*, and some parts of the grass are indigestible, so they'll pass through the hare and come out as waste *[1 mark]*. Also, some energy is lost to the environment when the Arctic hare uses energy for respiration *[1 mark]*.
b) (137 ÷ 2345) × 100 = **5.8** ***[1 mark]***
Efficiency of energy transfer = **5.8%** ***[1 mark]***
Award 2 marks for correct answer of **5.8%** without any working.
2 a) You could take a 1 m^2 sample area of his cabbage field and calculate the dry mass of the cabbages *[1 mark]*. You would then multiply the mass of the sample by the total area of the field *[1 mark]*.
b) One mark for suggestion and a second mark for associated explanation up to a maximum of four marks: e.g. he could use herbicides to kill weeds that compete with the cabbages for energy *[1 mark]*. Reducing competition means the cabbages receive more energy, so they grow faster and become larger, increasing productivity *[1 mark]*. / He could use fungicides to kill fungal infections that damage the cabbages *[1 mark]*. The cabbages would use more energy for growth and less for fighting infection, so would grow faster and become larger, increasing productivity *[1 mark]*. / He could use insecticides to kill insect pests that eat and damage the cabbages *[1 mark]*. Killing insect pests means less biomass is lost from the cabbages, so they grow to be larger, which means productivity is greater *[1 mark]*. / He could introduce natural predators to the field to eat cabbage pest species *[1 mark]*. This means the cabbages lose less energy and biomass due to damage caused by pest species, which increases productivity *[1 mark]*. / He could use fertilisers to provide the cabbages with all the minerals needed for optimum growth, e.g. nitrates *[1 mark]*. Adding fertiliser means the cabbages have all the minerals they need and this maximises the amount of energy they can use for growth/the efficiency of energy conversion *[1 mark]*.

Page 111 — Recycling in Ecosystems

1 a) A — nitrification *[1 mark]*,
B — nitrogen fixation *[1 mark]*
b) Process C is denitrification *[1 mark]*. Denitrification is where nitrates in the soil are converted into nitrogen gas by denitrifying bacteria *[1 mark]*. The denitrifying bacteria use nitrates to respire anaerobically, which releases nitrogen gas *[1 mark]*.
2 Carbon (in the form of CO_2) is absorbed by grass when it carries out photosynthesis — the grass converts carbon to carbon compounds in its tissues *[1 mark]*. Cattle (primary consumers) eat the grass and they incorporate the carbon compounds it contains into their tissues *[1 mark]*.

Page 113 — Succession

1 D *[1 mark]*
2 a) Primary succession *[1 mark]* because the sand is freshly exposed and there is no soil or organic matter to start with *[1 mark]*.
b) When grass dies, microorganisms decompose the dead organic material forming a soil *[1 mark]*. The formation of soil helps to retain water and makes the conditions less hostile, which allows larger plants (e.g. shrubs) to move in *[1 mark]*. The larger plants are better adapted for the improved conditions and out-compete the species already there, so they become the dominant species *[1 mark]*.

Page 115 — Investigating Ecosystems

1 a) Take a random sample of the population of daffodils in the field *[1 mark]*.
b) Several frame quadrats would be placed on the ground at random locations within the field *[1 mark]*. The percentage of each frame quadrat that's covered by daffodils would be recorded *[1 mark]*. The percentage cover for the whole field could then be estimated by averaging the data collected in all of the frame quadrats *[1 mark]*.
c) Including plant species that aren't daffodils (or ignoring daffodil plants) could lead to inaccurate percentage cover estimates being calculated in frame quadrats *[1 mark]*.

Module 6: Section 7 — Populations and Sustainability

Page 117 — Factors Affecting Population Size

1 ***5-6 marks:***
The answer fully describes and explains how the population sizes of both the predator and prey species vary over the first 10 years, using a range of figures taken from the graph.
The answer has a clear and logical structure. The information given is relevant and detailed.
3-4 marks:
The answer partly describes how the population sizes of the predator and prey species vary over the first 10 years and offers some explanation for this. Some figures from the graph are included.
The answer has some structure. Most of the information given is relevant and there is some detail involved.
1-2 marks:
The answer outlines how the population size of either the predator or prey species varies over the first 10 years. No explanation is given. A figure from the graph may be included.
The answer has no clear structure. The information given is basic and lacking in detail. It may not all be relevant.
0 marks:
No relevant information is given.
Here are some points your answer may include:
In the first three years, the population of prey increases from 5000 to 30 000. The population of predators increases slightly later (in the first five years), from 4000 to 11 000. This is because there's more food available for the predators. The prey population then falls after year three to 3000 just before year 10, because lots are being eaten by the large population of predators. Shortly after the prey population falls, the predator population also falls (back to 4000 by just after year 10) because there's less food available.

Page 119 — Conservation of Ecosystems

1 a) It provides wood for people to use today without depleting the woodland/reducing the ability of people in the future to take wood from the woodland *[1 mark]*.
b) Any two from: e.g. it maintains the woodland habitat for other organisms *[1 mark]*. / It allows new trees to grow from seeds produced by the mature standards *[1 mark]*. / The mature standards can be used to produce larger logs at a later date *[1 mark]*.
You're not expected to know the answer to this question, just to be able to come up with sensible suggestions.
c) So that the mature standard trees don't block out the light that the coppiced trees need to grow [1 mark].

Page 121 — Conservation of Ecosystems

1 E.g. in the Terai Arc, farmers are encouraged to plant mint hedges around their crops to protect them from being eaten and trampled by elephants and to avoid the elephants being killed. In the Maasai Mara, conservation trusts have helped the local people to make money from conservation or ecotourism projects rather than farming / to farm in a more sustainable way. In peat bog areas of the UK, government-funded programmes have given farmers money to farm in a more sustainable way, e.g. by reducing the number of livestock that graze on peat bogs. These ways are all similar because they allow the economic needs of the farmer to be met/they allow the farmer to continue to make a living, whilst also conserving the areas in which they farm. ***[1 mark per correct named example, plus 1 mark for a comparison of the examples.]***

Index

Index

Index